D1452010

Timescales
in Geomorphology

A publication of the British Geomorphological Research Group

Timescales in Geomorphology

Edited by

R. A. Cullingford
Department of Geography, University of Exeter
D. A. Davidson
Department of Geography, University of Strathclyde
J. Lewin
Department of Geography, University College of Wales, Aberystwyth

A Wiley–Interscience Publication

JOHN WILEY & SONS

CHICHESTER · NEW YORK · BRISBANE · TORONTO

British Library Cataloguing in Publication Data:

Timescales in geomorphology.
  1. Geomorphology—Methodology 2. Geological time
  I. Cullingford, R. A. II. Davidson, Donald A.
  III. Lewin, John IV. British Geomorphological Research Group
551.4   GB400.4   79-40517

ISBN 0 471 27600 6

Text set in 10/12 pt VIP Times, printed and bound
in Great Britain at The Pitman Press, Bath

Contributing Authors

M. G. ANDERSON, *Department of Geography, The University, University Road, Bristol, BS8 1SS.*

J. T. ANDREWS, *Institute of Arctic and Alpine Research and Department of Geological Sciences, University of Colorado, Boulder, Colorado 80309, USA.*

M. D. BRYAN, *Birmingham City Museum, Birmingham.*

P. A. BULL, *Christ Church, Oxford, OX1 1DP.*

K. W. BUTZER, *Departments of Anthropology and Geography, University of Chicago, 5828 S. University Avenue, Chicago, Illinois 60637, USA.*

A. P. CARR, *Institute of Oceanographic Sciences, Crossway, Taunton, Somerset, TA1 2DW.*

A. CALVER, *Geo Abstracts Ltd., University of East Anglia, Norwich, NR4 7TJ.*

M. CHURCH, *Department of Geography, University of British Columbia, 2075 Wesbrook Mall, Vancouver, BC, Canada, V6T 1W5.*

G. R. COOPE, *Department of Geological Sciences, The University, P.O. Box 363, Birmingham, B15 2TT.*

R. A. CULLINGFORD, *Department of Geography, University of Exeter, Amory Building, Rennes Drive, Exeter, EX4 4RJ.*

D. A. DAVIDSON, *Department of Geography, University of Strathclyde, Livingstone Tower, 26 Richmond Street, Glasgow, G1 1XH.*

K. J. EDWARDS, *Department of Geography, The Queen's University of Belfast, Belfast, Northern Ireland, BT7 1NN.*

R. FERGUSON, *Department of Earth and Environmental Science, The University, Stirling, FK9 4LA.*

A. C. IMESON, *Fysich Geografisch en bodemkundig Laboratorium, University of Amsterdam, Dapperstraat 115, Amsterdam–Oost, The Netherlands.*

R. L. JONES, *Department of Geography, Lanchester Polytechnic, Priory Street, Coventry, CV1 5FB.*

R. H. JOHNSON, *Department of Geography, The University, Manchester, M13 9PL.*

F. J. P. M. KWAAD, *Fysisch Geografisch en bodemkundig Laboratorium, University of Amsterdam, Dapperstraat 115, Amsterdam—Oost, The Netherlands.*

J. LEWIN, *Department of Geography, University College of Wales, Llandinam Building, Penglais, Aberystwyth, Dyfed, SY23 3DB.*

J. J. LOWE, *Geography Section, City of London Polytechnic, Calcutta House Precinct, Old Castle Street, London, E1 7NT.*

G. H. MILLER, *Institute of Arctic and Alpine Research and Department of Geological Sciences, University of Colorado, Boulder, Colorado 80309, USA.*

J. MORRISON, *Department of Geography, Lanchester Polytechnic, Priory Street, Coventry, CV1 5FB.*

D. N. MOTTERSHEAD, *Department of Geography, Portsmouth Polytechnic, Lion Terrace, Portsmouth, PO1 3HE.*

H. J. MÜCHER, *Fysisch Geografisch en bodemkundig Laboratorium, University of Amsterdam, Dapperstraat 115, Amsterdam—Oost, The Netherlands.*

R. J. PRICE, *Department of Geography, The University, Glasgow, G12 8QQ.*

R. J. RICE, *Department of Geography, The University, Leicester, LE1 7RH.*

J. ROSE, *Department of Geography, Birkbeck College, University of London, 7–15 Gresse Street, London, W1P 1PA.*

K. M. ROWNTREE, *Department of Geography and History, The Polytechnic, Sunderland, SR1 3SD.*

D. E. SMITH, *Department of Geography, Lanchester Polytechnic, Priory Street, Coventry, CV1 5FB.*

A. STRAW, *Department of Geography, University of Exeter, Amory Building, Rennes Drive, Exeter, EX4 4RJ.*

J. H. TALLIS, *Department of Botany, The University, Manchester, M13 9PL.*

M. F. THOMAS, *Department of Earth and Environmental Science, The University, Stirling, FK9 4LA.*

C. TURNER, *Sub-Department of Quaternary Research, The University, Cambridge, CB2 1TT.*

M. J. C. WALKER, *Department of Geography, St David's University College, Lampeter, Dyfed, Wales, SA48 7ED.*

A. WERRITY, *Department of Geography, The University, St Andrews, Fife, KY16 9AL.*

S. M. WISE, *Department of Geography, University of London, King's College, Strand, London, WC2R 2LS.*

P. WORSLEY, *Department of Geography, The University, No. 2 Earley Gate, Whiteknights Road, Reading, RG6 2AU.*

Contents

Preface

This book originates from a Symposium held by the British Geomorphological Research Group at the University of Hull, 4–5 January 1978. The aim of the meeting was to compare the various geomorphological methods which are used to investigate different timescales. The feeling was that there is a lack of communication between geomorphologists dealing with various timescales. The Symposium, besides fostering discussion between different types of geomorphologists, allowed an examination, by way of case studies, of whether the results from one timescale were applicable to another. Clearly such a theme is of central importance in geomorphology when any attempt is made to generalize about long-term landscape evolution on the basis of process or short-term measurements. The response to the Symposium theme was sufficiently strong to suggest that an edited volume on the topic would be welcome.

The resultant text bears only a partial resemblance to the original Symposium, since all papers have been edited so that they conform to the theme and additional papers have been included to broaden the book. After an introduction to available and appropriate timescales in geomorphology, the book is subdivided into three sections dealing with short (*ca.* 10^1 to 10^2 years), medium (*ca.* 10^3 to 10^4 years) and long (*ca.* 10^4 to 10^5 years and more) timescales. Each of these timescales is introduced by a review, and, together with the introduction, these review papers provide the structural and methodological framework for the book.

We thank all the authors for submitting their papers and completing revisions within a tight schedule. In particular we thank the review authors, John Andrews, Karl Butzer, Michael Church and Giff Miller, who, true to North American tradition, produced their papers in a very prompt manner. We are also very grateful to the many referees who made our job much easier. We thank the British Geomorphological Research Group for inviting us to undertake the editorial task. Last, but by no means least, we thank our respective departments at Exeter, Strathclyde and Aberystwyth for their knowing and unknowing support.

Centre Hotel, Birmingham,   ROBIN CULLINGFORD
14 December 1978   DONALD DAVIDSON
                                                                                         JOHN LEWIN

Editorial Note

Where reference is made to radiocarbon ages in years before the present (i.e. before AD 1950), the convention is followed that uncorrected dates are expressed in years bp, and corrected or 'calendar' dates in years BP.

Introduction

Timescales in Geomorphology
Edited by R. A. Cullingford, D. A. Davidson, and J. Lewin
© 1980 John Wiley & Sons Ltd

CHAPTER 1

Available and appropriate timescales in geomorphology

John Lewin

*Department of Geography,
University College of Wales, Aberystwyth*

In the 1950s and 1960s a refocusing of the timescales considered appropriate for study in geomorphology took place. This was both summarized and further developed in an influential paper by Schumm and Lichty (1965). Despite attempts at reconciliation the practical result, put crudely, has been the development of a schismatic science. Some geomorphologists have persisted with their interests in long-term geomorphological development, especially in an endeavour to reconstruct the sequence of Quaternary events and environments. Others have largely concerned themselves with the observation of contemporary processes, with morphometric studies, and with the statistical links between landform and environmental variables. At the same time, very considerable development of the available techniques (or at least of geomorphologists' use and understanding of them) has taken place in the last two decades, so that the mastering of particular dating methods, of time-series analysis, or of such topics as fluvial hydraulics, became individually absorbing preoccupations. In fact, some geomorphologists in the 1960s and early 1970s probably came to feel more at ease discussing their problems with engineers, archaeologists, or systems analysts than with geomorphological colleagues whose concerns could be so divergent.

This *eclectic* phase in the history of geomorphology has in practice proved extremely fruitful. The published archive of geomorphology has been enriched with insights of very contrasted kinds which are not in fact mutually exclusive [compare, for example, Andrews (1970), Butzer (1971), Chorley and Kennedy (1971) and Church (1972)]. The danger of geomorphology becoming enthralled and stultified by a single orthodox paradigm, like that associated with W. M. Davis (Chorley, 1965), has at least been avoided in recent years. Admittedly this multiplicity of approach is not especially identified as useful *in itself* in the methodological literature, possibly because of a philosophical divergence and compartmentalization previously suggested, and at least partly because some of the most persuasive 'methodological' literature has had a strongly proselytizing role (Chorley, 1962, 1965, 1978). This 'methodology' has especially concerned a limited cognitive realm somewhere between *what* is studied (hazard situations, coastal landforms, hillslope processes, etc.) and the *sensory techniques* (field instruments, dating techniques, etc.) with which such studies are undertaken, and in an extremely stimulating manner has exploited statistical and mathematical techniques within a systems approach (Bennett and Chorley, 1978). This approach appears at times to take an agnostic stand on the existence or relevance of the complexities of sequences in environmental change (Chorley, 1978, p. 6), which to other working geomorphologists have the most real of presences, particularly whilst they are slowly accumulating data on Late Cenozoic environments in a world-wide academic exercise in collaborative competition.

It can be argued that the substantive results of these varied approaches, as they have emerged in the past decade, have still not in themselves proved wholly satisfying when viewed in isolation. Thus, observations of contemporary processes (a beguiling term that can ambiguously refer equally to a progression of forms in time, like 'scarp retreat', or to physical or chemical transformations of state) have not proved a simple panacea solution to the problems of geomorphology. For example, the use of stream sediment load data for estimating rates of long-term denudation (usually quantized into yearly rates per standard area) is beset by problems of inadequate sampling (Walling, 1977) including those arising because of non-sampling of rare and intermittent events, the factor of sediment storage within catchments (Trimble, 1977), the effects of man (Meade, 1969), and the fact that actual yields may be responding to the availability of sediment following prior glacial conditions, so that time elapsed since glaciation may be significant (Church and Rider, 1972).

Even with all these problems, of course, observation of contemporary processes still can provide an invaluable route to the interpretation of preserved sediments and past environments, provided we appreciate that some phenomena of Pleistocene Earth (Bowen, 1978), or Devonian Earth for that matter (Allen, 1974), may have no known contemporary field analogue. Also, studies of contemporary rates and patterns of geomorphological activity may nowadays be undertaken without any strong regard for long-term landform development. Information may be demanded from geomorphologists on such matters as solute dynamics or coastal sediment transfers, where ecological conditions or managerial decision for the next decade rather than for the next or the last millennium are what matter. Such physical or chemical activity in the environment may be only tenuously linked to landform generation, but geomorphologists may be the ones who can analyse such activity for the general benefit of science or of human welfare. Here again the proviso must be made that in studying the near-present it is still necessary to consider and identify the timescales over which components of this present are effectively being produced or modified.

This consideration of 'process' studies suggests that the relative isolation of one outward-looking branch of geomorphology from another should not be carried too far. Our understandings of short-term and long-term landform developments are mutually dependent. An increasing appreciation of the limitations of direct process observation, and the need to extend such data in time, comes just when the complexities of the Holocene are being revealed, particularly through geo-archaeological work. Analysis of environmental space-time systems, with a much stronger emphasis on topics such as non-stationarity, non-linearity, or lead-lag situations, is developing in parallel with a very considerable improvement in the time-stratigraphic framework for longer term landform development which can calibrate just such systems in a geomorphological context. Geomorphologists may in essence agree, though not all would express it in the same way, that 'the majority of mesoscale landform assemblages represent a palimpsest of superimposed and interlocking process-response systems of highly varying relaxation times' (Chorley, 1978, p. 8). There would seem to be particular reason in considering the different timescales or time concepts in which geomorphologists can operate at present, to see how such variety may prove informative and how the study of different timescales may cumulatively prove enlightening.

This volume provides a series of studies undertaken using strongly contrasted time bases, moving in general order from ones involving measures of contemporary change to those concerned with millions of years of landform development. Particular problems occur in geomorphology because it is not simply the *length* of timespan which is involved, but also its *position* in time. For example, it appears that a number of relatively short but highly significant occurrences in the past may be critical for the understanding of present landforms (e.g. Kerney and *et al.*, 1964; Gage, 1970; Knox, 1972). Rather different techniques are needed for studying 500-year periods in the Pleistocene, from 2000 to 2500 BP, or immediately preceding the present.

Studies in this volume involve river channel, slope, glacial and coastal environments, and within chapters authors have frequently stressed the implications of work in one timescale for work in another. A number of chapters discuss rather new techniques, and the availability of new information and methods of approach is especially stressed in the review contributions of Church, Butzer, and Andrews and Miller. Any collection of independent studies and opinions such as this is necessarily somewhat diffuse. It may, however, be helpful to reconcile and link the different approaches by considering, repeatedly perhaps as the volume proceeds, the timescales over which geomorphological activities can best be observed. What timespans are *available*, and what are or would be *appropriate* to the kinds of study geomorphologists may wish to make?

Available Timespans

In practice we can only possess 'windows' of limited and varying opacity and size, giving a restricted view of the fluctuating pace of geomorphological change. For instance, we may have for just a few rivers of certain sizes some measure, continuously monitored, of solute concentration—but for only a minute proportion of geomorphological time at one particular point in a river catchment. Field observations may be restricted to a few occasions in one field season, or to the few years of 'PhD time', whilst historical documents or fortuitously preserved sediments may allow a dated reconstruction of some past environment which may be separated by decades, centuries or millennia from the next opportunity at which reconstruction is possible. Rates of change between reconstructions are integrals, whilst individual events or occurrences within or beyond the bounding reconstructions may be unknown. In addition, geomorphological evidence is of limited reliability: relevant historical data may be inaccurate, instrumental observations are liable to error, and dating techniques are often of questionable interpretation. Naturally some data are securely based, and they allow both quantitative analysis (see Thornes and Brunsden, 1977, and Bennett and Chorley, 1978) and the reconstruction of Quaternary environments in particular (Goudie, 1977; Bowen, 1978). Nevertheless, it is important to appreciate the considerable limitations that geomorphologists have to work with in different timescales, if only to provoke a search for a more satisfactory spectrum of available observations.

Four types of timescale evidence are used in geomorphology. The first results from direct field measurement of process and change. Such observations are seldom sustained for more than a decade—but see Leopold (1973) and Young (1978). They may thus fail to encompass the necessary suite of erosional and depositional events, and it is significant that both the Leopold and Young studies revealed changes that their initial, short-term observations did not foretell. Observations may also involve measuring changes whose dimensions approach the error inherent in the particular measurement techniques available, as most research workers in this field have been only too well aware (Young, 1960).

The second type of evidence involves the use of historical data, gathered perhaps for some other purpose, but which may well be most useful in showing geomorphological changes or in recording significant past events (e.g. Grove, 1972). Survey notes, maps, ground and air photography, and remote sensing imagery of a variety of types are useful here.

The third category concerns the dating of exposed surfaces by a range of techniques which include the relative weathering of rock surfaces and soil development (Birkeland, 1974), lichenometry (Mottershead, this volume, Chapter 8), and dendrochronology (Alestalo, 1971; Shroder, 1978). Fourthly, the geomorphologist may also use essentially stratigraphic methods which involve both relative and absolute age determinations. Such methods may equally involve localized interpretation of recent sediments, or a re-interpretation of macro-scale landforms in the light of recent developments in plate tectonics.

These types of evidence are often used best in combination for the understanding of a particular geomorphological situation, and techniques may be applicable over a range of timescales. Thus, lichen growth has been used both in the short term to determine the limits of river channel capacity (Gregory, 1976) as well as in combination with other relative age techniques for Late Quaternary chronology (Carroll, 1974). Reviews of research applications of many other techniques are given in later chapters by Church, Butzer, and Andrews and Miller.

Recent advances in extending the availability of timespans for geomorphological studies have occurred rather differently in the various branches of the subject. For example, it can be argued that geomorphologists have been slow to attempt studies in alluvial chronology (Butzer, this volume, Chapter 10), and perhaps slow in general to appreciate what can be learnt from sediments in slope, valley floor, ice marginal, coastal, or other environments. Again, examples showing what can be achieved appear later in this volume.

We may conclude our initial consideration of the availability of various timespans for geomorphological studies by emphasizing gaps that have yet to be filled. For instance, the time bases for the present understanding of stream network development are essentially derived from the following:

(a) observations in the short term of hardware models or rapidly evolving net-works—notably gullies in superficial deposits (Morisawa, 1964; Schumm, 1956; Flint, 1973; Gregory and Walling, 1973, pp. 369–378);

(b) attempts to relate network development to dated land surfaces (Ruhe, 1952);

(c) the association of river systems with geological structure and lithology, formerly in theoretical terms involving progressive adjustment to structure through river capture (see, for example, Davis, 1889, Brown, 1960, and Worssam, 1973), and now through the association of 'big rivers' with persistent structural depression areas (Potter, 1978);

(d) following the work of Horton, recent and extensive probabilistic–topological analysis of stream networks, involving comparison of observed and simulated network characteristics (reviewed by Werrity, 1972, and Jarvis, 1977), or the substitution of space for time (Abrahams, 1972).

It is clear that there are as yet few time-calibrated studies of network development other than in exceptional circumstances, and the testing of random, allometric, or other growth models so far must rest on a non-timescaled comparison of co-existing network geometries (Dacey and Krumbein, 1976). Slope studies show something of the same situation. On the one hand, there are numerous studies of the rates of operation of slope processes (Williams, 1973; Young, 1974); on the other, there are theoretical models (largely deterministic this time) of slope development (Carson and Kirkby, 1972; Young, 1972), but few models of form development that are calibrated in relative or absolute age terms (Savigear, 1952; Carter and Chorley, 1961; Welch, 1970; Brunsden and Kesel, 1973). It is not difficult to think of situations in which very little is known of the rates at which major landforms have changed, and the genuinely geomorphological application of chronometric techniques is potentially capable of considerable expansion.

Appropriate Timescales

One does not need to be an historical geomorphologist to appreciate that a whole range of timescales may be appropriate to geomorphology. Thus, the dimensions of 'contemporary' river channels may be responses to observed events of varying frequency (Harvey, 1969; Pickup and Warner, 1976), including extreme events (Baker, 1977; Costa, 1978) and the adjustments that may occur in their aftermath. Some river channel characteristics are inherited from prior Quaternary conditions, and it is necessary for students even of contemporary geomorphological activity to discover what the effective temporal dimensions of 'the present' are.

It is nevertheless quite impractical for an aimless concern for all and any timescale to be maintained, and some purposes may require selection of one set of timescales rather than another. Sedimentologists, for example, have derived much enlightenment from examining in juxtaposition *both* ancient sedimentary sequences *and* the within-annual sedimentation patterns of contemporary rivers. It is also true that some research fields are more fashionable, attract research funding more readily, and seem more 'relevant' than others.

'Appropriateness' can helpfully be judged on three grounds: on the objective in studying landforms, in terms of theoretical expectations concerning the behaviour of landforms with respect to time, and on the requirements of the particular landform studied. Rather short timescales might seem suitable for studies in applied geomorphology, though not exclusively so (Cooke and Doornkamp, 1974). By contrast with the recent expansion in concern for human welfare in human geography (Harvey, 1973; Smith, 1977), or even the explosion of interest in environmental geology, applied geomorphology remains curiously uncoordinated and inarticulate other than as a service aid for pre-conceived planning or engineering projects. Yet many possibilities do exist (Gregory, 1977; Hails, 1977); geomorphological activity is closely involved with other environmental processes, as in the dispersal of pollutants, and its relevance to a wide range of parallel sciences such as ecology and archaeology is so important that these sciences have often begun to develop geomorphologies of their own to fill the vacuum.

Theoretical expectations concerning landform–time relationships are now notably varied. Landforms may be interpreted as approaching a variety of equilibrium states (Chorley and Kennedy, 1971, pp. 201–203), of which static (Twidale, 1976), metastable (Schumm, 1974), steady-state (Hack, 1960) or dynamic equilibria appear common. Some geomorphologists have concentrated on the determination of relaxation times following systems disturbance (Graf, 1977), whilst others have been more concerned with the sequences of disturbances themselves. (See also Thornes and Brunsden, 1977, Chapter 6.)

Concerning particular landforms, we can only observe as a matter of fact that some landforms possess inherited characteristics to a much greater extent than others; ancient planed surfaces (Oberlander, 1974; Twidale, 1976), for instance, clearly require a vastly different study strategy from that required by beach profiles. Here again, though, the exclusive adoption of one particular time-scale may be inappropriate: short-term observations can aid in the interpretation of relict forms, whilst past 'catastrophe' may condition present processes. Both on a regional scale (Thomas, this volume, Chapter 22) and within a drainage basin, rates of activity may be effectively taking place on different timescales. Slow or episodic slope development, with net downslope sediment movement closely approximating total sediment flux, may occur alongside floodplains where the net rate of downvalley movement is accomplished partly via different complex stepwise and cyclical lateral sediment transfers. Both take place in a non-stationary environmental situation with fluctuations in climate and in the level of human activities.

In recent years some distinctly rewarding combinations of timescale availability have influenced geomorphological work to an increasing extent. These include:

(a) the combination of direct observation of activity rates and patterns with historical or sediment data to extend and qualify conclusions derived from brief observations alone;

(b) very considerable refinement to our understanding of Late Quaternary environments, based especially on the analysis of alluvial, glacial, and coastal sediments and forms in combination with radiometric dating and pollen analysis;

(c) the development or extension of dating techniques for short and long timescales. These techniques include radiometric, chemical, and correlative methods which should allow study of much longer timespans than hitherto, and a better understanding of particular environments (e.g. cave systems and sediments).

This volume provides both an up-to-date review of these timescales and techniques, and illustrations of the ways in which these may be applied in a variety of geomorphological contexts.

References

Abrahams, A. D. (1972). Environmental constraints on the substitution of space for time in the study of natural channel networks. *Geol. Soc. Am. Bull.*, **83**, 1523–1530.

Alestalo, J. (1971). Dendrochronological interpretation of geomorphic processes. *Fennia*, **105**, 1–140.

Allen, J. R. L. (1974). Studies in fluviatile sedimentation: implications of pedogenic carbonate units, Lower Old Red Sandstone, Anglo Welsh Outcrop. *Geol. J.*, **9**, 181–208.

Andrews, J. T. (1970). A geomorphological study of post-glacial uplift with particular reference to Arctic Canada. *Inst. Br. Geog. Spec. Publ.*, No. 2.

Baker, V. R. (1977). Stream-channel response to floods, with examples from central Texas. *Geol. Soc. Am. Bull.*, **88**, 1057–1071.

Bennett, R. J., and Chorley, R. J. (1978) *Environmental Systems: Philosophy, Analysis and Control*. Methuen, London.

Birkeland, P. W. (1974). *Pedology, Weathering and Geomorphological Research*. Oxford University Press, New York.

Bowen, D. Q. (1978). *Quaternary Geology*. Pergamon Press, Oxford.

Brown, E. H. (1960). *The Relief and Drainage of Wales*. University of Wales Press, Cardiff.

Brunsden, D., and Kesel, R. H. (1973). Slope development on a Mississippi river bluff in historic time. *J. Geol.*, **81**, 576–597.

Butzer, K. W. (1971). *Environment and Archaeology*. Aldine, New York.

Carroll, T. (1974). Relative age dating techniques and a Late Quaternary chronology, Arikaree Cirque, Colorado. *Geology*, **2**, 321–325.

Carson, M. A., and Kirkby, M. J. (1972). *Hillslope Form and Process*. Cambridge University Press, Cambridge.

Carter, C. S., and Chorley, R. J. (1961). Early slope development in an expanding stream system. *Geol. Mag.*, **98**, 117–130.

Chorley, R. J. (1962). Geomorphology and general systems theory. *U.S. Geol. Surv. Prof. Pap.*, 500–B.

Chorley, R. J. (1965). A re-evaluation of the geomorphic system of W. M. Davis. In *Frontiers in Geographical Teaching* (Eds. R. J. Chorley and P. Haggett). Methuen, London, pp. 21–38.

Chorley, R. J. (1978). Bases for theory in geomorphology. *Geomorphology: Present Problems and Future Prospects* (Eds. C. Embleton, D. Brunsden, and D. K. C. Jones) Oxford University Press, London, pp. 1–13.

Chorley, R. J., and Kennedy, B. A. (1971). *Physical Geography: A Systems Approach*. Prentice-Hall, London.

Church, M. (1972). Baffin Island sandurs. *Can. Geol. Surv. Bull.*, No. 216.

Church, M., and Rider, J. M. (1972). Paraglacial sedimentation: a consideration of fluvial processes conditioned by glaciation. *Geol. Soc. Am. Bull.*, **83**, 3059–3072.

Cooke, R. U., and Doornkamp, J. C. (1974). *Geomorphology in Environmental Management*. Clarendon Press, Oxford.

Costa, J. E. (1978). Holocene stratigraphy in flood frequency analysis. *Wat. Resour. Res.*, **14**, 626–632.

Dacey, M. F. and Krumbein, W. C. (1976). Three growth models for stream channel networks. *J. Geol.*, **84**, 153–163.

Davis, W. M. (1889). The rivers and valleys of Pennsylvania. *Nat. Geog. Mag.*, **1**, 183–253.

Flint, J. J. (1973). Experimental development of headward growth of channel networks. *Geol. Soc. Am. Bull.*, **84**, 1087–1094.

Gage, M. (1970). The tempo of geomorphic change. *J. Geol.*, **78**, 619–625.

Goudie, A. S. (1977). *Environmental Change*. Clarendon Press, Oxford.

Graf, W. L. (1977). The rate law in fluvial geomorphology. *Am. J. Sci.*, **277**, 178–191.

Gregory, K. J. (1976). Lichens and the determination of river channel capacity. *Earth Surface Processes*, , 273–285.

Gregory, K. J. (Ed.) (1977). *River Channel Changes*. Wiley, Chichester.

Gregory, K. J. and Walling, D. E. (1973). *Drainage Basin Form and Process*. Arnold, London.

Grove, J. M. (1972). The incidence of landslides, avalanches and floods in western Norway during the Little Ice Age. *Arct. Alp. Res.*, **4**, 131–138.

Hack, J. T. (1960). Interpretation of erosional topography in humid temperate regions. *Am. J. Sci.*, **258A**, 80–97.

Hails, J. R. (Ed.) (1977). *Applied Geomorphology*. Elsevier, Amsterdam.

Harvey, A. M. (1969). Channel capacity and the adjustment of streams of hydrologic regime. *J. Hydrol.*, **8**, 82–98.

Harvey, D. (1973). *Social Justice and the City*. Arnold, London.

Jarvis, R. S. (1977). Drainage network analysis. *Prog. Phys. Geog.*, **1**, 271–295.

Kerney, M. P., Brown, E. H., and Chandler, T. J. (1964). The Late-glacial and Post-glacial history of the Chalk escarpment near Brook, Kent. *Phil. Trans. Roy. Soc., B*, **248**, 135–204.

Knox, J. C. (1972). Valley alluviation in south-western Wisconsin. *Ann. Assoc. Am. Geog.*, **62**, 401–410.

Leopold, L. B. (1973). River channel changes with time: an example. *Geol. Soc. Am. Bull.*, **84**, 1845–1860.

Meade, R. H. (1969). Errors in using modern stream-load data to estimate natural rates of denudation. *Geol. Soc. Am. Bull.*, **80**, 1265–1274.

Morisawa, M. (1964). Development of drainage systems on an upraised lake floor. *Am. J. Sci.*, **262**, 340–354.

Oberlander, T. M. (1974). Landscape inheritance and the pediment problem in the Mojave Desert of Southern California. *Am. J. Sci.*, **274**, 849–875.

Pickup, G., and Warner, R. F. (1976). Effects of hydrologic regime on magnitude and frequency of dominant discharge. *J. Hydrol.*, **29**, 51–75.

Potter, P. E. (1978). Significance and origin of big rivers. *J. Geol.*, **86**, 13–33.

Ruhe, R. V. (1952). Topographic discontinuities in the Des Moines Lobe. *Am. J. Sci.*, **250**, 46–56.

Savigear, R. A. G. (1952). Some observations on slope development in South Wales. *Inst. Br. Geog. Trans.*, **18**, 31–52.

Schumm, S. A. (1956). Evolution of drainage systems and slopes on badlands at Perth Amboy, New Jersey. *Geol. Soc. Am. Bull.*, **67**, 597–646.

Schumm, S. A. (1974). Geomorphic thresholds and complex response of drainage systems. In *Fluvial Geomorphology* (Ed. M. Morisawa). State University of New York, Binghamton, N.Y., pp. 299–310.

Schumm, S. A., and Lichty, R. W. (1965). Time, space, and causality in geomorphology. *Am. J. Sci.*, **263**, 110–119.

Shroder, J. F., Jr. (1978). Dendrogeomorphological analysis of mass movement on Table Cliffs Plateau, Utah. *Quat. Res.*, **9**, 168–185.

Smith, D. M. (1977). *Human Geography: a Welfare Approach*. Arnold, London.

Thornes, J. B., and Brunsden, D. (1977). *Geomorphology and Time*. Methuen, London.

Trimble, S. W. (1977). The fallacy of stream equilibrium in contemporary denudation studies. *Am. J. Sci.*, **277**, 876–887.

Twidale, C. R. (1976). On the survival of paleoforms. *Am. J. Sci.*, **276**, 77–95.

Walling, D. E. (1977). Assessing the accuracy of suspended sediment rating curves for a small basin. *Wat. Resour. Res.*, **13**, 531–538.

Welch, D. M. (1970). Substitution of space for time in a study of slope development. *J. Geol.*, **78**, 234–238.

Werritty, A. (1972). The topology of stream networks, In *Spatial Analysis in Geomorphology* (Ed. R. J. Chorley). Methuen, London, pp. 167–196.

Williams, M. A. J. (1973). The efficacy of creep and slopewash in tropical and temperate Australia. *Aust. Geog. Stud.*, **11**, 62–78.

Worssam, B. C. (1973). A new look at river capture and the denudation history of the weald. *U.K. Inst. Geol. Sci. Rep.*, 73/17.

Young, A. (1960). Soil movement by denudational processes on slopes. *Nature, Lond.*, **188**, 120–122.

Young, A. (1972). *Slopes*. Oliver and Boyd, Edinburgh.

Young, A. (1974). The rate of slope retreat. *Inst. Br. Geog. Spec. Publ.*, No. 7, pp. 65–78.

Young, A. (1978). A twelve-year record of soil movement on a slope. *Z. Geomorph.*, **29**, Suppl., 104–110.

SECTION I

Short Timescales (*ca*. 10^1 to 10^2 years)

Timescales in Geomorphology
Edited by R. A. Cullingford, D. A. Davidson, and J. Lewin
© 1980 John Wiley & Sons Ltd

CHAPTER 2

Records of recent geomorphological events

Michael Church

Department of Geography
University of British Columbia

Introduction

By comparison with the usual scales of human experience, geomorphological processes are characterized, in most places and at most times, by relatively low rates of activity and by long elapsed times for cumulatively important effects to occur. Geomorphologists who wish to examine the contemporary evolution of landforms must seek means both to examine the sequence of events that alters the landscape and to determine its integrated effect over some period that is sufficient to reveal significant changes.

In this paper, contemporary time will initially be taken arbitrarily to refer to the last few hundred years—approximately the period (since the European 'scientific revolution') within which we have considerable records of any sort that are either intended directly for the study of nature, or can be turned to that purpose with minimal re-interpretation. Further, on the assumption that significant geomorphological events occupy timescales comparable to or much greater than those of the external forcing agency, which at the high-frequency end is usually some aspect of weather, we shall consider that diurnal effects represent the other bound of interest. In effect, the physics of material transfers will be ignored. However, sudden events, such as rockfalls or landslides, may still be considered since their antecedents do encompass scales of interest.

Some Properties of Geophysical Event Sequences

Changes in landscape involve transfers of water and of earth materials in complex process–response systems, and there are several ways of formalizing some part of any given system for analysis (compare Scheidegger, 1971, and Chorley and Kennedy, 1972, for contrasting approaches). Whichever approach is adopted, we usually end up with the problem of observing mass or energy fluxes, or changes in content of a reservoir or control volume. We define some means of making the observations and proceed to carry out observations over some period of time. There results a sequence of observations which specify magnitudes of fluxes, $\{q_t\}$, or successive states of a system parameter, $\{x_t\}$.

Because net change occurs very slowly, or involves large geographic areas, direct observation of the geomorphological parameter of interest (for example, rate of denudation) is commonly not feasible. The net amount of work accomplished is often estimated by observing the frequency distribution of an externally applied effective stress (usually a weather or hydrologically related stress) which is more easily measured, or is accessible from archives. It is transformed into the sequence of interest via a 'rating', 'calibration', or 'transfer' function which links the applied stress and material flux or strain. Wolman and Miller (1960) have developed such analysis in detail.

The change in the landscape over a period, $T = t_2 - t_1$, is measured either by the integration of fluxes, $\int_T q_t dt$, or by the net displacement of a system parameter, $(x_{t2} - x_{t1})$. Available event sequences are inevitably short in comparison with the timescale of significant landscape changes: this is particularly true of most observations explicitly designed for the study of the earth environment. Hence, the mean rate of the process, $\bar{q}$ or $\overline{\Delta x/\Delta t}$, or the frequency distribution, are often used to extrapolate to timescales of interest.

Unfortunately, the character of geophysical event sequences complicates this simple analysis. The frequency distribution of events does not sufficiently describe the properties of a sequence (Fig. 2.1). Three types of serial property are also important:

(i) trend;
(ii) short-term serial dependence, or persistence;
(iii) long-term serial dependence, or intermittency.

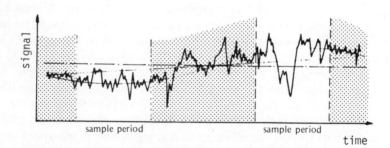

Fig. 2.1 Event sequence composed of (i) long term mean, (ii) linear trend, (iii) well-defined cycle, (iv) intermittent signal with $H \sim 0.8$. A typical sample period produces statistics that are biased with respect to the entire sequence. The second sample period shown here would see an exceptional sequence of events that might be interpreted as a short cycle

The first property is so well known that it will not be amplified here, except to remark that it includes well defined cyclic behaviour.

Persistence occurs when the present value of a sequence constrains adjacent values: short records do not then reveal the full, long-term variability of the sequence. Such short-term serial dependence is usually the result of continuity or storage constraints in nature, and may be studied via the correlogram or by investigating the Markovian properties of the event sequence (Yevjevich, 1972).

Intermittency is a much less well understood property of event sequences that reflects the tendency for (non-periodic) grouping of like values over long periods of time. When this occurs, cumulative effects, such as water or sediment storage, or net geomorphological work, may depart drastically from the mean condition. A statistic that measures this departure is the rescaled range (Hurst, 1951). Consider the sequence of cumulative sums of $\{q_t\}$,

$$\left\{ \sum_{t=1}^{n} q_t \right\} \qquad n = 1, 2, \ldots, N$$

These can be compared with the mean condition, $n\bar{q}$, for any n. The range of cumulative departures for any n (see also Figure 2.2) is

$$R_n = \frac{\max}{n} \left| \left(\sum_{t=1}^{n} q_t \right) - n\bar{q} \right| - \frac{\min}{n} \left| \left(\sum_{t=1}^{[n]} q_t \right) - n\bar{q} \right|$$

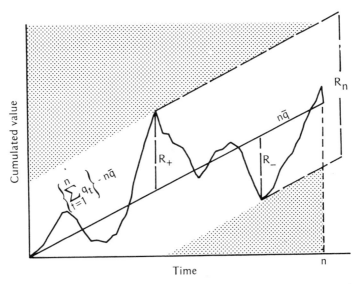

Fig. 2.2 Definition sketch for the sequence of cumulative sums and range of cumulative departures

Then the rescaled range is R_n/s, where s is the standard deviation of the sequence $\{q_t\}$. For random and short-memory processes, the rescaled range grows with the length of the sequence as $R_n/s \approx n^{0.5}$. For intermittent processes, it grow as n^H, where $H \neq 0.5$. For most geophysical processes, $0.5 < H < 1.0$ (cf. Mandelbrot and Wallis, 1969, and Fig. 2.3). Hence R_n increases out of expected proportion for simple stochastic processes and eventually unexpectedly extreme effects occur. The effect is called the 'Hurst phenomenon' after its discoverer. It carries the important implications that a short-term realization of the event sequence in nature will not sample all scales of variability in the process and that, in consequence, distribution statistics derived from the sample realization will be biased (Fig. 2.1).

The sources of intermittency in geophysical event sequences are not well understood. Two general mechanisms which give rise to the Hurst phenomenon are (1) a non-stationary mean in the process, and (2) a stationary stochastic process whose parameters give rise to substantial low frequency effects. Klemeš (1974) has reviewed the known processes of this second type. It may be impossible to discriminate amongst the possible

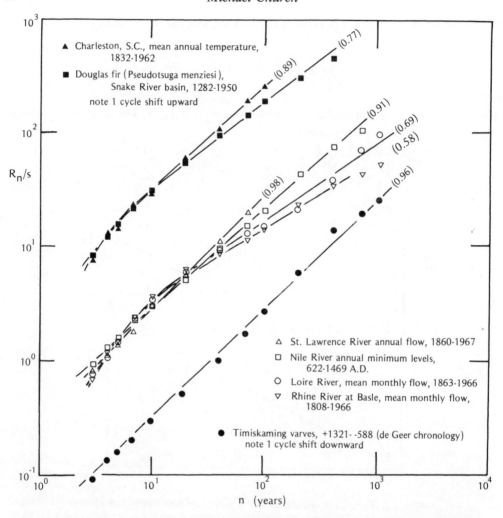

Fig. 2.3 Rescaled range plots for event sequences exhibiting intermittency. Data are from long geophysical event sequences representing climate, hydrological response and sedimentary response, and are replotted from diagrams in Mandelbrot and Wallis (1969). Their diagrams illustrate the range of sample estimates of R_n/s, but only the means are plotted here for clarity. The bracketed number on each plot is H for the main (linear) portion of the domain. $H > 0.5$ for all sequences, though for Rhine River data the difference is not significant. None of the other data shows any sign of approaching 0.5, even at the limits of their domains

sources of intermittent behaviour in most available data records (cf. Lettenmaier and Burges, 1978, and Fig. 2.1). Klemeš (1974) has gone on to demonstrate convincingly the sufficiency of non-stationarity to produce the Hurst phenomenon.

We now know that weather exhibits irregular spells on the synoptic and seasonal scale (Mitchell, 1976) and that climate similarly exhibits intermittent variability on all scales from a few years out. Fig. 2.3 includes examples of a long temperature sequence and a climatically sensitive tree ring record. Fig. 2.4 illustrates the spectrum of climatic variability over a wide range of timescales, and the conjectural response of some

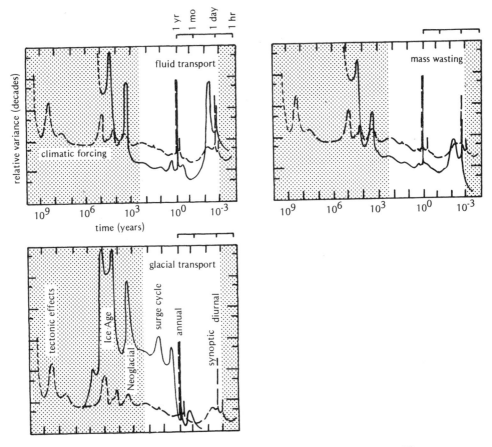

Fig. 2.4 Conjectural variance spectra for geophysical event sequences. The spectra are standardized on the annual cycle, and variance is plotted relative to that of the annual cycle. The logarithmic scales distort the variance contributions of the low frequency (left-hand) side by diminishing the area under the plot. The climatic spectrum is from Mitchell (1976): it represents thermal climate and is partly based on data. The response spectra are entirely conjectural. The highlighted area represents the domain of main interest in this paper

generalized geomorphological agencies. The response spectra have been sketched mainly on the notion that, as inertia increases in the sediment transporting system, response will be displaced towards lower frequencies. For example, the scale of synoptic weather events is considered to be very important for fluid transport of sediment: the range of sediment fluxes measured in rivers or in surf is far greater for individual storm events than it otherwise is over an entire year or, indeed, over periods of many years. This phenomenon is far less prominent for mass wasting—the annual cycle there being relatively important—and it is not detectable in glacial systems. In contrast, all significant variability in glacial transport systems occurs on timescales of Neoglacial and Glacial order: this induces further significant variability in other geomorphological transport systems. The period, near 10^5 years, at which fluid transport and mass wasting spectra increase without bound represents the supposed minimum time for significant Davisian evolution of the landscape. The spectrum for glaciation does not increase without bound since glaciation is too rare an event in earth history to contribute systematically to landscape evolution.

The presence of variability in several broad bands—not harmonics of each other—as illustrated in Fig. 2.4 would give rise to intermittent behaviour. Most available event sequences are of order 10^1 or 10^2 years long and would reveal only a portion of the variability carried in the significant low frequencies between 10^3 and 10^5 years. The effect of this low-frequency variability, if it is detectable, would be interpreted as a secular trend resulting from climatic change. For the truly non-stationary case wherein a consistent trend occurs throughout the data, $H = 1.0$ (see Klemeš, 1974). In summary, there appears to be sufficient ground to expect the Hurst phenomenon to appear in nearly all geophysical event sequences that respond to climatic forcing.

In geomorphological processes, a further complication ensues in that the stress–strain relationship between an applied stress, τ, and the resulting mass transfer, $q_t = q(\tau_t)$, may not be simple. It may reflect the prior history of the landscape. A simple illustration is the supply-limited character of washload transported in rivers. A rainstorm flood following a prolonged dry spell (or nival flood) may carry a large quantity of fine material that has been prepared for entrainment by repeated wetting and drying of soil (or by freeze–thaw), by local mass movements, by the effects of particular land uses, or has been exposed by land cover condition. On another occasion, an equivalent flood may carry far less sediment since it is restrained by other land use, by seasonal vegetation cover, or simply because insufficient time has elapsed since the last such event for a fresh supply of debris to be prepared for fluvial evacuation.

A second aspect of this issue is that $q(\tau)$ sometimes does not describe the simple effect of an applied force, but may result from the conjunction of several conditions. For example, the 'freeze–burst–thaw' cycle may be effective in mobilizing rock on a mountain wall only in the presence of water and a fortuitous configuration of rock crevices. In general

$$q(\tau) = f(\tau_i \mid x_j \geq x_{j\text{crit}}) \qquad i, j \geq 0$$

where the τ_i are effective stresses and the x_j are states with some threshold $x_{j\text{crit}}$ for the process to occur. Schumm has worked for many years on the issue of geomorphic thresholds, and now contends (Schumm, 1977) that they may be of two types (Fig. 2.5). Extrinsic thresholds are crossed when some external stress passes a critical level to produce an abrupt response in the system: intrinsic thresholds represent purely an historical progression of changes in a landscape system and require no new external stress.

The outcome of this complex pattern of geomorphological response is to render geomorphological event sequences more intermittent than the forcing sequence. Unfortunately, to characterize such a process requires a record whose length is considerably greater than T, the longest span over which intermittent behaviour recurs. Since most available event sequences exhibit intermittency to the limit of their length, we cannot be sure of characterizing them adequately.

Finally, over time spans comparable to the evolution of landscape, altogether exceptional events may occur. Gretener (1967) showed that the statistics of extremely improbable events makes their eventual occurrence very likely in geological time. Schumm and Chorley (1964), in their study of Threatening Rock, illustrated one class of 'improbable' events (periodic collapse of very large rock monoliths) that, recurring on the order of 10^3 years, dominates the development of a landscape. Further, they showed that each such event appears to be the culmination of a sequence that requires of the

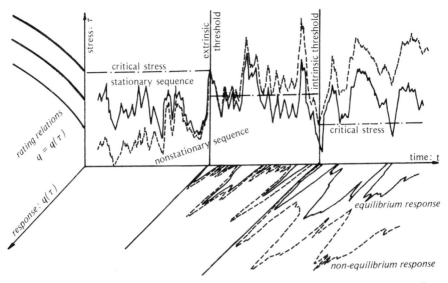

Fig. 2.5 Schematic diagram of stress and response sequences, incorporating thresholds. Each threshold crossing changes the critical level for response, as seen in the displacement of the stress-response relations on the left-hand 'wall'. The first threshold is 'extrinsic' (in Schumm's sense): the stress exceeds a certain level to produce the change. The second is intrinsic: it is not related to an immediate stress exceedance

order of 10^3 years to run its course, so that it is a continuing process.

In summary, short-term event sequences may provide a misleading impression of the long-term variability of a process, particularly where thresholds are important, as in many geomorphological cases. Most records that have been made within 'contemporary time' are too short to indicate the pattern of landscape evolution. The value of such records lies, rather, in the following contexts:

(1) their use to establish systematic physical relationships between applied stresses and material responses, where these can be functionally analysed, thence to study the mechanics of material transport;
(2) to study significant individual events (extreme events);
(3) to characterize the short-term, equilibrium behaviour of landforms in the present environment, for engineering purposes, and as a reference with which to compare the substantial effects of human activity.

'Contemporary time' might best be re-defined, then, as the (present) period within which a geomorphological process has maintained a substantially constant mean—that is, has undergone no important changes due either to non-stationarity of the forcing function or impingement upon some threshold. Such an epoch appears to be much shorter for most landscape-forming processes than has generally been appreciated in recent years, and may approach zero in some instances.

Direct Observations of Landscape Change

Instrument Records

Almost no parameter of direct geomorphological interest (i.e. pertaining to changing

landform configuration) is directly measured on a regular basis. Several important
environmental system parameters, principally pertaining to weather, water flows and
levels, and sedimentation, are regularly observed by government agencies, and these
provide the usual basis for assessing rates of geomorphological processes in the present
day. In this section, some of these data will be used to demonstrate the spatial variability
of geophysical event sequences.

Fig. 2.6 shows the record of mean annual flows at three of the longest continued
stream gauges in British Columbia, Canada. The Fraser River record refers to a very
large watershed. The sequence is evidently non-stationary within the record—it looks not
unlike the record of Fig. 2.1, and $H = 0.70$. Slaymaker (1972) has attempted to isolate
the reason for the apparent trend in Fraser River flows, but no simple cause could be
documented: in particular, no general change in precipitation was found. Comparing the

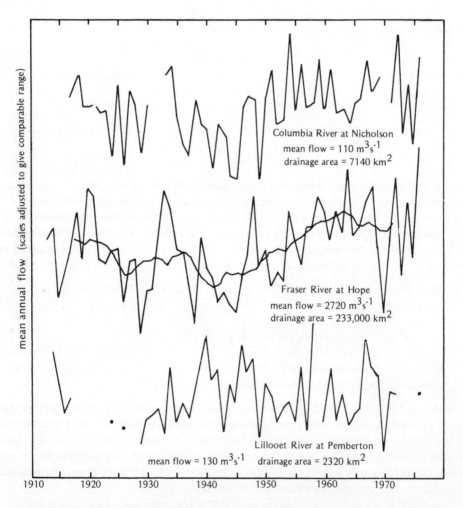

Fig. 2.6 Mean annual flows over $n \sim 60$ years for three rivers. A ten-year running
mean is also plotted for Fraser River to emphasize the long term changes (data of
Water Survey of Canada, 1974, with additions for the most recent years). Fraser
River and Columbia River exhibit significant intermittency, but Lillooet River does
not

other two records, it is clear that upper Columbia River, draining parts of the Canadian Rocky Mountains and Selkirk Mountains, shows the same trend ($H = 0.70$), but that Lillooet River, a tributary within the Fraser basin, does not ($H = 0.52$). The effect is evidently regional, but not general. In fact, Lillooet basin is 22% glacierized. It is probable that a cooler climate since about 1950 has reduced evaporation and tipped the regional water balance in favour of increased runoff. The effect is not evident in Lillooet basin, where the warmer preceding decades produced increased glacier melt. The supposition accords with the 20th century pattern of glacier fluctuations in the Canadian Cordillera (cf. Gardner, 1972, for the Rocky Mountains; W. H. Mathews, personal communication, 1978, confirms the pattern for the southern Coast Mountain region). Whatever the cause of the pattern, the example illustrates that trends or low-frequency fluctuations in geophysical records need not be regionally consistent since various antecedent conditions may influence them. Wallis (1977) has given other illustrations of pattern variability amongst records in his discussion of water resources data, and Goudie (1972, 1977) has demonstrated this by means of a comparison of many of the world's longest streamflow records.

In general, then, the statistics of geophysical event sequences that may be derived from instrument records should always be referred to the period of record and to the immediate locale: they should be expected to yield biased results if they are used to extrapolate beyond the period of record unless either (i) the record can be shown unequivocally to be stationary with $n > T$, the limit of intermittency, or (ii) the Hurst coefficient, H, can be estimated reliably. In any event, the record may yield biased regional results. In addition to limiting the value of records for direct inferences about the evolution of landscape, this situation has serious implications for simulation analyses of landform development (Ahnert, 1976), and for the space-for-time substitution (Brunsden and Kesel, 1973) in studying geomorphological processes.

So far as evolution of landscape goes, however, we are ultimately concerned with net change. This result is the integral of a process (or mean, which is the same thing). Provided we are no longer interested in the higher order statistics of the process, we may infer this result considerably more conveniently by examining net change of state, $x_{t2} - x_{t1}$, instead of by monitoring the process. Although such changes are more reliably examined, for most geomorphological processes, on the longer time scales discussed later in this book (Butzer, Chapter 10; Andrews and Miller, Chapter 18), important information can be gained from direct observation, or from interpretation of associated effects in contemporary time. A variety of methods are available: the usefulness of some of them is restricted to historical times.

Photographic Records

Direct comparisons of landform configuration at different times are most readily made using photographs. About 100 years of record might be recovered using photographs, but most early photographs were taken for purposes other than landscape studies, so that it is up to the present-day worker to discover the potential value of an old print and to provide a contemporary comparison. In some regions, historical photographic resources are available that might be used systematically. For example, the physiographic explorations of western North America during the late 19th and early 20th centuries by the United States and Canadian Geological Surveys produced important photographic archives, and various boundary surveys in the two countries have been useful. Schumm and Lichty (1963) were able to reconstruct a history of channel and floodplain changes extending over nearly a century for the Cimarron River in Kansas using historical photographs. Similarly, Gardner (1972) was able to demonstrate the pattern of glacier retreat and glacial sedimentation in the central Canadian Rockies for a comparable period beginning near the late 19th century climax.

Experimental use of vertical aerial photography to aid topographic mapping began in North America shortly after World War I, and systematic files date from about 1925. Hence, as many as 50 years might be encompassed by such records, although most of the world has been photographed only since 1950. Because of the high resolution afforded and the possibility of making systematic measurements in photogrammetric machines, this resource represents a major source of information about landform changes over time. Fig. 2.7 illustrates the use of aerial photography to study changes in a river bend where an influx of coarse gravel from upstream and abundant wood debris in the channel have produced a complex recent history. The episodic character of the major changes of course is evident. Several papers in this volume analyse similar events using comparable material.

The recent advent of satellite photography has, for the first time, introduced the possibility of synoptic scale observations of the earth's surface. Geomorphological applications (distinct from geological, physiographic, or hydrological applications) are as yet rare, probably because of resolution problems.

More recently, sequences of photographs have been assembled specifically for geomorphological purposes. A remarkable example was provided by Rapp (1960), who was able to compare photographs of talus cones on Spitsbergen taken as far back as 1882 (by Gerhard de Geer) with his own photographs to determine the extent of mass movement over 70 years. Allen (1970) used Rapp's observations as test data in a theory of avalanching materials. He deduced that avalanches containing 10^4 kg of rock per metre of width move on the order of 100 m, results that are confirmed by Rapp's observations, and further that such a movement will recur with a period of the order of 10^2 years under present conditions.

Maps and Historical Documents

Maps and other historical descriptions extend records back by several hundred years. An important problem is to determine the accuracy of such sources. Maps can often be checked if assuredly fixed reference points are plotted: often, there is no such assurance available. Although contours began to appear on topographic maps in the mid-19th century, even today it is only special project maps of very restricted areas that provide sufficient resolution for changes in elevation or contour to be measured. Planimetric information, particularly changes in river channel and coastline location, can often be obtained.

Brice (1977) used map and aerial photographic evidence to study lateral shifts of the Middle Sacramento River, California, over a century. Simons *et al*. (1974) used early engineering surveys to study the effect of engineering works on the morphology of part of the Mississippi River over a similar period.

Rich historical resources are often available in Europe: Sundborg (1956), following a technique adopted by Sten de Geer, used cadastral maps going back to the mid-18th century to compile changes in the river meanders of Klarälven and to study the growth of Klarälven's delta (Sundborg and Heijkenskjöld, 1972).

The use of other historical documents is remarkably demonstrated by Grove's (1972) presentation of the record of glacier advances, floods, and mass movements extracted from land rent records of the northern Jostedalsbre district of Norway. The record extends right through the Little Ice Age of the 17th to 19th centuries and documents

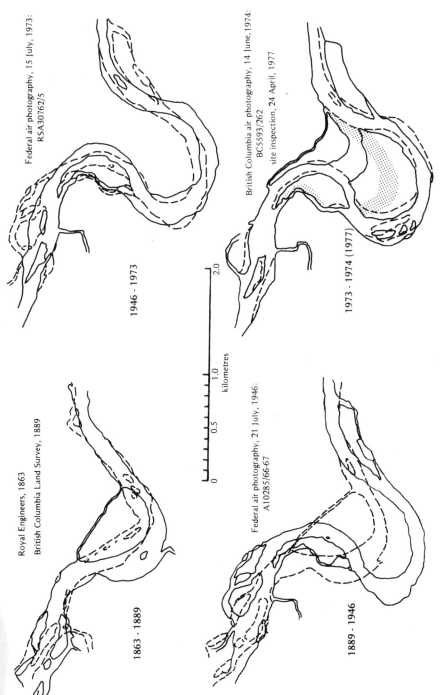

Royal Engineers, 1863
British Columbia Land Survey, 1889

1863 - 1889

Federal air photography, 21 July, 1946:
A10285/66-67

1889 - 1946

Federal air photography, 15 July, 1973:
RSA30762/5

1946 - 1973

British Columbia air photography, 14 June, 1974:
BC5593/262
site inspection, 24 April, 1977

1973 - 1974 (1977)

0   0.5   1.0   1.5   2.0
kilometres

Fig. 2.7 Comparison of the course of Bella Coola River (British Columbia) at the big bend near Bella Coola village on six occasions between 1863 and 1977. In each diagram the solid lines represent the later date, except that the stipple pattern represents the change after 1974 in the final frame. The data are derived from historical surveys to 1889 (there also exists a 1905 topographical survey), from vertical aerial photography since 1946, and site inspection (1977). The early maps are not entirely accurate, hence part of the change before 1946 may be spurious. The maps show that normal loop extension continued from 1863 to 1973, when a major cutoff occurred. Since 1973 the river has shifted steadily across most of the former meander again. At present the curvature is too severe near the point indicated by the date (1977) and further major changes may be anticipated

the spatially transgressive and temporally non-stationary character of geomorphological event sequences in response to climate fluctuations. Further examples are included in this volume.

Interpretation of Associated Effects

Botanical Effects

Growth, condition, and succession of vegetation are influenced by stability of substrate. Further, many woody plants will yield reliable dating and cross-dating from the consistent response of annual growth to environmental conditions (Fritts, 1976). Hence, interpretation of geomorphological processes can sometimes be made from the growth and condition of woody plants (Alestalo, 1971).

Trees have most commonly been used as chronological indicators for the age of substrate (*e.g.* Sigafoos and Hendricks, 1969, 1972, amongst many references); in particular, Neoglacial moraines have been dated in this way. However, the response of a tree to disturbance can often be interpreted to provide evidence of geomorphological processes as well as dating. Tilting of a tree when the substrate is disturbed leads to production of distinctive reaction wood and other morphological changes: these have been used by LaMarche (1966) (800-year record) and by Parker and Josza (1973) (100-year record) to study river bank erosion, by Zoltai (1975) (160-year record) to study soil movement on frost-patterned ground, and by Shroder (1978) (200-year record) to study movement of boulder tongues. Shear or rupture of growth-producing cambial tissue beneath the bark produces growth suppression and scars. These features, as well as breakage and felling followed by sprouting, have been used to date flooding, particularly along ice-choked rivers (Sigafoos, 1964; Parker and Josza, 1973), and avalanche activity (Potter, 1969).

Burial or exposure is detectable in living trees by differences between stemwood and rootwood morphology, by the occurrence of adventitious roots, or by sprouting. These characteristics have been used by LaMarche (1968) to determine rates of slope denudation in the California White Mountains.

Various plants are, of course, climatically sensitive in many regions and provide one of the main techniques for extending climatic records (Fritts, 1976), so that indications of the climatic sequence that prompted geomorphological events can often be gained as well. Although the geomorphological processes that affect the plant may be sporadic, the plant preserves a continuous seasonal record of its history, so that complete event sequences are preserved. There are numerous complications in the response of living organisms to the environment which affect the interpretation of environmental history from them, yet they appear to present one of the best opportunities available for the interpretation of palaeoenvironments on timescales between several decades and several hundred years.

Records in Depositional Environments

The most obvious source of information about geomorphological processes (at least about depositional processes) lies in the sediments themselves. The main complicating factors in the study of deposits are (i) the episodic nature of many depositional processes (Schumm, 1975, 1977) and (ii) the probability that erosion will occur periodically in most terrestrial depositional environments. Either effect leads to an incomplete record.

Where spatially transgressive events occur consistently in one direction for some time, surface morphology may yield a useful history. The development of beach dunes, deposition of small moraines in front of a retreating glacier, and shifting river meanders are examples. Hickin (1974) was able to study the evolution of meander bends on Beatton River over several centuries by mapping point bar ridge patterns which were dated dendrochronologically.

There are problems associated with the study of the terrestrial sedimentary record stemming from the long-term instability of almost all such environments. Fig. 2.8 presents a schematic diagram of the main sediment transfers and storage points. Reliable records may be recovered only from sites that conform to the following requirements:

(i) they have been active and subject to similar processes throughout the period of interest;

(ii) they are purely aggradational (hence, no disconformities appear in the sedimentary record);

(iii) the deposits are locally homogeneous (i.e. sediment inputs are well distributed over the receiving area—otherwise a very difficult sampling problem must be faced);

(iv) the sedimentary processes are seasonally distinctive, so that a chronology may be inferred, *or* there exists the possibility for absolute dating.

Such sites are usually restricted to bogs, lakes, and submarine basins, though river floodplain accumulations may remain stable for periods much longer than the horizon of this review. Environments that are most likely to yield stable sites are indicated in Fig. 2.8.

The resolution with which an event sequence may be reconstructed from the sediments depends on the timescale for bedding repetition. Annual rhythmites are found in many lacustrine deposits and in some others where tempo is controlled by seasonal climate (for example, evaporites). Fluvial deposits are apt to be conditioned by synoptic weather events. Synoptic within-annual sequences may be found (Peach and Perrie, 1975), but many sequences are complex and difficult to interpret. Some environments are dominated by rare, irregular events (e.g. extreme floods or mudflows on alluvial fans; subaqueous turbidity flows), and some reveal no usable sequence within the limits of fortuitously included, datable material.

Although physical properties have traditionally provided the basis for interpretation of sedimentary sequences, chemical—particularly differential isotopic—properties are of increasing importance on all timescales. Radioactive isotopes that circulate in the atmosphere are particularly interesting since, once isolated in sediments, they become chronometers by virtue of the fixed rate of radioactive decay. Isotopes with half-lives of between a few years and a few hundred years may be useful within the horizon of contemporary time. Table 2.1 indicates the main candidates for use. Among them, ^3H (tritium) has been most extensively used, to date ice and groundwater. Silicon-32 has been used for similar purposes, very large sample volumes being required for this isotope. Bomb-caesium has been used to determine recent sedimentation rates, as has ^{210}Pb (references in Table 2.1 and in Wise, this volume, Chapter 9). Some of the rarer isotopes will become traceable with recently developed mass spectrometric techniques for detection.

Nuclear releases and accidents have proved perversely useful on a few occasions for studies of sedimentation processes (Haushild *et al.*, 1975). Other useful, man-induced indicators in the sedimentary column include trace metals, the result of increasing industrial activity after about 1800 in northwest Europe and eastern North America (Oldfield *et al.*, 1978), and pollen indicators of the otherwise known decline or introduction of certain plants, mainly within the last two centuries (Anderson, 1974).

Michael Church

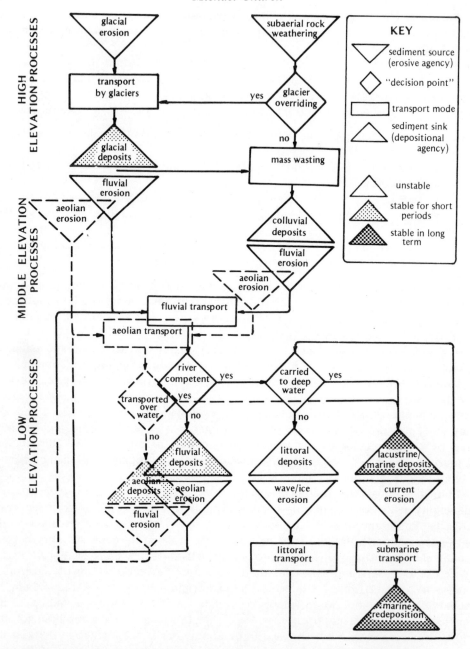

Fig. 2.8 Schematic diagram of the main sediment transfer patterns and storage points in the landscape. The dashed portion in the lower part of the diagram indicates an aeolian stream that parallels the fluvial stream: the latter is much more important. A variety of more complex pathways are not shown in order to preserve clarity

Conclusions

Significant changes in landscape almost always occur in time frames much longer than the few hundred years that we may, by any reasonable definition, call 'contemporary'.

Table 2.1 Radioactive isotopes with short half-lives

Isotope	Half-life (years)	Origin	References for geochronology
^{3}H	12.3	Upper atmosphere, bomb, reactors	Payne (1967)
^{32}Si	350 ± 150	Upper atmosphere	Nijampurkar and Somayajulu (1974)
^{39}Ar	260	Upper atmosphere (very rare)	
^{90}Sr	27.7	Bomb	
^{137}Cs	27	Bomb	Ritchie *et al.* (1973)
^{210}Pb	22.3	^{238}U decay series	Krishnaswamy *et al.* (1971)

Analysis of geophysical records reveals intermittent behaviour over periods far longer than almost all records. Because of threshold effects and complex functional relations, geomorphological responses are apt to be more intermittent than most of the climatic and hydrological sequences available for inspection. Hence, contemporary records of geomorphological events are not likely to represent the long-term behaviour sufficiently well to provide any firm basis for understanding landscape evolution.

Useful information about the processes and recent tempo of landscape change can often be gained by means more expeditious than analysis of instrument records of related events. Amongst the techniques available, those based on the behaviour of woody plants and on the chemical character of sediments appear to be particularly promising for the future. An important application of information pertaining to contemporary time is to study the influence of environmental processes on human activities and the increasingly pervasive reciprocal effects. These techniques may be especially sensitive in this respect.

In this introductory review, the writer has deliberately restricted references to recent examples that seem instructive. The regional character of the work referred to (mainly northwestern North America and northern Europe) is also deliberate. Whilst many important studies have thereby been slighted, to do more would invite the appearance of a book: the collection of papers that follows goes some way towards that end.

Acknowledgement

Dr. B. A. Kennedy kindly reviewed and duly approved this tract.

References

Ahnert, F. (1976). Brief description of a comprehensive three-dimensional process–response model of landform development. *Z. Geomorph.*, Suppl. **25**, 29–49.

Alestalo, J. (1971). Dendrochronological interpretation of geomorphological processes. *Fennia*, **105**, 140 pp.

Allen, J. R. L. (1970). The avalanching of granular solids on dune and similar slopes. *J. Geol.*, **78**, 326–351.

Anderson, T. W. (1974). The chestnut pollen decline as a time horizon in lake sediments in eastern North America. *Can. J. Earth Sci.*, **11**, 678–685.

Brice, J. C. (1977). *Lateral Migration of the Middle Sacramento River, California*. United States Geological Survey, Water Resources Division, Menlo Park, Calif., WRI-77/052, 51 pp. (National Technical Information Service, PB-271-6G2).

Brunsden, D., and Kesel, R. H. (1973). Slope development on a Mississippi River bluff in historic time. *J. Geol.*, **81**, 576–597.

Chorley, R. J., and Kennedy, B. A. (1972). *Physical Geography–a Systems approach*. Prentice Hall, London, 370 pp.

Fritts, H. C. (1976). *Tree Rings and Climate*. Academic Press, London, 567 pp.

Gardner, J. (1972). Recent glacial activity and some associated landforms in the Canadian Rocky Mountains. in *Mountain Geomorphology* (Eds. H. O. Slaymaker and H. J. McPherson) B. C. Geographical Series, No. 14, pp. 55–62.

Goudie, A. S. (1972). The concept of Post-Glacial progressive desiccation. *Univ. Oxford, School Geog., Res. Pap.*, No. 4, 48 pp.

Goudie, A. S. (1977). *Environmental Change*. Clarendon Press, Oxford, 244 pp.

Gretener, P. E. (1967). Significance of the rare event in geology. *Am. Assoc. Petrol. Geol. Bull.*, **51**, 2197–2206.

Grove, J. M. (1972). The incidence of landslides, avalanches, and floods in western Norway during the Little Ice Age. *Arct. Alp. Res.*, **4**, 131–138.

Haushild, W. L., Dempster, G. R., Jr., and Stevens, H. H., Jr. (1975). Distribution of radionuclides in the Columbia River streambed, Hanford Reservation to Longview, Washington. *United States Geol. Surv. Prof. Pap.*, No. 433–0, 35 pp.

Hickin, E. J. (1974). The development of meanders in natural river channels. *Am. J. Sci.*, **274**, 414–442.

Hurst, H. E. (1951). Long-term storage capacity of reservoirs. *Am. Soc. Civil Engrs. Trans.*, **116**, 770–808.

Klemeš, V. (1974). The Hurst phenomenon: a puzzle? *Wat. Resour. Res.*, **10**, 675–688.

Krishnaswamy, S., Lal, D., Martin, J. M., and Meybeck, M. (1971). Geochronology of lake sediments. *Earth Planet. Sci. Lett.*, **11**, 407–414.

LaMarche, V. C., Jr. (1966). An 800-year history of stream erosion as indicated by botanical evidence. *United States Geol. Surv. Prof. Pap.*, No. 550–D, 83–86.

LaMarche, V. C., Jr. (1968). Rates of slope degradation as determined from botanical evidence, White Mountains, California. *United States Geol. Surv. Prof. Pap.*, No. 352–I, pp. 341–377.

Lettenmaier, D. P., and Burges, S. J. (1978). Climate change: detection and its impact on hydrological design. *Water Resour. Res.*, **14**, 679–687.

Mandelbrot, B. B., and Wallis, J. R. (1969). Some long-run properties of geophysical records. *Water Resour. Res.*, **5**, 321–340.

Mitchell, J. M., Jr. (1976). An overview of climatic variability and its causal mechanisms. *Quat. Res.*, **6**, 481–494.

Nijampurkar, V. N., and Somayajulu, B. L. K. (1974). An improved method of Silicon-32 measurement of groundwaters. *Proc. Indian Acad. Sci.*, **80**, 289–298.

Oldfield, F., Thompson, R., and Barber, K. W. (1978). Changing atmospheric fallout of magnetic particles recorded in recent ombotrophic peat sections. *Science*, **199**, 679–680.

Palmer, H. S. (1863). *North Bentinck Arm Route. Report of a Journey of Survey from Victoria to Fort Alexander via North Bentinck Arm*. Royal Engineers Press, New Westminster, 30 pp. + map insert.

Parker, M. L., and Josza, L. A. (1973). Dendrochronological investigations along the Mackenzie, Liard and South Nahanni Rivers, N. W. T. Part I: Using tree damage to date landslides, ice jamming and flooding. In *Hydrologic Aspects of Northern Pipeline Development*. Canada, Task Force on Northern Oil Development. Environmental–Social Committee, Northern Pipelines. Report No. 73–3, pp. 313–464.

Payne, B. R. (1967). Isotope techniques in the hydrologic cycle. *Geophys. Monogr.*, **11**, 62–68.

Peach, P. A., and Perrie, L. A. (1975). Grain-size distribution within glacial varves. *Geology*, **3**, 43–46.

Potter, N., Jr. (1969). Tree-ring dating of snow avalanche tracks and the geomorphic activity of avalanches, Northern Absaroka Mountains, Wyoming. *Geol. Soc. Am. Spec. Pap.*, No. 123, 141–165.

Rapp, A. (1960). Talus slopes and mountain walls at Temelfjorden, Spitsbergen. *Norsk Polarinst. Skr.*, **119**, 96 pp. + plates.

Ritchie, J. C., McHenry, J. R., and Gill, A. C. (1973). Dating recent reservoir sediments. *Limnol. Oceanol.*, **18**, 254–263.

Scheidegger, A. E. (1971). *Theoretical Geomorphology.* Springer, New York, 2nd ed., 435 pp.

Schumm, S. A. (1975). Episodic erosion: a modification of the geomorphic cycle. In *Theories of Landform Development* (Eds. W. N. Melhorn, and R. C. Flemal). 6th Ann. Geomorphology Symp., Binghamton, N. Y., State University of New York, Pubs. in Geomorphology, pp. 69–86.

Schumm, S. A. (1977). *The Fluvial System.* Wiley-Interscience, New York, 338 pp.

Schumm, S. A., and Chorley, R. J. (1964). The fall of Threatening Rock. *Am. J. Sci.*, **262**, 1041–1054.

Schumm, S. A., and Lichty, R. W. (1963). Channel widening and floodplain construction along Cimarron River in southwestern Kansas. *United States Geol. Surv. Prof. Pap.*, No. 352–D, pp. 68–88.

Shroder, J. F., Jr. (1978). Dendrogeomorphological analysis of mass movement on Table Cliffs Plateau, Utah. *Quat. Res.*, **9**, 168–185.

Sigafoos, R. S. (1964). Botanical evidence of floods and floodplain deposition. *United States Geol. Surv. Prof. Pap.*, No. 485–A, 35 pp.

Sigafoos, R. L., and Hendricks, E. L. (1969). The time interval between stabilization of alpine glacial deposits and establishment of tree seedlings. *United States Geol. Surv. Prof. Pap.*, No. 650–B, pp. 89–93.

Sigafoos, R. L., and Hendricks, E. L. (1972). Recent activity of glaciers of Mt. Rainier, Washington. *United States Geol. Surv. Prof. Pap.*, No. 387–B, 24 pp.

Simons, D. B., Schumm, S. A., and Stevens, M. A. (1974). Geomorphology of the Middle Mississippi River. *United States Army Engineer Waterways Experiment Stn., Vicksburg, Miss., Contract Rpt.*, No. Y-74-2, 110 pp.

Slaymaker, H. O. (1972). Recent fluctuations in the mean discharge of the Fraser River. In *Contemporary Geography: Research Trends* (Ed. R. Leigh). B. C. Geographical Series, No. 16, pp. 3–14.

Sundborg, A. (1956). The River Klarälven: a study of fluvial processes. *Geog. Ann.*, **38**, 126–316.

Sundborg, A., and Heijkenskjöld, R. (1972). Klarälvsdeltat i Karlstad. *Ymer*, Ar. 1972, pp. 14–25.

Wallis, J. R. (1977). Climate, climatic change, and water supply. *Eos*, **58**, 1012–1024.

Water Survey of Canada (1974). *Historical Streamflow Summary. British Columbia to 1973.* Water Resources Branch, Inland Waters Directorate, Canada Dept. of Environment. 694 pp.

Wolman, M. G., and Miller, J. P. (1960). Magnitude and frequency of forces in geomorphic processes. *J. Geol.*, **68**, 54–74.

Yevjevich, V. (1972). *Stochastic Processes in Hydrology.* Water Resources Pubs., Fort Collins, Colo., 276 pp.

Zoltai, S. C. (1975). Tree ring record of soil movements on permafrost. *Arct. Alp. Res.*, **7**, 331–340.

Timescales in Geomorphology
Edited by R. A. Cullingford, D. A. Davidson, and J. Lewin
© 1980 John Wiley & Sons Ltd

CHAPTER 3

Hillslope processes and deposits in forested areas of Luxembourg

A. C. Imeson, F. J. P. M. Kwaad and H. J. Mücher
University of Amsterdam

Introduction

Forested areas are of interest in geomorphology inasmuch as they provide opportunities for studying processes operating under reasonably natural conditions. The low rates of erosion observed have frequently been considered to approach the 'geologic norm' of erosion described by Lowdermilk (1934). Less is known about these processes, however, than those operating under conditions of accelerated erosion; frequently the processes are assumed to be the same but to be confined to restricted areas or to operate at slower rates.

An indication as to the timescales appropriate to the study of contemporary erosion processes in forested areas of Luxembourg has been obtained in two ways: firstly, by directly measuring the effect of particular processes in the field over short timespans of 1 or 2 years; and secondly, by studying recent colluvial deposits, presumably produced by contemporary processes. Here colluvium is defined as a loose, non-stratified, non- or ill-sorted, heterogeneous mixture of various size grades, found on the lower parts or at the base of slopes; if it contains rock fragments, these are angular.

The problems encountered in, and possibilities offered by, these approaches will be considered in this paper and illustrated by the results of the Luxembourg study. The object of studying both colluvial deposits and contemporary processes together is to enable more confident conclusions to be drawn about the significance of the results. Of particular interest is the degree to which colluvium reflects the processes responsible for its formation. If such relationships can be established from combined investigations of this kind, or from experiments, extrapolations from process measurements can be better evaluated and conditions which have led to the accumulation of colluvium in the past might be inferred. Unfortunately, however, relationships between process measurements and colluvium are in practice difficult to establish. At present, process studies are hampered by the lack of standardized methods of measurement of known efficiency, and under forest by a lack of knowledge about the processes themselves. The study of colluvium is hindered by the absence of precise micromorphological and sedimentological criteria for determining conditions of transport.

Process Measurements and Colluvium

In the case of accelerated erosion where large amounts of material are deposited by surface wash processes, the relationship between process and deposit is clear because other processes are usually relatively insignificant. However, under forest, processes insignificant on agricultural land may combine to produce appreciable colluvial deposits. From the study of these colluvial deposits one can learn several things:

(a) when the colluvium was formed; in Luxembourg, pollen analysis in combination with radiocarbon datings and historical data was used for this purpose (Riezebos and Slotboom, 1974, 1978; Kwaad and Mücher, 1977, 1979); also, the presence in the colluvium of certain heavy minerals from a volcanic eruption in the Eifel of a known age (Hulshof *et al.*, 1968; Jungerius *et al.*, 1968; Pissart *et al.*, 1975; Juvigné, 1977) has been used as an age indicator for the colluvium (Jungerius and Mücher, 1970; Kwaad and Mücher, 1979);

(b) whether one or several periods of colluviation have occurred, interrupted by periods of soil formation; this is based on field evidence (colour, content of stones, presence of buried soils, etc.) and on micromorphological characteristics of the colluvium (Mücher *et al.*, 1972);

(c) the rate of formation of the colluvium, based on considerations of thickness and period of formation of the colluvium (Kwaad, 1977);

(d) the environmental conditions under which the colluvium was formed (whether arable land, forest, etc.), based on pollen analysis and historical data (Riezebos and Slotboom, 1974, 1978; Kwaad and Mücher, 1977, 1979; Kwaad, 1977);

(e) the nature and relative importance of the processes which contributed to the formation of the colluvium; research concerning this point has not made much progress yet; Kwaad (1977) compared the grain-size composition of material collected in splash boards under forest in northern Luxembourg with that of natural colluvium on the same slope and found a close resemblance; Mücher and de Ploey (1977) studied the structural characteristics of deposits formed under controlled laboratory conditions and compared these with natural deposits.

These points will be illustrated in more detail in the course of this chapter.

Processes on Forested Slopes

Mineral material is transported downslope in temperate forests in a variety of ways, many of which reflect the natural functioning of the particular forest ecosystem. The relative importance of these processes is not yet known, neither are details of their areal or temporal variations.

Transport of material by overland flow is often possible over small areas in many forests in spite of the generally high infiltration capacities. Rainfall and hence soil moisture and sorptivity are unevenly distributed owing to the effects of the canopy and topography (Zaslavsky and Sinai, 1977) and forest soils may be locally, or even extensively, water repellent. In any case, water may carry soil particles some tens of centimetres downslope through the interlocking leaves of the litter layer before infiltrating into the A1 horizon.

Perhaps the most important processes under forest, due to the restricted occurrence or travel distance of overland flow, are those associated with splash erosion. Of particular importance here is the role played by the soil fauna in exposing mineral soil and creating opportunities for splash erosion. Under certain conditions in Luxembourg, earthworms may remove all fallen litter from half of the forest floor within a few months of the leaf fall, and elsewhere by the late summer and early autumn between 20 and 70% of the ground may be covered by animal mounds and wormcasts. Animals (voles and moles) displace material directly downslope by burrowing and are important transporters of material in their own right.

It might be thought that material splashed from soil exposures soon becomes trapped in the litter and washed into the A horizon before it can travel very far. On gently sloping or flat land this may be the case. On moderately to steeply sloping terrain and on wind-exposed slopes, a considerable proportion of material splashed from soil exposures is transported by the leaves onto which it becomes attached downslope to colluvial accumulations or river channels (van Zon, 1978).

Measurement of Sediment Transport on Slopes

The rates of sediment delivery by the processes mentioned above have usually been measured by intercepting and collecting the sediment being transported downslope. Examples of this approach are illustrated in Figs. 3.1 and 3.2, where the monthly amount of material transported downslope by splash and litter, respectively, are shown. Although illustrative, particularly in terms of seasonal variations and short-term time-scales, the absolute efficiency of the trapping device is difficult to establish. Maintaining the efficiency of the trap at the same level is easier but in practice unforseen difficulties often arise, particularly with the forest fauna, which influence the accuracy of the collection. Another difficulty is in isolating the effect of different processes. In general, problems faced by collecting devices are similar to those described for plot experiments by Boughton (1967).

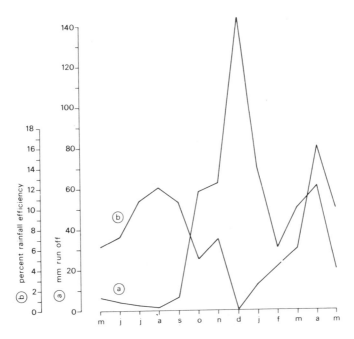

Fig. 3.1 Rainfall efficiency and runoff in the wooded Haarts catchment, northern Luxembourg, 1973–1974. (a) Runoff was measured at a gauging station equipped with a V-notch weir and an Ott water level recorder. (b) Rainfall efficiency is the amount of splashed soil in mg per mm of rain; it can also be expressed as a monthly percentage of the yearly total (Kwaad, 1977)

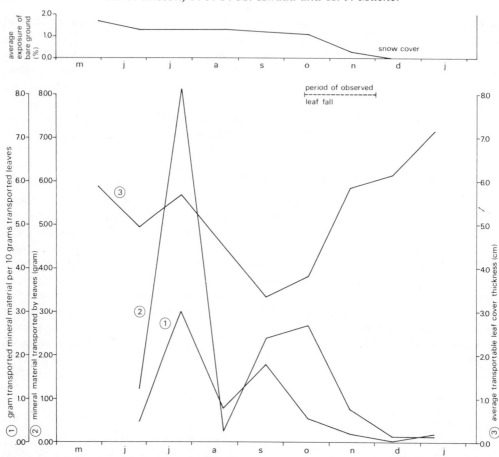

Fig. 3.2 Percentage of bare soil under beech forest in the Honsschlaed catchment, southern Luxembourg. Average thickness of the transportable part of the litter layer (3), amount of mineral matter transported as attached to leaves, in g per metre of slope width (2) and in g/10 g transported leaves (1). Period of measurement May 1976–January 1977 (van Zon, 1978)

The heterogeneity of forest conditions means that many measurements are required before statistical parameters of the population can be estimated satisfactorily. The laboratory costs entailed in handling all of the samples that would be collected prohibit this in most cases and only a limited range of conditions can usually be investigated. Similar restraints inhibit the continuation of most measurements for more than a few years. Yearly variations in climate and animal population fluctuations which have an unknown but probably large effect on sediment delivery therefore make the long-term significance of the measurements difficult to assess. Even if measurements were to be continued for 10 or 20 years the effect of the changes in forest management which have occurred in the past (van der Poel, 1976) on the forest fauna would still remain unknown. It is for these reasons that it is helpful to examine colluvial deposits.

The Study of Colluvial Deposits

The importance of slope deposits in the study of landscape development has been recognized by, amongst others, Butler (1959), Demek (1969), Walker (1962), and Young (1972). However, in contrast to marine and fluviatile deposits, relatively little is known about slope deposits and they are mostly defined according to their assumed genesis rather than on the basis of the structure of the material itself (Fairbridge, 1968; Soil Survey Staff, 1962). Yet just as palaeosols provide information on the stable phases of landscape development, so slope deposits give an insight into the conditions prevailing during and before (via pedorelicts) their accumulation. Further, when soil profiles are developed in them, information can be obtained about the relative age of the deposits. At present, there is unfortunately no accepted descriptive classification of slope deposits. Beckmann (1967) was one of the first to attempt this using micromorphological criteria but he limited his work to the study of solifluction deposits in the Sierra Nevada (Andalusia).

The initial phase of an investigation of slope deposits usually involves recognizing them as depositional materials. In many cases this can be readily done macroscopically in the field on the basis of, for example, differences in texture and colour, or the presence of charcoal, anthropogenic material, stone lines, or buried soils. When this is difficult, as in the loess soils of The Netherlands, micromorphological evidence is important. Criteria used by Mücher (1974) as indicative of loess colluvium in this area included papules, sharply bounded nodules, plant and root fragments parallel to the surface, and buried mudcrusts and pedorelicts (for example, rounded aggregates from other soil horizons). Some of the pedorelicts may, of course, reflect transportation within the soil profile by processes of soil homogenization rather than former erosion. In addition to micromorphological analyses, pollen, heavy mineral, and grain size distributions may be used under certain conditions to establish transport.

After establishing that the material is indeed a slope deposit, the next phase of investigation often involves subdividing it into various zones or layers, largely on the basis of macromorphological field evidence (colour, texture, stoniness, roots, structure, presence of buried soil horizons, etc.). This subdivision can be controlled or refined by the analyses of bulk and undisturbed samples, by means of variations in grain-size distributions, pH, S and T values, clay and heavy mineral composition, and by micromorphological description and interpretation. Micromorphological investigation is particularly useful because it provides insight into the degree to which differences indicated from other laboratory work (for example, grain size, pH, and organic carbon determinations) reflect sedimentological differences, soil formation, or both.

When buried soil horizons are found in slope deposits, these allow a distinction to be made between relatively stable periods with soil formation dominating over erosion or sedimentation and relatively unstable periods with translocation of slope material dominating over soil formation (Butler, 1959). When such periods of slope stability and slope instability are placed in chronological order, a sequence of events which gave rise to the polygenetic profile as we can observe it can be inferred. There is always a possibility, of course, of missing certain events due to excessive erosion during (one of) the next unstable period(s), by which all traces of a preceding stable period may be erased.

The most difficult phase of investigation is the interpretation of the mode of formation of the deposit. Whereas a large amount is known about the origin of sedimentary structures in marine and fluviatile deposits, the study of slope deposits is, by comparison, in its infancy.

Two approches have been employed to study the effect of particular processes on colluviation: (1) direct observation in the field and (2) experimental work in the field and laboratory. On the basis of experimental work, Mücher and de Ploey (1977) were able to draw conclusions about the mode of redeposition of loess from the Pleniglacial A of the Weichselian in Belgium. They arrived at the following conclusions:

(a) Pluvial runoff (overland flow with raindrop impact), supplied with or without extra runoff at the upper end of the erosion flume, gave rise to laminated deposits, tightly packed and moderately differentiated in size and mineral species.

(b) After flow (the flow that occurs in the field during a short period after rainfall has ceased) and meltwater flow were simulated by adding runoff at the upper end of an erosion flume. If the discharge and suspended load were moderate (0.8 l min^{-1} dm^{-1} and 20,000 mg l^{-1}, respectively), the sediments produced were very well laminated, well sorted, minerally differentiated, and loosely packed.

(c) When splash (material transported exclusively under raindrop impact) was applied to loess materials, no lamination, no sorting, and practically no mineral differentiation were produced that could be observed in the thin sections.

However, such experimental work still needs to be done for the forest soils of Luxembourg. A difficulty with slope deposits is that the depositional structures are not only determined by the nature of the processes of erosion and deposition, but also by the nature of the material itself, e.g. by its grain-size composition.

An Example from the Luxembourg Ardennes

The results of a number of studies in the neighbourhood of Wiltz in Luxembourg will be discussed below in an attempt to illustrate the relationship between the timescales associated with present day processes and the accumulation of colluvial deposits. In this area (Fig. 3.3) the Ardennes have a relative relief of about 90 m in which relatively gently sloping upper slopes, representing the remnants of an old planation surface, contrast with the steeply incised lower and middle slopes resulting from later stream incisions. The upper slopes are cultivated, but the steep middle and lower slopes are wooded either with beech, or mixed coppiced oak and beech, or with spruce fir or pine plantations. Many of the upper valley courses are dry and under forest; these contain a stony dark brown colluvial deposit. A similar deposit is also often found above the characteristic break of slope which occurs at the edge of the incision. This colluvium is distinct from the colluvium currently accumulating on agricultural land.

Forest Colluvium

In the field the colluvium found under forest was interpreted as such amongst other things on the basis of its colour and texture, and by the fact that it often rested on a stone line or truncated Bt horizon of an older soil profile. At first the entire deposit, usually up to 80 cm deep, depending on its position in the dry valley, was thought to have accumulated under the present forest vegetation.

Micromorphological criteria confirming the deposit to be colluvium (Kwaad and Mücher, 1977) were:

(1) The presence of many sharply bounded and mostly sub-rounded lithorelicts with colours in incident light ranging from grey to yellow-orange, brown and red. The various forms or stages of iron segregation found and exhibited by intermixed fragments of the same rock type would not be expected if the detritus had formed *in situ*. The presence of fresh (grey) rock fragments, which must have been

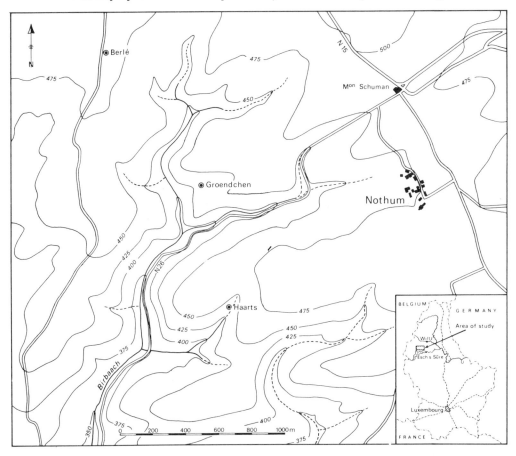

Fig. 3.3 Location of sites in northern Luxembourg where colluvium was studied. At the Berlé site farmland colluvium occurs (Kwaad and Mücher, 1979). The Groendchen and Haarts sites are located near the centre of two dry valleys in which woodland colluvium is found (Kwaad and Mücher, 1977; Kwaad, 1977)

relatively recently supplied, and the general lack of weathering rinds, indicate a recent displacement of the material.

(2) The occurrence of sharply bounded and sub-rounded ferric nodules next to diffuse ferric nodules apparently formed *in situ*.

(3) The presence of pedorelicts in the form of some papules and a few para-aggregates.

(4) The occurrence of charcoal fragments of various dimensions.

The initial assumption that all of the colluvium had formed under forest was not supported by palynological evidence (Riezebos and Slotboom, 1974; Kwaad, 1977). This suggested that only about the upper 10 cm of colluvium had formed under forest (Fig. 3.4). From ^{14}C determinations it appeared that accumulation had begun about AD 1400. From the pollen content it would seem that the forest colluvium in the upper part of the deposit dates from about AD 1800. At the site shown in Fig. 3.4 at the centre of the dry valley in the Haarts catchment, it is estimated that colluvium has accumulated at a rate of 6 cm per 100 years since the present coppiced oak/beech woodland was established round about AD 1800. Field evidence did not establish that the colluvium

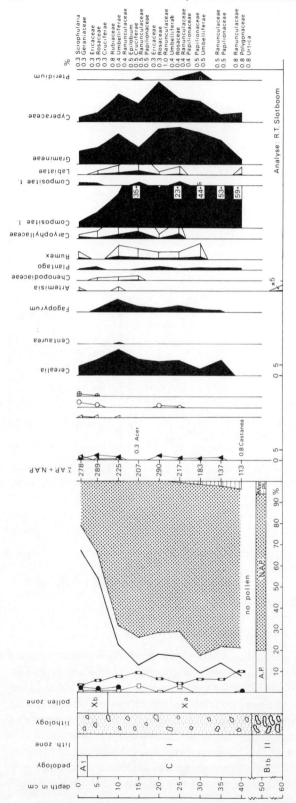

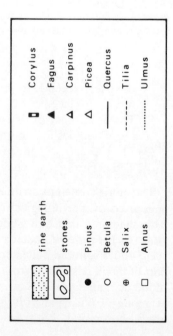

Fig. 3.4 Pollen diagram of the colluvium in the upper part of the Haarts valley. Location is given in Fig. 3.3. The colluvium forms the top 45 cm of the profile. It overlies a buried IIBtb horizon of a truncated soil profile (Kwaad, 1977). The pollen percentages are given relative to the total amount of tree pollen (A.P.) and non-tree pollen (N.A.P.)

underlying the forest colluvium was not formed under forest, but the stone line and truncated B horizons did indicate rather severe erosion preceding its deposition. Further, a land-use map of Luxembourg was compiled in 1770 by the Comte de Ferrari at a scale of about 1:50,000 (re-issued in 1970). From this it would seem that much less woodland existed in the Wiltz area than today and that in the Haarts catchment at the site illustrated in Fig. 3.4, marshy meadowland was mapped. The sudden increase in tree pollen from 30 to 75% at a depth of 10 cm is thought to indicate reafforestation shortly after this time.

The upper 10 cm or so of colluvium found in the dry valley probably reflects processes of erosion occurring under woodland. Although it lacks stratification this does not mean that the deposit was not formed as a result of overland flow. Nevertheless, on the basis of the grain-size distribution, processes associated with animal activity and splash are thought to have been largely responsible for its accumulation. The size distribution of the material caught in splash traps bears a close resemblance to that of the colluvium (Kwaad, 1977). As a result of splash creep, 10% of this material was larger than 1 cm. In the colluvium material coarser than 1 cm amounted on average to about 6%.

Present Day Processes on Forested Slopes

The results of measurements of various processes on slopes in the Wiltz area have been reported by Imeson (1976), Imeson and Kwaad (1976), and Kwaad (1977). Most of these were made on the slope above the profile illustrated in Fig. 3.4. Overland flow was neither observed nor measured (Imeson and Jungerius, 1974). Processes which have been studied and which are thought to be important in terms of the supply of material to the colluvial deposits are splash erosion and zoogenic erosion. Fig. 3.5 summarizes some of the results obtained.

Of particular importance for the amount of erosion is the area of bare mineral soil exposed to rain splash. Areally this varies with the soil moisture and the slope. The damper areas contain large numbers of animal mounds and these are mainly found in the dry valley floors and close to the river channels. On the steeper slopes, which are also found relatively close to the rivers and which are also fairly moist, mineral soil is also frequently exposed because the litter cover is not maintained. The amount of transport at various sites was found to vary considerably throughout the year with the amount of bare ground, which reached a peak in August and September (Fig. 3.5, line 1). The amount of material caught is, of course, equally dependent on the amount of rainfall, but not in a simple manner. Probably because of seasonal changes in drop-size distribution produced by the effect of the forest canopy, rainfall is more efficient in eroding soil during the summer (see Fig. 3.1). It would seem that because the rainfall is more erosive during the summer and late autumn, when the maximum amount of soil is exposed, peak erosion on the slopes occurs at this time (Fig. 3.5, line 3).

From the measurements described above, it was estimated that splash erosion supplied 0.36 kg per metre-width of slope per year to the colluvial deposits during the period of measurement. The downslope displacement of material excavated by burrowing animals (mice and voles) amounted to 0.18 kg per metre-width of slope per year. Not measured, but possibly equally important, was the downslope transport of material by litter (van Zon, 1978). If the amount of colluvium beneath the investigated slopes formed after AD 1800 is expressed in the same way, a supply of 2.5 kg per metre-width of slope per year is indicated. This is larger by a factor of 5 than the rate of supply from the slopes, excluding material supplied by litter transport. This discrepancy is not considered to be discourag-

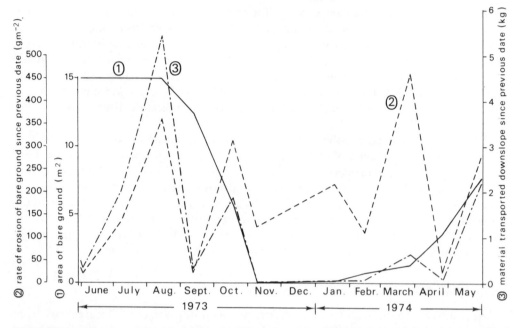

Fig. 3.5 Monthly rate of erosion under deciduous forest in northern Luxembourg due to animal burrowing and raindrop impact (Imeson, 1976; Imeson and Kwaad, 1976). (1) Area of bare ground produced by animal burrowing (mounds), in m^2 per 1650 m^2 of slope (total surface area of 22 experimental plots, each 15 m long and 5 m wide). (2) Rate of erosion of bare ground as determined with splash traps, in g m^{-2}. (3) Total amount of soil material transported downslope from bare areas by rainsplash erosion, in kg/1650 m^2

ing in view of the short length of measurement and the sensitivity of splash erosion to the area of bare soil. Further, the relatively large rate of accumulation of colluvium in the valley bottom could reflect the contribution of material from upvalley and the fact that some of the colluvium could have been supplied during high-magnitude rainfall events with a long return period that were not experienced during the period of measurement. It is a great over-simplification to consider the accumulation of colluvium as a two-dimensional case. As mentioned earlier, the mechanical composition of both recent colluvium and material collected in traps on the hillslopes is similar.

Evaluation

From the investigation of the colluvium and the measurements of erosion, an idea of the magnitude of sediment delivery can be obtained and, as expected under forest, this is relatively low. Inasmuch as the two types of information indicate a similar order of magnitude there is a fair amount of certainty in assuming this to be appropriate. However, the process measurements revealed erosion to be dependent not just on the climate but also upon dynamic properties of the forest ecosystem. To estimate reliably the average rate of sediment delivery during the 200 years or so over which the contemporary processes have operated just from the measurements made on the slopes over a few years, is clearly impossible. Some indication of the long-term average is provided by the colluvium, but for reasons mentioned earlier it is no more than this.

The main contribution of the study of the colluvium to an understanding of the rate of action of the contemporary forest processes was the discovery that the contemporary processes had only operated for the last 200 years or so and had supplied only about 10 cm of colluvium. Without this information it would have been tempting to extrapolate from the process measurements much further back in time. The other important information provided was that the colluvium found in the valley bottom had properties which indicated that it could have been formed by contemporary processes.

The process measurements, in addition to revealing the order of magnitude of erosion under forest, indicated that the rate of erosion under forest is measurable at weekly or monthly intervals. It is known that erosion rates in the Ardennes are relatively low compared with elsewhere in Luxembourg so that measurements can often be made over even shorter periods. Because the rate of erosion is dependent on the amount of bare soil, which in turn reflects the composition of the forest, soil moisture conditions, animal activity, and slope, this implies that persistent patterns in these factors are likely to be reflected in long-term rates of erosion. It would be expected, for example, that steeper and damper areas in a forest would lose relatively much more material than elsewhere. It would seem important, therefore, to establish how persistent such conditions are.

Conclusions

The study of forest processes and colluvium described here indicates the difficulty involved in attempting to extrapolate measurements made over a timescale of 1 or 2 years to longer periods. Measurements made so far indicate that erosion rates are likely to be extremely variable and, until more is known about this variation, extrapolation will remain difficult. It is essential to consider erosion processes in forests in the context of the total forest environment. Since man has influenced most, if not all, forests in many subtle ways there will always be uncertainty in assuming that contemporary processes have operated similarly in former forest environments. Furthermore, the reconstruction of former forest environments exactly enough to predict erosion rates seems hardly possible.

Fortunately, slope deposits may provide a link between present day processes and the rates of action of these and similar processes in the past. Developing this link is, in the opinion of the authors, an interesting field for further research.

References

Beckmann, W. (1967) Ein Beitrag zur Kenntnis der Mikrostruktur von solifluidal bewegtem Bodenmaterial in der Sierra Nevada (Andalusien). *An. Edafol. Agrobiol.*, **26,** 351–360.

Boughton, W. C. (1967). Plots for evaluating the catchment characteristics affecting soil loss. 1. Design of experiments. *N. Z. J. Hydrol.*, **6,** 113–119.

Butler, B. E. (1959). Periodic phenomena in landscapes as a basis for soil studies. *C.S.I.R.O. Australia, Soil Publ.*, No. 14, 20 pp.

Demek, J. (1969). Importance of slope deposits in the study of landscape development. In *Quaternary Geology and Climate* (Ed. E. H. Wright). Proc. VII Inqua Congr., Vol. 16. National Academy of Sciences, Washington, D.C., No. 1071, pp. 130–133.

Fairbridge, R. W. (1968). *The Encyclopedia of Geomorphology*. Encyclopedia of Earth Sciences Series, Vol. III. Reinhold, New York, 1295 pp.

Hulshof, O. K., Jungerius, P. D., and Riezebos, P. A. (1968). A Late-glacial volcanic ash deposit in southeastern Belgium. *Geol. Mijnbouw*, **47,** 106–111.

Imeson, A. C. (1976). Some effects of burrowing animals on slope processes in the Luxembourg Ardennes—the excavation of animal mounds in experimental plots. *Geog. Annaler*, **58,** 115–125.

Imeson, A. C., and Jungerius, P. D. (1974). Landscape stability in the Luxembourg Ardennes as exemplified by hydrological and (micro) pedological investigations of a catena in an experimental watershed. *Catena*, **1**, 273–295.

Imeson, A. C., and F. J. P. M. Kwaad (1976). Some effects of burrowing animals on slope processes in the Luxembourg Ardennes. The erosion of animal mounds by splash under forest. *Geog. Annaler*, **58**, 317–328.

Jungerius, P. D., Riezebos, P. A., and Slotboom, R. T. (1968). The age of Eifel maars as shown by the presence of Laacher See ash of Allerød age. *Geol. Mijnbouw*, **47**, 199–205.

Jungerius, P. D., and Mücher, H. J. (1970). Holocene slope development in the Lias cuesta area, Luxembourg, as shown by the distribution of volcanic minerals. *Z. Geomorphol, N. F.*, **14**, 127–136.

Juvigné, E. (1977). La zone de dispersion des poussières émises par une des dernières éruptions du volcan du Laachersee (Eifel). *Z. Geomorphol, N. F.*, **21**, 323–342.

Kwaad, F. J. P. M. (1977). Measurements of rainsplash erosion and the formation of colluvium beneath deciduous woodland in the Luxembourg Ardennes. *Earth Surface Processes*, **2**, 161–173.

Kwaad, F. J. P. M., and Mücher, H. J. (1977). The evolution of soils and slope deposits in the Luxembourg Ardennes near Wiltz. *Geoderma*, **17**, 1–37.

Kwaad, F. J. P. M., and Mücher, H. J. (1979). The formation and evolution of colluvium on arable land in northern Luxembourg *Geoderma*, **22**, in press.

Lowdermilk, W. C. (1934). Acceleration of erosion above geologic norms. *Am. Geophys. Union Trans.*, **15**, 505–509.

Mücher, H. J. (1974). Micromorphology of slope deposits: the necessity of a classification. In *Soil Microscopy* (Ed. G. K. Rutherford). Proc. 4th Int. Working-meeting on Soil Micromorphology, Kingston, Ontario, pp. 553–566.

Mücher, H. J., Carballas, T., Guitián Ojea, F., Jungerius, P. D., Kroonenberg, S. B., and Villar, M. C. (1972). Micromorphological analysis of effects of alternating phases of landscape stability and instability on two soil profiles in Galicia, N. W. Spain. *Geoderma*, **8**, 241–266.

Mücher, H. J., and de Ploey, J. (1977). Experimental and micromorphological investigation of erosion and redeposition of loess by water. *Earth Surface Processes*, **2**, 117–124.

Pissart, A., Bastin, B., Juvigné, E., and Thorez, J. (1975). Étude génétique, palynologique et minéralogique des dépôts périglaciaires de la Vallée de la Soor (Hautes Fagnes, Belgique). *Ann. Soc. Géol. Belg.*, **98**, 415–439.

Poel, P. W. van der (1976). Influence of environmental factors on the growth of the beech. *Catena*, **3**, 203–214.

Riezebos, P. A., and Slotboom, R. T. (1974). Palynology in the study of present-day hillslope development. *Geol. Mijnbouw*, **53**, 436–448.

Riezebos, P. A., and Slotboom, R. T. (1978). Pollen analysis of the Husterbaach peat (Luxembourg): its significance for the study of subrecent geomorphological events. *Boreas*, **7**, 75–82.

Soil Survey Staff (1962). *Soil Survey Manual*. U.S. Dept. Agriculture. Washington, D.C., Handbook No. 18, 503 pp.

Walker, P. H. (1962). Soil layers on hillslopes: a study at Nowra, N.S.W. Australia. *J. Soil Sci.*, **13**, 167–177.

Young, A. (1972). *Slopes*. Oliver and Boyd, Edinburgh, 288 pp.

Zaslavsky, D., and Sinai, G. (1977). *'Surface Hydrology' Nota 1917*. Inst. voor Cultuurtechniek en Waterhuishouding, Wageningen, 127 pp.

Zon, H. J. M. van (1978). *Litter Transport as a Geomorphic Process*. Fys. Geogr. en Bodemk. Lab., Universiteit van Amsterdam, Amsterdam, Publ. 26, 136 pp.

Timescales in Geomorphology
Edited by R. A. Cullingford, D. A. Davidson, and J. Lewin
© 1980 John Wiley & Sons Ltd

CHAPTER 4

Channel plan changes following large floods

Malcolm G. Anderson

Department of Geography,
University of Bristol

and Ann Calver

Geo Abstracts,
Norwich

Introduction

There has been a lack of work, either theoretical, empirical or experimental, which has been concerned with sudden or catastrophic channel plan changes. Scheidegger (1975) has discussed the problems and current limitations of theoretical modelling in this field, whilst experimental investigations of channel pattern controls have been confined to exploring results of *gradual* changes in the independent variables (Schumm and Kahn, 1972). Moreover, the conditions of such experimental flume studies are relatively uniform, yielding channel patterns which are more regular in their behaviour than are frequently found in natural rivers. This paper seeks to comment upon channel plan changes following large floods from empirical field evidence. As we shall discuss in more detail below, investigations of this type can be few because of the requirement for empirical evidence for pre- and post-flood periods, as well as during the event itself.

Brice (1974) provides evidence of the evolution of meander loops in certain North American rivers, and records the gradual channel pattern shifts that can be determined from alluvial deposits and aerial photograph evidence, and more recent such studies are reported in the book by Gregory (1977). Undoubtedly gradual channel plan changes provide the principal route through which mathematical modelling of a river channel pattern will proceed from modelling of a regular pattern in uniform conditions, and thus empirical documentation of gradual pattern changes in the field can be seen as a necessary and informative prerequisite for this purpose. In order that both past environments and current channel patterns are correctly interpreted, however, consideration has to be afforded to the role of catastrophic flood events. The authors have argued elsewhere in relation to hillslope changes associated with a major flood that the magnitude–frequency concept as introduced by Wolman and Miller (1960) needs modification, since landscape response can be different in *form* to events of different magnitude as threshold conditions are surpassed (Anderson and Calver, 1977). Moreover, the time which has elapsed since a flood event occurred is of geomorphological significance since even if the flood-produced features do last the mean recurrence interval of their formative event, their degree of degradation can be of importance to landscape appearance in the short term. In addition, the current emphasis on contemporary process investigations of fluvial phenomena tends to lessen awareness of the true probability of large events having occurred in the recent past. The probability of a flood event equal to or larger than the 100-year event occurring in a 100-year period is 0.63, so there is a reasonable probability that certain studies detailing gradual channel plan changes are influenced by, or are operating within, environmental constraints created by a recent large event.

Whilst there is evidence that large events need closer examination in the context of channel plan change than has so far been afforded to them, three principal factors, noted above, prescribe the relative complexity of so doing: the occurrence of non-linear responses and threshold conditions (for example, channel bank stability); the difficulty of knowing precisely the order of, and the time elapsed since, the more recent large events; and, thirdly, dating precisely the most recent major flood event. It is this last factor, together with subsequent adjustments of channel plan, which restricts severely the sites at which such an analysis can be undertaken. Specifically, answers to the following need to be ascertained if the general geomorphological implications of large flood events are to be assessed in the context of channel plan changes:

(1) the nature of channel adjustment
    (i) at the time of the last major flood,
    (ii) shortly post-flood, and
    (iii) after tens of years post-flood;
(2) identification of the various rates of channel plan changes in the river reach—likely to be linked to a valley floor configuration criterion which may or may not facilitate channel plan changes;
(3) an assessment in the light of (1) and (2) above of the impact of *previous* large events in the river reach examined, perhaps for which no quantitative dating information exists, but for which historical sources may at least note their occurrence.

A field area where perhaps answers to these questions can be attempted is Exmoor. This upland area has three factors which commend it in the current context. Firstly, on 15 August 1952 a storm occurred of such intensity (Bleasdale and Douglas, 1952) that a flood event with an estimated recurrence interval in excess of 150 years resulted. Secondly, in the intervening 25-year period there has been no storm event even approaching this order of magnitude of recurrence interval. Finally, there exists for this region a good coverage of aerial photograph data, together with field photographs and field notes taken some 6–8 weeks after the flood in August 1952. Such data provide an excellent means of assessing both immediate post-flood change and longer term changes, as the discussion below will illustrate. Table 4.1 summarizes the available data used in this study. In particular, the detailed field notes and photographs taken shortly after the flood provide evidence which is critical to assessing channel plan changes associated with the 1952 Exmoor flood in a stream typical of those draining north Exmoor—that of Hoaroak Water.

Channel Change in Hoaroak Water

Abandoned channel courses are apparent on the valley floor of Hoaroak Water, firstly from curvilinear depressions, often additionally delineated by vegetation changes, and

Table 4.1 Base data available for Exmoor floods

Date	Large flood event	Aerial photograph coverage	Field notes, field photographs
1796	Mentioned in Dobbie and Wolf (1953)	—	—
1946 (13 May)	—	1:9800	—
1947 (11 April)	—	1:8600	—
1952 (15 August)	Detailed in Bleasdale and Douglas (1952)	—	—
1952 (September–October)	—	—	Meteorological Office, Institute of Geological Sciences
1969 (17 February)	—	1:32,000	—
1971 (5 September)	—	1:12,000	—
1973 (29 April)	—	1:7700	—
1977 (16 May)	—	Infrared, 1:13,000	Anderson and Calver (1977)

secondly from sections through the valley floor deposits exposed in the present channel banks which show infilled former channels.

Hoaroak Water is one of the streams draining the north of Exmoor, south-west England, and reaching the Bristol Channel coast at Lynmouth via the East Lyn river (inset, Fig. 4.1). The area is underlain by Devonian rocks: in the reach of Hoaroak Water of particular concern in this paper, from SS 747426 to SS 747431, south-westward dipping Hangman Grits crop out, with the overlying Ilfracombe Slates on the upper part of the west valley side (Whittaker, personal communication). In this 450 m reach of Hoaroak Water, valley floor elevation decreases from 360 to 345 m above sea level and the floor varies in width from about 30 to 70 m. Valley-side slopes are convexo-concave in section and support gleys, podzols, and brown earth soils and rough moorland vegetation. The main part of Fig. 4.1 shows the present channel (surveyed in 1977) and the remnants of abandoned channels discernible at present from surface configuration and from the bankside exposures of the valley floor deposits. Fig. 4.2 shows the reach, looking downvalley from near the southern limit, with A and B corresponding to the lettering on Fig. 4.1.

The earliest aerial photographs available for this area (1946 and 1947) show that some of the now abandoned channels coincide with those occupied by flowing water in 1946–47. (There is very little difference observable at the 1:8600–1:9800 scales in the position of the active channel between May 1946 and April 1947.) In other places the channel active in 1946–47 is roughly coincident with the present channel, whilst in other places still, no trace of the 1946–47 channel path is today apparent on the valley floor or in the exposed sections (although possibly some traces would be exposed by excavation of the valley floor deposits). The most noticeable difference between the 1946–47 channel plan and that of the present is that the former has a more sinuous course: the present channel shows some degree of meandering but to a much lesser extent than does the 1946–47 channel. This is the case not only where 1946–47 channel remnants can be seen in the field (Fig. 4.1) but also in the middle of the reach where the 1946–47 channel course is not readily distinguishable in the field but where its course is known from the aerial photographs.

The information that is available on the large flood on Exmoor in 1952 suggests that

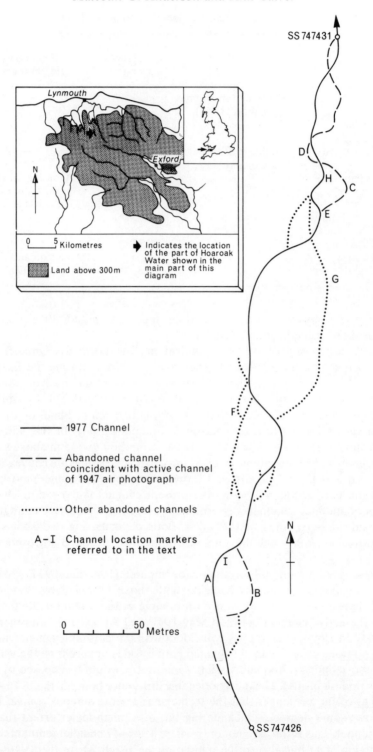

Fig. 4.1 Active and abandoned channels in part of Hoaroak Water,
Exmoor

Fig. 4.2 Hoaroak Water, looking northward down-valley, 1977. A and B provide cross references
with Fig. 4.1

an appreciable part of the change in channel plan between 1946–47 and the present can
be attributed to adjustments in the stream course during and shortly after the passage of
the flood. The rainfall of 15 August 1952 and the wet antecedent conditions which
helped to promote the flooding have been described by Bleasdale and Douglas (1952)
and Marshall (1952), and these conditions were estimated by Carson and Kirkby (1972,
p. 158) to have a recurrence interval of over 150 years. Various aspects of flow dynamics
and geomorphological changes associated with the flood have been described (Bleasdale
and Douglas, 1952; Dobbie and Wolf, 1953; Gifford, 1953; McClean, 1953; Kidson,
1953; Green, 1955) and we have discussed some geomorphological changes in the
post-flood period (Anderson and Calver, 1977). Of particular interest in the present
context of channel plan changes are unpublished 1952 photographs (Institute of
Geological Sciences and Meteorological Office) of the part of Hoaroak Water of
concern: one such photograph, taken on 7 October 1952, looking southwards up the
valley, is reproduced as Fig. 4.3. These photographs, together with unpublished 1952
field notes and published data on Exmoor in general, indicate that the August 1952 flood
was responsible for the deposition of coarse debris over much of the valley floor in this
reach of Hoaroak Water, and that changes in channel position were brought about
following the overtopping and, in a number of cases, blocking of pre-existing channels.
Although hillslope runoff along this reach of valley was considerable at the time of the
flood, the disposition of the valley floor debris suggests that it was deposited by the main
downvalley flow through the area. Such deposition and the potential for associated
channel plan changes in a reach depended on the existence of sufficient upstream

Fig. 4.3 Hoaroak Water, looking southward up-valley, October 1952. C, D and E provide cross references with Fig. 4.1 NERC copyright. Reproduced by permission of the Director of the Institute of Geological Sciences, London S.W.7

drainage area to give rise to a high capacity flow to transport debris to the reach, on the existence of a wide enough valley floor to attenuate the flow to some degree and to permit the establishment of a new spatially distinct channel path, and, of course, on the existence of sites of erodible or re-workable material. [Such criteria for the behaviour and effects of the 1952 flood have been detailed for Cannon Hill valley some 4 km to the west of Hoaroak Water (Anderson and Calver, 1977).]

Whilst it is thus very likely that the passage of the 1952 flood was responsible for a substantial part of the change in channel position between 1946–47 and the present, a number of factors suggest that the change was not necessarily accomplished in one simple and complete step. Firstly, as will be discussed below, there is evidence from aerial photographs that the channel in places underwent some degree of gradual migration between 1969 and the present and, presumably, did so between 1952 and 1969, and (although the valley floor deposits were different before the flood) between 1946 and 1952. Secondly, it is doubtful that changes in channel position associated with the passage of the flood in 1952 were necessarily made *directly* to what was to become the relatively stable post-flood channel. An example of such short-term stages in channel re-positioning can be seen with reference to Fig. 4.1 and 4.3: letters C and D provide cross-references. It is apparent that a substantial part of the abandonment of the pre-flood meandering channel via C and D was completed by the time of the photograph (7–8 weeks after the flood), and, indeed, a section exposed in the eastern side of the present channel bank at point E suggests that at least the upstream part of the old channel loop was largely filled by the coarse debris of the main passage of the flood. The main water flow of 7 October 1952 is substantially to the west (right, on photograph) of the present day channel at E: that is, the main stream nearly 2 months after the flood was in places following neither the pre-flood channel course nor that which was to become the stabilized post-flood channel. Another photograph (Bleasdale, Meteorological Office) likewise indicates only partial use of what was to be the surviving channel by the water flow of, in this case, September 1952; this photograph also shows some degree of braiding of the water flow over the debris-covered valley floor. A comparison of the channel form of the present (1977) on the one hand, and that of Fig. 4.3 and Bleasdale's photograph on the other, suggests that since September/October 1952 what has become the surviving channel of those shallow watercourses over the flood debris has incised slightly into those deposits over parts of the reach (enabling, incidentally, sections of valley floor deposits and old infilled channels to be seen), and this small measure of incision has presumably to some extent stabilized the channel course through the unconsolidated debris.

We have so far discussed the difference between the channel pattern of 1946–47 and the present day pattern and, in particular, the part played by the 1952 flood in bringing about these differences. Returning to Fig. 4.1, it can be seen that there are apparent in the field a number of abandoned channel segments which do not coincide with the active channel of 1946–47. The following possibilities exist for the date(s) of occupation of these abandoned channels: (i) pre-1946; (ii) intermediate stage in adjustments associated with the 1952 flood; (iii) in the period 1947 to before the 1952 flood; and (iv) after the completion of the 1952 flood modifications. The last two cases, that is, of occupation of the now-abandoned channel courses since 1947 but not during the adjustments closely associated with the large 1952 flood, are believed to be unlikely in view of the lack of large runoff events in this area during those periods and (see below) in view of the slow rate of lateral movement of the channel over periods when aerial photographic covers allow monitoring of the migration. The possibility of these channel remnants (that is, those represented by the dotted line in Fig. 4.1) being intermediate stages in 1952 adjustments will be clear from the description above of channel changes associated with Fig. 4.3, and such is likely to be the case for the segment of abandoned channel immediately to the west of the 1977 channel at point E (and, possibly, for the channel remnant to the west of that). That the abandoned channel immediately west of point E was occupied sometimes *after* the passage of the main flood, rather than before it, is favoured in that it occupies an area of relatively low elevation among the valley floor deposits which, had the channel dated from before the flood, would probably have been covered with debris.

The remaining possibility for the date of occupation of the channel courses not used in 1946–47 or at present is, as mentioned above, that they were occupied earlier than the time of the 1946 aerial photograph. This is particularly likely where some indication of their topographic expression (i.e. as small-scale relief features rather than as active water-containing channels) appears on the 1946 aerial photograph, and such indications are naturally more commonly seen at the *edges* of the valley floor, particularly as meander scar features. Abandoned channel remnants at F and G (Fig. 4.1) are believed to be examples of channels occupied *before* 1946. In places it appears likely that there may be more than one pre-1946 channel occurring in a valley cross-section. Unless braiding of well established channels (as opposed to that of superficial water courses over flood debris) has occurred in the past, this suggests that the channel position of more than one pre-1946 date of occupation is still evident, whether of the channel between catastrophic changes in plan or of preserved stages, particularly at the valley floor edges, in lateral migration across the valley floor. (It should perhaps be noted that the degree of infill of abandoned channels is not particularly useful for relative dating purposes because of differences in the nature of deposits, in the small-scale topography and, especially, because of the possibility of rapid infilling during floods.) The question of mode of abandonment of the pre-1946 channels necessarily remains speculative to some degree. Exposed sections in the present channel banks show the valley floor to be composed of a variety of deposits. Some suggest flood-filled channels in sites other than those known to correspond to 1952 infillings, whilst others show silt and thin bedded deposits more characteristic of gradual channel changes. Thus, both catastrophic and more slowly acting processes appear to have been active. It is difficult to date any pre-1952 catastrophic changes since little detailed documentation exists of earlier large flows in the Hoaroak area. Dobbie and Wolf (1953, p. 541) do, however, quote an earlier publication (Chanter, 1907) which mentions a large flood at Lynmouth in 1796 which 'may have been similar in intensity to that of August 1952'.

The *gradual* change in position of the channel in Hoaroak Water has been mentioned above. Aerial photographs covering periods not known to have included severe runoff events allow the investigation of gradual channel migration, and in Hoaroak Water such photographs date from 1969 and more especially, because of the photograph scales and quality, from 1971 to the present. In the reach of Fig. 4.1 changes are minor—the bend at point H has migrated slightly towards the eastern valley edge, and near point I the 1977 channel is straighter than that of 1971. The detail of such changes may be expected to be influenced by the inhomogeneity of the valley floor deposits, and over long periods the changes are therefore likely to be rather less systematic than changes reported (see, for example, the section on channel pattern in Gregory, 1977) on meandering streams in more homogeneous finer grained alluvial deposits.

Conclusion

From channel remnants visible in the field together with the field notes and photo-graphs detailed in Table 4.1 we have been able to elucidate the recent history of channel plan changes, including those associated with a large, rare runoff event. In the area studied the changes associated with the large flood were seen to be more complex than those associated with the traditional idea of 'cutting off' of meanders, though they nevertheless involved a general reduction in sinuosity. This stands in contrast, and indeed a geometrically necessary contrast, to the frequently reported increases of sinuosity associated with slower channel migration. This study has called for very precise dating of channel plan location and the associated deposits: such precision in dating is required to distinguish between rapid flood-induced changes and longer term more gradual changes, and in this context the availability of field notes and photographs taken in 1952 shortly after the flood was particularly important.

Twenty-five years after the large flood, the pre-flood channel courses remained apparent on the surface of parts of the reach studied despite flood deposition and surface degradation: the flood deposits on the valley floor and within former channels will remain until erosion, whether in-channel or overbank flood erosion, reaches those sites. The present channel plan in this stretch of Hoaroak Water is very substantially that dating from the early post-flood period and changes since then are essentially minor modifications to this plan.

Where particular criteria were met in other areas of Exmoor affected by the flood, there were channel changes similar to those of Hoaroak Water. These criteria were sufficient drainage area, sufficient valley floor width, and the availability of sufficient debris. In such areas, as we have seen above, the flood had markedly more effect on channel plan change than did the commonly experienced day-to-day flows over the last 30 years: in these areas 'average' channel migration would not be a valid concept over this period. Areas of Exmoor that experienced the flood but which did not meet the criteria noted above did not experience noteworthy changes in channel plan. A large runoff event is therefore by no means necessarily effective in bringing about channel plan changes if other conditions are not met in a particular reach of channel, but where it does alter the channel plan the effect may, as we have seen, last for a substantial period. That large drainage areas and wide valley floors favour channel plan changes suggests that downstream areas may (in the absence of protective engineering works) be more prone to such changes: this is counteracted to some degree, however, by the fact that intense rainfalls are less likely to affect the whole of large as opposed to small catchments. Floods can, of course, change aspects of the channel other than its plan form and these changes can occur in areas not meeting the criteria for plan alteration. In Cannon Hill valley, Exmoor (Anderson and Calver, 1977), for example, in reaches where the valley floor is narrow and the channel confined by valley side slopes, the flood caused cross-section changes, particularly deepening and undercutting. In such situations of a channel adjacent to a valley side slope, hillslope stability characteristics have been seen to be important to the detail of channel cross-section, the Cannon Hill channel having suffered slumping and partial infill from failed hillslope material: change of channel *plan* by this means appears, however, to be limited.

This investigation has shown the relative importance of short-term flood adjustment and slower, more continuous changes to channel plan over tens of years, in an area that *has* experienced a large event in that time. Compared with Exmoor, few areas in Britain have experienced such a large recurrence interval runoff event so recently. Over longer periods of time, however, a more complete range of magnitudes of runoff events is experienced in any area. Over somewhat longer periods than the present investigation details, the *potential* aggregate channel migration by gradual lateral erosion is increased significantly, and so the relative importance of high runoff events may be less than in the particular period and type of area this study has considered. It is important to note that some of the criteria for accommodating channel plan change—both in flood and under gradual migration—can undergo change in their spatial distribution over long periods of time: sources of easily erodible debris, for example, can change over time, as also may the valley floor width. These controlling factors are themselves in part influenced by channel behaviour: the distribution of erodible debris in Hoaroak Water was, for example, changed by the passage of the 1952 flood. The spatial distribution of sites amenable to significant change in channel plan may therefore be expected to vary over time. The occurrence of actual channel plan change varies with the magnitude–frequency distribution of runoff events within these controls of valley floor sedimentary and morphological characteristics.

References

Anderson, M. G., and Calver, A. (1977). On the persistence of landscape features formed by a large flood. *Trans. Inst. Brit. Geog.*, **2**, 243–254.
Bleasdale, A., and Douglas, K. (1952). Storm over Exmoor on August 15, 1952. *Meteorol. Mag.*, **81**, 353–367.
Brice, J. C. (1974). Evolution of meander loops. *Geol. Soc. Am. Bull.*, **85**, 581–586.
Carson, M. A., and Kirkby, M. J. (1972). *Hillslope Form and Process*. Cambridge University Press, Cambridge.
Chanter, J. F. (1907). *A History of the Parishes of Lynton and Countisbury*. Commin, Exeter.

Dobbie, C. H., and Wolf, P. O. (1953). The Lynmouth flood of August 1952. *Proc. Inst. Civ. Engrs.*, **2**, 522–588.

Gifford, J. (1953). Landslides on Exmoor caused by the storm of 15th August, 1952. *Geography*, **38**, 9–17.

Green, G. W. (1955). North Exmoor floods, August 1952. *Bull. Geol. Surv. Gr. Br.*, **7**, 68–84.

Gregory, K. J. (Ed.) (1977). *River Channel Changes*. Wiley, Chichester.

Kidson, C. (1953). The Exmoor storm and the Lynmouth floods. *Geography.*, **38**, 1–9.

Marshall, W. A. L. (1952). The Lynmouth floods. *Weather*, **7**, 338–342.

McClean, W. N. (1953). The Lynmouth flood of 15th August 1952. *J. Inst. Wat. Engrs.*, **7**,157–159.

Scheidegger, A. E. (1975). *Physical Aspects of Natural Catastrophes*. Elsevier, Amsterdam.

Schumm, S. A., and Kahn, H. R. (1972). Experimental study of channel patterns. *Geol. Soc. Am. Bull.*, **83**, 1755–1770.

Wolman, M. G., and Miller, J. P. (1960). Magnitude and frequency of forces in geomorphic processes. *J. Geol.*, **68**, 54–74.

Timescales in Geomorphology
Edited by R. A. Cullingford, D. A. Davidson, and J. Lewin
© 1980 John Wiley & Sons Ltd

CHAPTER 5

Pattern changes in a Scottish braided river over 1, 30, and 200 years

A. Werritty

Department of Geography,
University of St. Andrews

and R. I. Ferguson

Department of Earth and Environmental Science,
University of Stirling

Introduction

Rates of change associated with the development of fluvial landforms have been extensively reported in the recent literature on channel processes. Ideally such data should provide a reliable basis for comparative studies of channel changes over varying timescales, but in reality such comparisons are beset by numerous difficulties.

One major problem arises in assessing the importance of frequent small-scale episodic changes relative to that of the rarely observed catastrophic event (Wolman and Miller, 1960). Simple extrapolation from a short-term field survey is hazardous in that the record of channel events may have been atypical and thus unrepresentative of the long-term trends. Conversely, the use of periodic source materials such as aerial photographs may constitute a sampling interval which is too coarse to identify the impact of each individual flood event. Further difficulties arise from the changing status of environmental variables at different timescales (Schumm and Lichty, 1965). Climate, for example, can be regarded as fixed in 'steady' time but as one moves from 'graded' to 'cyclic' timescales it ceases to be invariant and in the guise of climatic change becomes instead a major controlling variable.

At a more pragmatic level, difficulties arise from the variable quality and availability of such diverse source materials as aerial photographs, large-scale topographic maps, and cadastral surveys. The detailed reconstruction of channel changes in Britain is generally restricted to a timespan of little more than a century. National topographic mapping at a large scale did not commence until the 1860s and extensive aerial photography not until the 1940s. Older source material is sometimes available but its use must be accompanied by rigorous checks on source reliability if detailed comparisons with later sources are to be attempted. Even modern sources may be less than ideal for geomorphological purposes: there are still parts of Britain for which repeated near vertical aerial photography is not available.

Most recent studies of the development of fluvial landforms have concentrated upon undivided channels in fine-grained alluvium (e.g. Leopold, 1973; Hickin and Nanson, 1975). Rates of change in braided channels have received far less attention except for short-term studies by sedimentologists investigating the origin of contemporary alluvial deposits in semi-arid and proglacial environments (Bluck, 1974; Smith, 1970, 1974; Fahnestock and Bradley, 1973). Braiding is nevertheless also widespread in temperate piedmont and mountain-valley environments. In this paper we examine the behaviour of a river of this neglected type, the River Feshie on the edge of the Cairngorm Mountains in Scotland, and discuss the variability of its channel pattern over timescales from a year to two centuries as revealed by field survey, aerial photographs, and large-scale maps.

The Catchment of the River Feshie

The River Feshie is a major tributary of the upper Spey, draining an area of 235 km^2 on the west side of the Cairngorm Mountains. Much of the catchment consists of a sparsely vegetated plateau at 700–900 m above sea level, but the main river flows for much of its length in a narrow steep-sided glen flanked by a well preserved sequence of terraces. Most of the tributary development is above 500 m either to the east on the Cairngorm plateau surface or to the south in the Gaick area. Mean annual precipitation in both is of the order of 1500 mm. Moinian schist comprises most of the underlying bedrock except for the eastern side of the glen, which includes part of the Cairngorm granite (Hinxman and Anderson, 1915). Both lithologies are present in the bedload sediments with the schist being by far the more abundant. The relief of the area has become more rugged and precipitous by the activity of Pleistocene glacier ice, most notably via a series of glacial breaches in the headwaters. One of these gives rise to the apparent 'capture' of the headwaters of the River Dee (Linton, 1949). In the Gaick area to the south a local zone III ice cap has been mapped by Sissons (1974), and it seems likely that the upper valleys of the main eastern tributaries of the Feshie sustained contemporaneous nival activity, possibly reactivated during the Little Ice Age (Young, 1975; Sugden, 1977).

The modern channel pattern is partly determined by the characteristics of the runoff regime, which is extremely flashy. The overall mean flow for 1951–74 at Feshiebridge is 8.1 m^3 s^{-1} with a tendency for higher flows in winter. Floods occurred at most times of the year, the largest on record being *ca.* 200 m^3 s^{-1} on 28 September 1961. Unfortunately, no figure is available for the mean annual flood because of the instability of the rating curve, particularly at high flows, which led to the abandonment of the station in 1974 and exclusion from the Flood Studies Report (NERC, 1975).

Given such a regime and a general channel slope of 0.01, a bankfull discharge of only 3 m^3 s^{-1} is sufficient for the main channel to plot in the braided region of Leopold and Wolman's (1957) well known graph. The overall mean discharge thus implies that the whole of the channel is potentially braided, yet in only three reaches is a braided channel particularly well developed (Fig. 5.1). Two constraints serve to minimize braiding in the remaining reaches. For much of its length the main channel is restricted in terms of its floodplain development by a well preserved sequence of high terraces developed in coarse fluvioglacial outwash (Young, 1976). The second and lesser constraint is that a limited number of reaches are incised into bedrock, including the meltwater gorge at Feshiebridge and some of the reaches between the two east-bank tributaries (Allt Fhearnagan and Allt Garbhlach). In the absence of such constriction the channel is free to develop the intense and active braiding characteristic of the Glen Feshie Lodge, Blackmills, and Spey confluence reaches (Fig. 5.1).

In this paper we concentrate on the upper, most southerly, braided reach near Glen

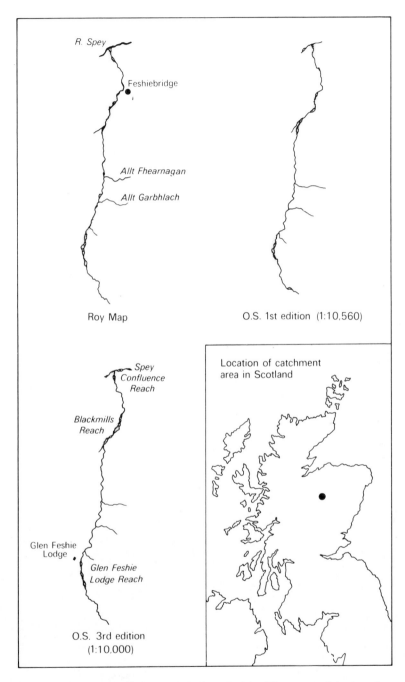

Fig. 5.1 Braided reaches of the River Feshie. The same three reaches (stippled) appear braided on the Roy Map, 1749–1751, the O.S. County Series First Edition, 1869, and the O.S. 3rd (National Grid) Edition, 1971

A. Werritty and R. I. Ferguson

Feshie Lodge. The general morphology of the valley floor here is well shown in Fig. 5.2. The river normally occupies, but occasionally overflows, a partially anastomosing and gently sinuous channel shallowly cut into a terraced valley floor of coarse fluvioglacial outwash deposits. The terraces carry sparse remnants of Caledonian pine forest but much of the lowest floodplain is unvegetated. In this setting the channel does not display the complete freedom of lateral movement characteristic of contemporary proglacial sandar (e.g. Krigström, 1962), but braiding is far more extensive and better developed than the single islands and bars examined in lowland England by Knighton (1972). It is on a much

Fig. 5.2 Upper braided reach, Glen Feshie Lodge. Oblique aerial view of upper braided reach looking north from national grid reference 845915 on 23 July 1962 (Cambridge University Collection: copyright reserved; AGJ 28)

ıarger scale than that observed in upland northern England by Hitchcock (1977), and more complex than any of the channel patterns described by Bluck (1976) in his illuminating typology of low-sinuosity rivers in Scotland. The closest British comparison is probably the lowest part of the River Spey to which the Feshie is tributary and whose morphology and recent history have been outlined by Lewin and Weir (1977).

The 200-Year Timescale: Historical Maps

The oldest planimetric survey dates from the Roy map of 1749–51 at a scale of approximately 1:36,000. Although a remarkable cartographic achievement for its time, it is not sufficiently detailed or accurate to permit quantitative measurements of channel pattern. Nevertheless, qualitative evidence of braiding was clearly evident in the Glen Feshie Lodge reach, and careful scrutiny reveals a distinctive pattern of eastern and western channels which was to be a recurrent theme over the next 220 years (Fig. 5.1). The eastern channel in particular proved to be especially stable in the three successive editions of the 1:10,560 and 1:10,000 scale maps produced by the Ordnance Survey over a timespan of almost exactly 100 years (Fig. 5.3).

In order to use these map data to their fullest extent, quantitative indices of braiding were evaluated (Smart and Moruzzi 1972; Howard *et al.*, 1970), but it soon became apparent that any results would be arbitrary and misleading. For example, the 1899/1971 comparison would appear to suggest an increase in braiding during the present century. However, the real reason is a cartographic effect in that the 1971 map was based upon large-scale aerial photography at a high stage of the river, whereas the two earlier editions of the County series were based upon a nineteenth-century topographic survey. Fortunately, the first two editions of the County series can be directly compared (Table 5.1 and Fig. 5.3). In qualitative terms a decrease in main channel sinuosity can be observed together with an increase in the degree of braiding, especially pronounced in the upstream reaches. There was also the re-emergence of the two dominant eastern and western channels already noted on the Roy map 150 years earlier, and a marked increase in the extent of the bare gravel on the unvegetated bar surfaces. Braiding adjacent to the Lodge was much intensified as evidenced by the capture of a small marginal stream, whereas the eastern channel proved to have a very stable alignment. Upstream in the main glacial breach, the braiding intensity was greatly increased, as was the development of unvegetated bar surfaces.

The 1899/1971 comparison is complicated by the change in survey methods. However, there appeared to be an overall decrease in channel sinuosity and possibly an increase in the degree of braiding, although this may have been a stage effect. The extent of the unvegetated bar surfaces was much reduced. The eastern and western channel alignments were still visible, but some of the marginal distributaries were no longer actively connected with the main stream. Thus the nineteenth century distributary adjacent to the Ruigh-aiteachain bothy now became a 'misfit' with a much reduced discharge. In one of the glacial breaches the nineteenth century distributary disappeared beneath the surface of an alluvial fan and the extensive braiding around the lobate island in the main glacial breach became rationalized into three main channels whose respective dominance was subject to intermittent switching.

The 30-Year Timescale: Aerial Photography

Many of these features are revealed in much greater detail by changing the timescale

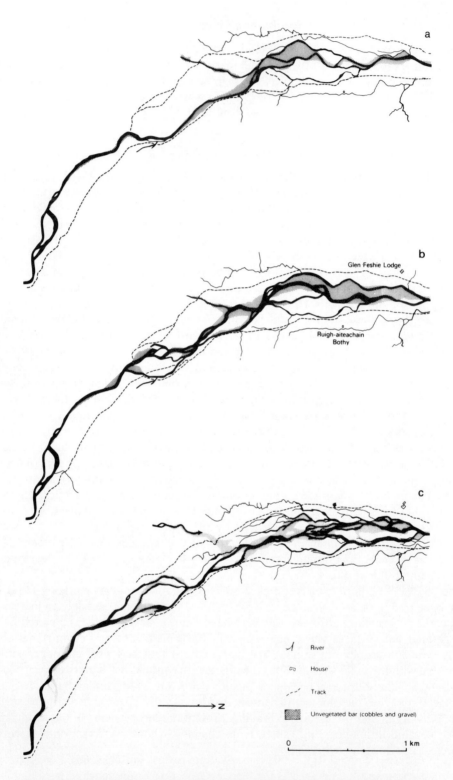

Fig. 5.3 Upper braided reach: 1869–1971. Changing channel patterns mapped in successive editions of O.S. large scale maps: (a) six-inch county series (Inverness-shire) first edition survey 1869; (b) six-inch county series (Inverness-shire) second edition resurveyed 1899; (c) National Grid Series 1:10,000 scale (derived) 1971

Table 5.1 Pattern changes near Glen Feshie Lodge, 1869–1977

Symbols indicate whether each measure of channel pattern increased (+) or decreased (−) between successive dates

Year	Source	Degree of braiding	Sinuosity of main channel	Extent of bare gravel
Ordnance Survey Maps				
1869	1:10,560 County series, 1st ed.			
		+	−	+
1899	1:10,560 County series, 2nd ed.			
		?+	−	−
1971	1:10,000 National Grid edition			
Aerial photographs				
1946 (7 October)	RAF			
		−	?+	+
1955 (2 July)	RAF			
		+	−	+
1964 (2 September)	RAF			
		?+	?−	No change
1966 (22 August)	Ordnance Survey			
		No change	No change	+
1967 (11 June)	Meridian Airmaps			
		−	? No change	+
Field surveying				
1977 (1 April)	plane table map			

from 100 to 30 years. Increasingly the sampling frequency identifies much more accurately the nature of the channel pattern changes over the interval 1946–77. However, comparative interpretation is still problematic because of the diverse nature of the source materials which range from high-quality vertical photography through RAF fan photography to low-angle obliques.

For comparative purposes the channel systems, active areas and, vegetated bars were scribed on to an emulsion-backed surface using a Sokkisha MS-27 mirror stereoscope with parallel displacer at scales between 1:10,000 and 1:11,900. Visual inspection of these three elements from five sets of photographs readily identified the magnitude and direction of channel pattern changes. More detailed comparison required mapping at a constant scale, and this was achieved by tracing the channel systems on to acetate film using a stereoscopic Bausch and Lomb zoom transferscope. Planimetric control was obtained by using the 1971 Ordnance Survey 1:10,000 sheet as a base map. Even with this improved source material it still proved impossible to develop accurate quantitative indices of channel change. Thus Table 5.1 represents a purely qualitative assessment indicating the direction of the changes recorded in the channel comparisons of Fig. 5.4.

In 1946 the dominance of distinct eastern and western channels was one again evident, as has already been noted in the map-based comparisons. In this instance two scales of braiding are apparent: a macro-braid extending over most of the reach (AB in Fig. 5.4a) coupled with micro-braiding around small ephemeral bars at the southeast corner of the main braid system (BC). This latter reach, linking the western channel to the then

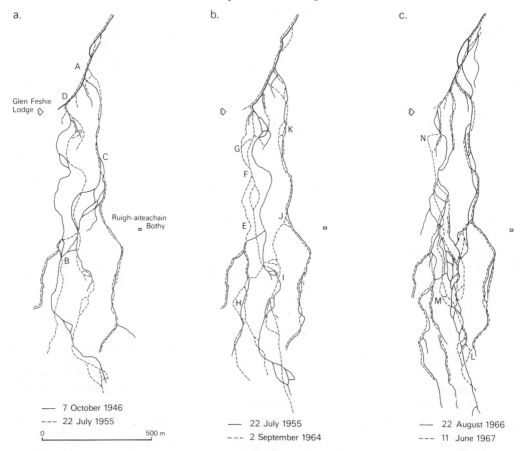

Glen Feshie
Lodge ◊

A

D

C

Ruigh-aiteachain
◻ Bothy

B

—— 7 October 1946
--- 22 July 1955

0   500 m

b.

◊

G

F

K

E

J

◻

H

I

—— 22 July 1955
--- 2 September 1964

c.

◊

N

◻

M

L

—— 22 August 1966
--- 11 June 1967

Fig. 5.4 Channel patterns from aerial photographs: 1946–1967. Changing channel patterns
in the upper braided reach: (a) 7 October 1946 to 22 July 1955; (b) 22 July 1955 to
2 September 1964; (c) 22 August 1966 to 11 June 1967

equally large eastern channel, was to prove a very unstable element over the next 30
years. Often its role was to transfer a proportion of the main channel discharge into the
eastern channel (1946, 1964). At other times this link was severed and the eastern
channel became a small 'misfit' contained by a series of lateral bars (1955, 1976). Apart
from braiding around a series of mobile bars upstream from B, the 1946 main channel
was characterized by high sinuosity and relatively low intensity of braiding. By 1955 this
pattern had been further intensified and braiding in the main channel had virtually
vanished whilst the overall sinuosity marginally increased (Fig. 5.4a, Table 5.1). The
unvegetated bar surfaces associated with the now inactive BC reach were rapidly being
recolonized. Simultaneously, a new sinuous channel had been established between B and
D, locally replacing floodplain remnants with new active areas 70 m east of the 1946
channel. This stable sinuous pattern was still in evidence in a low-angle oblique dating
from July 1960 (Cambridge University Collection, ACH64).

In September 1961 a peak discharge of 200 m³ s⁻¹ was registered at Feshiebridge.
This represented the largest event over the whole of the gauging record and the resultant
transformation of the floodplain is readily apparent in a second low-angle oblique dated

July 1962 (Fig. 5.2). The increasingly sinuous channel of the late 1950s was obliterated, probably in a few hours, and replaced by a highly fragmented unstable braided pattern. Even several years after the event the 1964 vertical photographs still recorded the impact of this flood: scouring of the floodplain, channel switching and re-excavation of former marginal channels (e.g. EFG re-occupied a 1946 channel, Fig. 5.4b), and the creation of an overall pattern much more akin to a constrained sandur. Over the past 17 years recovery of the channel system has taken the form of simplification and rationalization of the more unstable elements rather akin to the processes observed between 1946 and 1955. Thus the legacy of the 1961 flood has remained the dominant element in channel changes up to 1978, with marginal features such as the bar complex at H remaining stable whilst the continued processes of migration and switching in the main channel have generally been confined to the area scoured by the flood.

The development of the Glen Feshie Lodge reach over the period 1946–64 can be summarized as follows:

(i) a stable eastern channel which has become increasingly a 'misfit';

(ii) a highly mobile western channel whose sinuosity and propensity to braid are inversely related in a cyclic manner: braiding appears to be the immediate response to large floods, but increased meandering and rationalization of the channel pattern are characteristic during post-flood recovery;

(iii) a series of major vegetated lobate bars in the upstream reach where channel switching rather than lateral migration appears to be the dominant process;

(iv) the emergence of a series of nodes along the main channel. These are relatively stable and are associated with the initiation or termination of channel switching. Clearly identified with large stable floodplain remnants, they are less evident on the unvegetated bar surface adjacent to the Lodge.

A final comparison based upon aerial photography can be made over a very short timespan—the 9-month period from August 1966 to June 1967 (Fig. 5.4c). The second largest flood in the gauging record occurred on 18 December 1966 (*ca.* 180 m^3 s^{-1} at Feshiebridge). Its effect was almost entirely confined to reorganizing tributary development along the western channel by lateral shifts of up to 60 m. Although the intensity of braiding was little changed, the width of the active area was considerably increased in those parts of the reach devoid of vegetated bars. Comparable rates of channel change, although not so extensive across the whole channel reach, have been recorded over the shortest timescale of 1 year using field survey methods.

The 1-Year Timescale: Field Measurements

At the short timescales that are relevant to studies of braided rivers, field and documentary evidence are complementary. In general, and certainly in the case of Glen Feshie, published maps and aerial photographs of different dates provide the best evidence of the overall extent and complexity of channel changes at timescales from centuries down to a few years. However, ground survey has an important role to play in bringing this general picture into sharper focus by concentrating on more local changes over shorter intervals of time. It can also reveal local height differences that are too small to detect on published maps or to measure accurately from aerial photographs taken at normal flying heights. This third dimension of valley floor morphology may be very significant for river behaviour, especially in times of flood, and slight changes in elevation may also be the only clues to progressive aggradation or degradation.

Our field programme in Glen Feshie combined levelling with plane table mapping in order to assess the microrelief of part of the upper braided reach, its alteration over a single year, and its relationship to the documentary information on channel patterns and changes discussed above. In May 1976 five sections 250–280 m long were levelled across the valley floor between landmarks at the edges of the lowest conspicuous terrace. In order to level as many sections as possible in a limited time, distances were measured by tacheometry from a central station on each section and are thus accurate only to the nearest metre, but as will be seen this proved sufficiently accurate for subsequent comparison. The same sections were re-levelled in May 1977 shortly after a 1:500 map had been compiled, using plane table and telescopic alidade, to show the main channels, depositional features, and vegetation patterns in this part of the valley floor. A simplified and reduced version of this map is reproduced in Fig. 5.5 to show the locations of the western halves of the five transects. The sections as levelled in 1976 and 1977 are presented in Fig. 5.6.

The 1976 levelling made it abundantly clear that both vegetated and gravelly areas that look homogeneous on aerial photographs possess a complicated microrelief of degraded cut banks, inactive channels, and former bars, some with a relief of 1 m, which is as much as parts of the currently active river channel. All major features identified in 1976, together with some new ones, were apparent in the repeat levelling a year later. The main features could also be identified on the plane table map, and the combination of mapping with levelling proved invaluable for correlating the microrelief revealed by the different transects and relating it to the historical changes in channel pattern summarized in Fig. 5.4. Many of the inactive channels identified in the field could thus be dated tentatively and are labelled in Fig. 5.5 with the last year in which they are known to have been active.

The extent of migration of the main channel since the earliest available aerial photography is clearly shown by this reconstruction, but it would be wrong to deduce from overall shifts of up to 100–150 m in 31 years that widespread bank erosion at some 3–5 m per year has occurred. In several places successive sets of photographs show that the river has shifted without destroying intervening vegetation, so although bank erosion is locally rapid some of the biggest changes in channel pattern must have occurred by sudden switching of the river's course.

One such switch was beginning at the time of the original field survey and can be traced in Fig. 5.6. In 1976 all five sections lay across a gradual rightward curve of the main channel. This was joined from the left between sections A and C by a stable distributary, which in turn was fed by a tributary stream. Downstream, between sections C and D, a new distributary branched off leftwards over the grassy but freshly gravel-strewn floodplain. This new branch was then narrower and far shallower than the main channel, but by May 1977 it had captured the entire flow of the river and cut itself a suitably wide and deep channel. At section D the new course was on more or less the same line as the 1976 distributary but at section E it lay some 35 m further west, and 80 m away from the 1976 main channel which it did not rejoin for 400 m. At both sections a channel over 10 m wide had been excavated to a maximum of about 1 m below the 1976 surface level.

Apart from revealing the details of this switch the repeated levelling suggests a cause. Fig. 5.6 shows that the 1976 channel at sections D and E was perched at a higher level than the grassy depression further west to which the river switched within a year. The 1976 channel at sections A to C was not potentially unstable in this way and had only migrated a few metres even by April 1978.

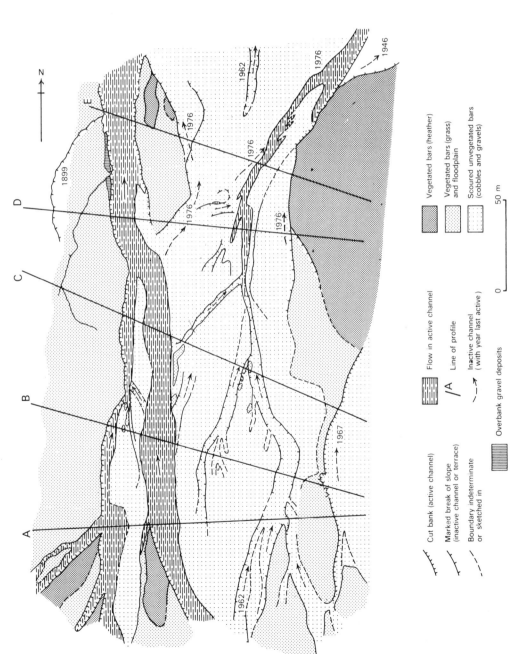

Fig. 5.5 Upper braided reach in April 1977. Simplified plane table map of part of braided reach showing location of transects and former channel systems

Vegetated bars (heather)

Vegetated bars (grass) and floodplain

Scoured unvegetated bars (cobbles and gravels)

Flow in active channel

Line of profile

Inactive channel (with year last active)

Cut bank (active channel)

Marked break of slope (inactive channel or terrace)

Boundary indeterminate or sketched in

Overbank gravel deposits

0   50 m

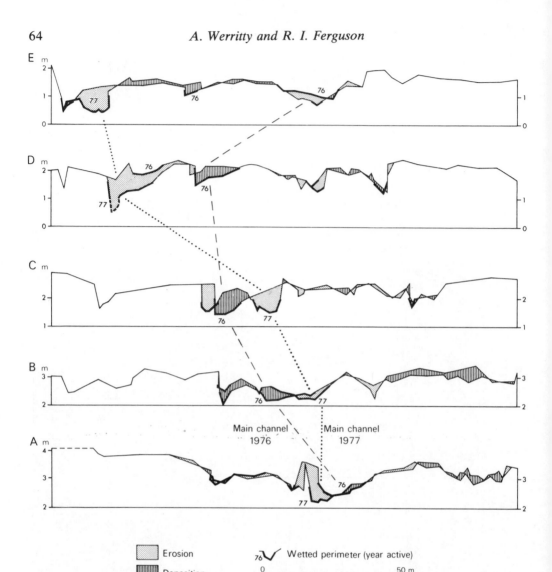

Fig. 5.6 Levelled transects. Sections levelled 31 May–1 June 1976 and 28 May–1 June 1977 along transects of Fig. 5, looking downstream. Heights are in metres above arbitrary datum. Vertical exaggeration: ×10

The new course past sections D and E can be recognized by comparison with Fig. 5.4 as the line of an old channel that was active in 1946 (BD in Fig. 4a) and again in 1964 (EF in Fig. 4b) but not in 1955 or 1967. It is evidently a preferred line that is periodically reoccupied and scoured out, then abandoned and largely filled again following a switch to some other line. For such a cycle to persist, the relative attractiveness of alternative courses must be reversed between switches. If the potential for switching lies in height differences—the perching phenomenon noted above—then repeated switching requires that active channels at low levels are gradually aggraded, or inactive channels are scoured, or both.

The complete cycle cannot be demonstrated from field measurements over a single year, but comparison of the 1976 and 1977 sections in Fig. 5.6 does lend some support to the idea. The extensive gravel bar complex east of the river in Fig. 5.5 is traversed by a system of small channels draining past sections B, C, and D to the 1976 main channel at Section E. These channels are normally fed only by groundwater seepage from the main river, but between 1976 and 1977 they were deepened by 0.1–0.5 m, presumably by an overbank flood or floods. Evidence of deposition in the active channel past sections B and C is also provided by Fig. 5.6. A submerged diagonal riffle near section B in 1976 developed over the year into an exposed mid-channel cobble bar extending 70 m downstream past section C (Fig. 5.5), where 0.8 m of deposition had taken place on the axis of the bar. The separation of the stream into two channels was accompanied by rapid lateral erosion: Fig. 5.6 shows that the deepest part of the main channel shifted 20 m to the right and scoured to a depth of 0.9 m below the former slip-off slope, while the 1 m high turf-topped cut bank of the left hand channel retreated over 4 m in the year by the undercutting and slumping. Despite this erosion the net effect of the changes was to raise slightly the average bed height. Slight aggradation is also apparent at section B, together with a rise in water level compared with the downstream sections. This can be interpreted as a backwater or ponding effect due to the building up of the bar downstream.

These observations over a single year are an unreliable guide to any longer term trend, but resurveying in April 1978 confirmed them. The combination of bar growth and ponding in the main channel, plus scouring of inactive channels, gives precisely the destabilizing tendency needed to induce further switches, and by August 1978 a new east-bank distributary had indeed developed near transect C.

Whether or not these speculations are correct, the switches themselves are almost certainly triggered by overbank floods. The falling stage of one such flood was observed on the afternoon of 31 October 1977. In the area of Fig. 5.5 the river was running just below bankfull, with surface velocities in excess of 2 m s^{-1} past sections C and D. The long mid-channel bar was completely submerged and fresh sand drapes and plant debris on the grassy left-bank floodplain testified to a peak stage at least 0.1 m above bankfull. Downstream of the area shown in Fig. 5.5 the entire unvegetated floodplain, with a maximum width of 160 m, was still inundated and normally dry channels were occupied by fast-flowing water. This area had been mapped and levelled earlier in the month when one section of channel was found to be perched. On a return visit in April 1978 it had largely been abandoned in favour of a nearby channel, inactive at the time of mapping but at a lower level. It seems probable that the switch began in the flood. Once water could spill over from the main channel, the lower level of the previously dry channel would encourage a rapid increase in water depth and consequently also in velocity and bed shear stress. The resulting scour would increase the channel's capacity and lead to its capturing an ever greater share of the total discharge of the river.

We have insufficient streamflow data to assess the frequency of bankfull discharge in this reach of the Feshie, but the overbank flood just described probably had a recurrence interval of less than 1 year. At Lagganlia, 11 km downvalley, 25 mm of rain fell in the 24 h to 9 a.m. on the day of the flood, a precipitation intensity equalled or exceeded once a year on average since records began there in 1971. Heavy precipitation and floods do not necessarily go together in the Cairngorms, where much winter precipitation is in the form of snow. However, the precipitation figures probably underestimate the flood frequency. This is because heavy snowfall without consequent flooding appears to be outweighed by snowmelt flooding not preceded by heavy rainfall: the 1960s streamflow records for Feshiebridge show that the dry month of April experienced mean and maximum discharges higher than in the snowy months of February and March and surpassed only in the more variable conditions of December and January. Further indirect evidence that the Feshie overflows its banks at least once a year comes from the already noted deepening of normally dry channels, from the disappearance from these dry channels by April 1978 of most of 80 painted pebbles left in them in April 1977, and from changes in the distribution over the floodplain of turf blocks, tree trunks, and other water-borne debris.

Discussion

The observations of Schumm and Lichty (1965) on time, space, and causality in geomorphology apply to the Feshie along with other rivers. We have shown that over 200 years different reaches have retained distinctive channel patterns that can be explained by spatial variations in valley topography and other environmental conditions that are virtually fixed at this 'graded' timescale, even though over geologic time they have evolved in response to climatic change and other controls not relevant in the short term.

The more detailed record made available by aerial photography in the last 30 years reveals the dynamic nature of the modern equilibrium between river and environment. Considerable local fluctuations have occurred in channel position, degree of braiding, sinuosity, and vegetation pattern. There also appears to be a relationship between channel pattern and the incidence of high-magnitude events. Major floods such as that of 1961 obliterate the former channel pattern and replace it with a chaotic braided system with many unstable elements. Reworking of the bar and bed materials by lower flows tends to result in a rationalization and simplification of the channel system into a single, rather sinuous main channel which occasionally divides around major medial bars. This process continues until it is disrupted by the next major flood. If this hypothesis is correct, the channel pattern revealed in any individual aerial photograph or topographic survey is to a large extent conditioned by the most recent major flood and the subsequent length of time available for recovery of the channel system.

At a shorter timescale again, our field observations over a single year suggest that at least some of the channel changes within the overall equilibrium can be understood in terms of hydraulic processes associated with individual floods and conditioned by the detailed morphology of the existing channel and floodplain.

The changing relationships at different timescales mean that there may be more to the past than simple extrapolation of the present. Locally, indeed, the past is often one of the keys to the present—as with the legacy of Pleistocene glaciation in Glen Feshie. Yet in all branches of geomorphology a better knowledge of present day processes and changes can help avoid misinterpretation of the past. Our investigations of channel changes in the Feshie point to two conclusions that are more generally relevant in this way.

The first concerns the magnitude and frequency of events responsible for channel change. The coarseness of the valley floor sediments might suggest that only the biggest, relatively rare, floods are capable of substantial erosion. However, aerial photographs and field observations show that channel changes are frequent and ubiquitous, and indirect evidence suggests that major channel switches have been triggered by floods small enough to recur about once a year. These floods are nevertheless overbank ones, implying a substantially higher frequency of bankfall discharge than found by Hey (1975) for non-braided gravel rivers elsewhere in Britain. The flashy hydrologic regime, and the high velocities characteristic of braided channels, offset the high threshold of sediment motion and mean that the behaviour of the Feshie is in broad accordance with

Wolman and Miller's (1960) dictum that most geomorphic work is done by events of modest magnitude and fairly high frequency. The channel changes of the Feshie may not appear modest, but they are certainly relatively frequent.

The second noteworthy result of our investigations is that the normal short-term behaviour of the Feshie is not restricted to channel migration by bank erosion. Channel switching is also common, with consequences that include rapid local aggradation and scour—in this case by up to ±1 m in a single year in a floodplain whose total relief at any one section is less than twice this figure. Another by-product of channel switching is the deposition of sheets of coarse gravel and cobbles on top of floodplain vegetation, 1 m above the bed of the main river channel. As Ritter (1975) points out in his discussion of an analogous deposit, an exposure showing coarse sediments overlying finer ones with a soil horizon would normally be interpreted as evidence for a major episode of valley aggradation. This could be wrong in the case of the Feshie, which has been downcutting throughout postglacial time.

The braided pattern of the Feshie is exceptional in Britain today, but similar rivers must have been common in the early Holocene when catchments further south and at lower levels had skeletal soils and vegetation, flashy hydrologic regimes, and a fresh mantle of unconsolidated glacial outwash. Our study shows that evidence of major channel changes on the part of such rivers need not imply changes in climate, base level, or other long-term controls. The lesson is that palaeoenvironmental inferences from coarse fluvial deposits must be made cautiously and with due regard for the considerable short-term and small-scale variability of the braided river environment.

Acknowledgements

We thank the following individuals and organisations: the Nature Conservancy Council and Lord Dulverton for permission to conduct research in Glen Feshie and Lord Dulverton for the use of a private road; the Universities of St Andrews, Hull, and Stirling for field support; the British Geomorphological Research Group for a grant to R.I.F. from its research fund; Dr. J. A. T. Young of Edinburgh University for the loan of aerial photographs; Mr. S. Armstrong of Lagganlia Outdoor Centre for precipitation records and a flood warning; the Scottish Development Department for streamflow records; and the cartographer of the Department of Geography, St. ·Andrews University.

References

Bluck, B. J. (1974). Structure and directional properties of some valley sandur deposits in southern Iceland. *Sedimentology*, **21**, 533–554.

Bluck, B. J. (1976). Sedimentation in some Scottish rivers of low sinuosity. *Trans. Roy. Soc. Edinburgh*, **69**, 425–456.

Fahnestock, R. K., and Bradley, W. C. (1973). Knik and Matanuska Rivers, Alaska: a contrast in braiding. In *Fluvial Geomorphology* (Ed. M. Morisawa). (State University of New York, Binghamton, N.Y., pp. 220–250.

Hey, R. D. (1975). Design discharge for natural channels. In *Science, Technology and Environmental Management* (Eds. R. D. Hey and T. D. Davies). Saxon House, pp. 73–88.

Hickin, E. J., and Nanson, G. C. (1975). The character of channel migration on the Beatton River, northeastern British Columbia, Canada. *Geol. Soc. Am. Bull.*, **86**, 487–494.

Hinxman, L. W., and Anderson, E. M. (1915). The geology of mid-Strathspey and Strathdearn. *Mem. Geol. Surv. Scotl.*, H.M.S.O.

Hitchcock, D. (1977). Channel pattern changes in divided reaches: an example in the coarse bed material of the Forest of Bowland. In *River Channel Changes* (Ed. K. J. Gregory). Wiley Chichester, pp. 207–220.

Howard, A. D., Keetch, M. E., and Vincent, C. L. (1970). Topological and geometrical properties of braided streams. *Wat. Resour. Res.*, **6,** 1674–1688.

Knighton, A. D. (1972). Changes in a braided reach. *Geol. Soc. Am. Bull.*, **83,** 3813–3822.

Krigström, A. (1962). Geomorphological studies of sandur plains and their braided rivers in Iceland. *Geog. Annaler*, **44,** 328–436.

Leopold, L. B. (1973). River channel change with time: an example. *Geol. Soc. Am. Bull.*, **84,** 1845–1860.

Leopold, L. B., and Wolman, M. G. (1957). River channel patterns: braided, meandering and straight. *Prof. Pap. U.S. Geol. Surv.*, No. 282–A.

Lewin, J., and Weir, M. J. C. (1977). Morphology and recent history of the lower Spey. *Scott. Geog. Mag.*, **93,** 45–51.

Linton, D. L. (1949). Some Scottish river captures re-examined: I. The diversion of the upper Geldie. *Scott. Geog. Mag.*, **65,** 123–132.

NERC (1975). *Flood Studies Report*. Natural Environment Research Council, London.

Ritter, D. F. (1975). Stratigraphic implications of coarse-grained gravel deposited as overbank sediment, southern Illinois. *J. Geol.*, **83,** 645–650.

Schumm, S. A., and Lichty, R. W. (1965). Time, space and causality in geomorphology. *Am. J. Sci.*, **263,** 110–119.

Sissons, J. B. (1974). A late-glacial ice cap in the central Grampians. *Trans. Inst. Br. Geog.*, **62,** 95–114.

Smart, J. S., and Moruzzi, V. L. (1972). Quantitative properties of delta channel networks. *Z. Geomorphol.*, **16,** 268–282.

Smith, N. D. (1970). The braided stream depositional environment: comparison of the Platte River with some Silurian clastic rocks, north-central Appalachians. *Geol. Soc. Am. Bull.*, **81,** 2993–3014.

Smith, N. D. (1974). Sedimentology and bar formation in the upper Kicking Horse river, a braided outwash stream. *J. Geol.*, **82,** 205–223.

Sugden, D. E. (1977). Did glaciers form in the Cairngorms in the 17th–19th centuries? *Cairngorm Club J.*, **18,** 189–200.

Wolman, M. G. , and Miller, J. P. (1960). Magnitude and frequency of forces in geomorphic processes. *J. Geol.*, **68,** 54–74.

Young, J. A. T. (1975). Ice wastage in Glen Feshie, Inverness-shire. *Scott. Geog. Mag.*, **91,** 91–101.

Young, J. A. T. (1976). The terraces of Glen Feshie, Inverness-shire. *Trans. Roy. Soc. Edinburgh.*, **69,** 501–512.

Timescales in Geomorphology
Edited by R. A. Cullingford, D. A. Davidson, and J. Lewin
© 1980 John Wiley & Sons Ltd

CHAPTER 6

The significance of cartographic sources in determining coastal change

Alan P. Carr

*Institute of Oceanographic Sciences,
Taunton*

Introduction

This paper falls into three distinct, but interrelated, parts. The initial section seeks to establish the inherent reliability of cartographic sources with reference to selected coastal examples. The middle section then compares the results of a number of short-term topographic surveys and research experiments with the apparent trends established from the extended cartographic record. The final part looks briefly at one or two other techniques which help to supplement data over the timespan where maps and charts are most effective and draws overall conclusions.

The Royal Commission on Coast Erosion and Afforestation (1911) summarized the view of the then Director-General of the Ordnance Survey, Col. Hellard, as: 'old charts and maps in the Ordnance Survey Department furnished no evidence of any real value as to the changes on the coast-line'. Similarly, Diver (1933), in reviewing the cartographic evidence for changes in part of Poole Harbour, Dorset, England, had considerable misgivings. He described various maps and charts as: 'approximate; valueless, not reliable; distorted by elongation; featureless; of no importance, inaccurate'. Often maps and charts were merely derived from earlier sources; thus, Jos. Avery's map of about 1720 occurs in no less than seven allegedly revised editions up to 1794, while Mackenzie's chart of 1785 was published by Heather in 1812 and Norie in 1816 and 1827, and the land detail was again used in the 1835 Admiralty chart. Taylor's erroneous survey of 1765 reappeared under Steel's name in 1815 and the outline of the first edition of the Ordnance Survey of 1811 was adopted by Dessiou in 1813 and the Greenwood brothers in 1826. The errors are common to all.

Nevertheless, in spite of the warnings of Helland in general, and Diver for a specific site, as well as those of other workers, there has been a continuing use of cartographic sources as evidence of geomorphological change. It is not surprising that this should be so because, notwithstanding their shortcomings, maps and charts have potential value for quantification; they provide a ready means of comparison and permit an immediate visual impact. In general there is a greater element of objectivity about them than in, say, the literary evidence which is often incorporated in politically motivated tracts or is highly ambiguous in interpretation. (We are not concerned here with extending cartographic interpretation back to pre-seventeenth century times by the use of place-name evidence as de Boer (1969) effectively did in respect of the evolution of Spurn Point in Yorkshire.)

The initial part of this paper concentrates on map evidence as it affects the coastline. The reasons for this are three-fold. Firstly, changes are at a maximum in the coastal environment and therefore *may* be large enough to be depicted on successive topographic surveys, at least in areas of unconsolidated sediment. Secondly, although early surveyors had major problems in the representation of detail (and nowhere was this more apparent than along the coast), there were both hydrographic and land surveys to complement one another in such an environment. This is especially true of the nineteenth century. Lastly, it is in coastal areas that most examples have become apparent because of the nature of the author's own research. Those quoted are confined to England and Wales.

In an earlier paper (Carr, 1962), the various aspects which influenced the value of maps and charts at three coastal sites were discussed. It is intended initially to summarize that work and to add one or two other examples.

Limitations in the Evidence Provided by Maps and Charts

Technical Accuracy

Apart from the occasional estate map, primarily constructed for litigational purposes, eighteenth century and earlier land surveys were generally of low accuracy and drawn to a small scale. Even as late as 1769 Wyld thought that there was no point in producing theodolites capable of reading to an accuracy of better than one minute when that was the best that graphical plotting could achieve and it was graphical, rather than mathematical, solutions that were adopted for triangulation. Some secondary control was provided by perambulators which were wheeled along the existing roads, and the remaining detail was added by sketching. The first extensive triangulation network began in the 1780s under General Roy, while the Ordnance Survey was founded in 1791. It took until the mid-nineteenth century for reasonably accurate medium to large-scale maps (i.e. 1:10,560 and larger) to become widely available in Britain.

The state of marine navigation and survey was at least as unsatisfactory and resulted in frequent complaints by the Royal Society during the eighteenth century. The sextant was used initially only for vertical angles while Robinson (1957) noted that, up to the time of Mackenzie, position fixing for hydrographic charts was still by compass even where land detail was based on theodolite triangulation. The station pointer did not come into being for plotting data until about 1774.

Even more recently, changes in surveying techniques militate against the comparability of data. In marine surveys examples include the use of echosounders instead of leadlines, and the employment of microwave and other position-fixing techniques instead of surveying sextants. While these particular instances result in improvements in coverage, detail, and accuracy, these do not always follow. For instance, aerial surveys do not necessarily provide the same accuracy of detail as measurements on the ground but are much quicker to carry out and therefore of value in areas where there is difficult access or limited time, as in the survey of a specified low water level.

Problems with instrumental techniques and plotting methods were gradually reduced over time. So, too, were actual errors and discrepancies of style of representation, but traces of bad survey and derived information continue to exist, as will be demonstrated.

Insufficient attention is given to the plotting accuracy which can be attained on various scales. Survey Computations (Winterbotham, 1926) stated that in general the coordinates of a point would be accurate to 150 ft (45 m) on a scale of 1:63,360, with other scales having similar limitations. This effectively means that for Chesil Beach, Dorset, England, recession of the crest between 1852–53 and 1968–69 surveys only exceeded the potential plotting error at 1:10,560 along one relatively short length of beach (Carr and Gleason, 1972).

Tanner (1978) observes that 'not every measurable distance on a published map is correct, even within the limits set by scale. The (United States) Geological Survey standards for horizontal accuracy state that ". . . at least 90% of the well-defined map points shall be plotted correctly within one-fiftieth of an inch (0.5 mm) on the published map" '. What of the remaining 10%? What about the ill-defined points?

Surveying Errors and Anomalies

As Carr (1962) has noted, rivers used to cause special difficulties for early surveyors and Norden's estate survey of the Orford area of Suffolk, England, dating from 1601, proved no exception with scale errors of up to 100% at some points (Carr, 1969). However, similar discrepancies were still apparent two-and-a-half centuries later. In the maps and plans undertaken for tithe redemption during the period *ca*. 1840 the format proposed by the Tithe Commissioners was adhered to only loosely and barely one third of the surveys gained full recognition and approval. For example, along the northeastern and eastern shore of Swansea Bay, South Wales, there were nine parishes at the time, one of which was in sole ownership and therefore not surveyed at all. For the remainder, two different scales were used, and there are various distance, orientation, and other errors. One tide level is included on each map but this may be an arbitrary high or low, while in one case the level is unspecified. Only one surveyor records his name and only three maps give survey dates.

Almost contemporaneous with the tithe surveys was John Coode's study of Chesil Beach (Coode, 1853). Coode's original beach profile and crest-line data still exist and are meticulous in the way in which they are recorded. Even so, on the accompanying site map, which is reproduced on a smaller scale in his published paper, the landward side of the Fleet lagoon is incorrect (Carr and Gleason, 1972). It appears merely to have been sketched but as a result some doubt must be cast on the accuracy of the remaining survey data. In this particular instance the problem could largely be resolved because it was possible to verify the recorded tide heights and survey datum. The predicted 1852–53 tide heights were recomputed by the Hydrographic Department on the author's behalf and compared with Coode's observed values. Normally such checks are not available.

Another example in England quoted by Carr (1962) is that of Stert Island, in Bridgwater Bay, Somerset, where the high water mark of the first edition of the 1:10,560 map has become the vegetation boundary of the second, while the shingle limit on the eastern side of the island appears to have been transformed into the high water mark.

Partial Revision

The effects of the partial revision of a map or chart has been a frequent source of difficulty and, in particular, it has often been hard to tell if areas which remained unchanged cartographically were actually so in the prototype. One notable example was the dune system at Braunton Burrows, North Devon, where the appropriate Ordnance Survey 1:63,360 map claimed full revision in 1957–58 but actually still had the contours as surveyed in 1885–86. Meanwhile the dune ridges had moved laterally by up to 120 m and the area above 30 m (100 ft) had increased 35-fold (Kidson and Carr, 1960).

On other occasions maps have been amended without the survey or publication dates being altered. Sometimes a written topographic description proves to be at variance with an apparently contemporaneous survey or two surveys provide contradictory data. The question then comes as to which, if either, was correct and if it is possible to reconcile them. Reyce's *Breviary* (1618) description of the position of the mouth of the River Ore is an example of anomalous literary evidence, while there is well over 500 m difference between the 1837 and 1838 survey positions for the distal point of Orfordness shingle spit (Carr, 1969), even though both sources are apparently reputable.

Occasionally reports in journals and newspapers supplement the limited survey data available. The repeated shifts in the position of the lifeboat station at Braunton Burrows, North Devon, between 1846 and 1892 (Blackley, *et al.*, 1972) gives an indication of the instability of that length of shoreline which cannot be gained by the map and chart evidence alone.

The Relation of Short-term to Longer-term Trends

It is pertinent to ask whether there is a specific timescale which is relevant in the elucidation of geomorphological change along the coast and in the study of littoral processes. In other words, the problem to be posed is how typical are short-term data? Also, can representative results be obtained by experimental field techniques of limited duration? What timescales are we, or should we be, examining? Is it possible to separate sequences and trends from mere oscillations and, if so, what period must be covered to ensure that this goal is achieved?

The object of this section is to compare the results of a number of short-term studies, ranging from a day to a year or so, with results over a more extended timescale. In this context 'long term' is of the order of 100 years. For this purpose two sets of data will be examined. These are the results of a number of beach and offshore tracer experiments and series of beach profiles. Thereafter the agreements and discrepancies between 'short-term' techniques and cartographic evidence over a longer period will be assessed.

Tracer Studies

Pebbles of a distinct geological type, but with the same hydraulic characteristics as the indigenous material, were used to examine longshore transport rates on Chesil Beach, Dorset, during 1969 and 1970 (Carr, 1971, 1975). The results of these tests showed that the maximum transport rate of the tracer material was 343 m in 24 h but only 2103 m after about 4 months (mean longshore movement 88 and 627 m respectively). The well known grading of the pebbles alongshore would imply no net transport over the long term on this beach. In parallel studies in Swansea Bay, South Wales, sand-size tracer labelled with radioactive scandium (^{46}Sc) was deployed offshore on the sea bed (Heathershaw and Carr, 1977) and sand, coated with fluorescent dyes, on the beach. The results of both series of experiments suggested that initial calculations produce excessive transport rates and a period of time is required for the sediment to come into equilibrium with the mobile layer on the sea bed. Offshore this appears to have been of the order of 2 weeks, and about 2 days onshore. Although both periods are short in a geomorphological sense they are long as far as tracer studies are concerned and, importantly, they are different from each other and from those at Chesil Beach and Slapton Beach, Start Bay, Devon (Gleason, *et al.* 1975). The results cast doubt on the very high drift rates calculated from many brief tracer investigations undertaken elsewhere, such as those listed by the United States Army Coastal Engineering Research Center (1973).

Slapton and Chesil beaches are also of interest because of the way in which certain pebble shapes are selected out of the range of the tracer population initially injected (Carr, 1975). Several instances occurred where there was less than a 0.001 statistical probability of the material recovered being derived from this parent population, although the 'labelling' proved that it must have been so. Different recovery rates (as well as types of material) under different environmental conditions (e.g. swell as compared with wind waves) again demonstrate the unrepresentativeness of field experiments of this nature and timespan.

Beach Profiles

During 1965–66 a series of cross-sections were surveyed at a number of sites along Chesil Beach. Although swash only rarely reached the beach crest (which was as much as 14.7 m above mean sea level), it was found that for some sections the variability of the upper part of the beach face during the survey period actually exceeded the apparent change recorded between 1852–53 and 1965–66 (this, of course, reflects not only the physical processes during 1965–66 but also the repeatability of the 1852–53 sections and the representativeness of the 1852–53 survey conditions).

Results of research into changes in the distal point of the Orfordness shingle spit are of interest both on a detailed and on a gross scale. For example, as many as 34 sections were surveyed annually between 1956 and 1970 (Carr, 1965, 1972). During that period very few of the profiles showed a consistent trend throughout. Longer term, mainly cartographic, data covering the period from the beginning of the ninteenth century suggest that over this more protracted timescale any site up to 1.4 km north of the 1970 distal point would have displayed both erosion and accretion at some time or other. The ridge structure of the spit suggests evolution from the north over a still longer timespan. Carr (1969, 1970) found that the written record could provide some potentially valuable information prior to that afforded by maps and charts. Nevertheless, he resorted to 'geomorphological evidence', that is, information based on physical criteria, for the period before 1600 AD.

Monthly surveys across the beach along the eastern shore of Swansea Bay were undertaken for a period of approximately 18 months until April/May 1977, with a further survey in October 1977, i.e. at the end of a 2-year period (Blackley and Carr, 1978). Calculation of changes in the volume of beach material based on the figures derived from the 18-month and 2-year periods provide a very different picture and if the data were to be extrapolated from either series, widely divergent conclusions would be produced. Beach gradients can be calculated from this work, from aerial surveys carried out for the British Transport Docks Board between 1968 and 1975, and from maps and plans dating from the 1840s onwards. The results of the 1975–77 beach profiles indicate no clear trends but the photogrammetry based over a 7-year timespan confirms the steepening of the beach recorded by the various earlier cartographic sources. Does this mean that the recent data are unrepresentative or that the long-term trend has now ceased?

Fig. 6.1 shows the erosion and accretion pattern for the offshore banks in the eastern half of Swansea Bay. The implications of these changes were discussed by Carr and Blackley (1977) and need not be considered here. What is of interest in the present context is the extent to which these data can or cannot be confirmed, not only by intervening cartographic sources but, especially, by modern techniques.

Whilst hydrographic surveys in 1859–60 and 1974 effectively map the whole eastern

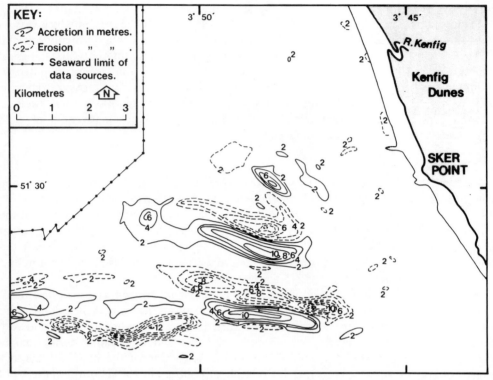

Fig. 6.1 Part of Swansea Bay, South Wales. Comparison of 1859 and 1974 hydrographic charts showing erosion and accretion

part of the bay, all the intermediate surveys cover only a portion of the area of interest. Nevertheless, these intermediate surveys help to confirm the long-term trends, showing specific locations at 'half-way' stages (Carr and Blackley, 1977). Sailing directions in the various editions of the appropriate volume of Admiralty Pilot also provide supporting evidence. At the same time, simply taking the crest-line of the various banks on each survey, rather than their overall positions, does not necessarily lead to the same conclusions. Further ambiguities arise because of the changing methods of depth sounding and position fixing over time, referred to earlier, as well as the sound navigational policy of always recording 'least depth' on the charts. This exaggerates the volume of sediment present. If one calculates the apparent changes in volume, not just of the banks but of the whole surveyed eastern area of the bay, there is a loss of sediment of 12.3×10^6 m³ between 1859 and 1974. The whole of this, and more, would be eliminated if the conversion of the earlier datum to that of the 1974 survey was in error by as little as 0.1 m, which is the attainable limit of accuracy. When this is compounded with the limitations on technique, and the way in which the isopleths of change have been derived, it is clear that while displacement of the banks may be, and in this instance is, real, the use of data for more sophisticated means of analysis and comparison are not necessarily justified. However, the 1859–1974 charts do provide an overall picture of changes of the banks within that period.

Present day techniques which may shed light on trends include tracer studies, such as those described above, and geophysical methods, principally in this case side-scan sonar.

The results of the tracer study for South Kenfig Patches, a sandbank about 4 km off the east coast of Swansea Bay (Heathershaw and Carr, 1977), *could* be interpreted as being compatible with the longer term displacement of the offshore banks, but it is not necessarily so, nor do they describe the transport pattern in more than the one area where the test was undertaken. Side-scan sonar, continuous seismic profiling and echo sounding are all capable of giving some information regarding sediment transport, for example by depicting orientation of sandwaves and mega-ripples. In the latter case the structure may be limited merely to an ebb or flood tide. Whilst sandwaves are of longer duration, they too may be destroyed, for example, by storm waves. Over much of the area of the banks no obvious orientation features exist and even contemporary transport paths are not clear although they may be inferred by current meter and wave data.

The examples listed in this section have been restricted both as to location and number. However, they go some way towards answering the questions posed at the beginning. Long-term records have the effect of averaging the changes that have occurred over the corresponding timespan. They may well include the effects of extreme events but are not explicit in so doing. Thus they represent the sum but not the range of conditions that have been experienced and may partially reflect factors and circumstances that have been superseded. The progressive extension of breakwaters at the entrance to Port Talbot Docks and tidal harbour in Swansea Bay appears to have had a corresponding effect on the foreshore. Calculations based solely on maps and plans pre- and post-dating the series of engineering works would be interpreted as showing a linear response and thus fail to reflect the present day dynamic equilibrium. Short-term records and experiments *may* show a new or recent trend at variance with earlier conditions and thus be valid and significant. For construction works of limited duration, it may be that these types of data and extrapolations based upon them are what are required although it it unlikely that, in a geomorphological sense, a representative range of conditions is met. It must be reiterated, however, that even analyses based on surveys spaced a long time apart do not guarantee that extremes have been experienced in the meantime or that the conditions when the data were acquired were representative.

Some Alternative Techniques and Their Applicability

Probably the most promising field for new methods in dating lies in the areas of geochemistry and the applications of radioactive isotopes. Wise (this volume, Chapter 9) has described the use of caesium (^{137}Cs) and lead (^{210}Pb) radionuclides for dating. The determination of the ^{210}Pb content is based on the measurement of the daughter polonium (^{210}Po) activity. Certain assumptions, such as the lack of post-depositional mobility, have to be made and the method is applicable only to fine-grained sedimentary deposits, i.e. silts and mud. Nevertheless, with the half-life for lead being 21.0 years, a useful timespan of the order of a century is possible. This enables dating to be carried out over a timescale not dissimilar from that over which quantitative cartographic methods may be utilized (e.g. Robbins and Edgington, 1975). Some work has been undertaken in the United Kingdom by the Institute for Marine Environmental Research using this technique, including the dating of samples from offshore in Swansea Bay. Although the preliminary results are encouraging, it is not yet possible to answer the problem posed by Fig. 6.2.

Another approach is to try and identify metallic pollutants present in the sediments themselves. For example, the increasing use of zinc for galvanizing from about 1870 means that there is a likelihood of much higher levels of this metal being present in

Alan P. Carr

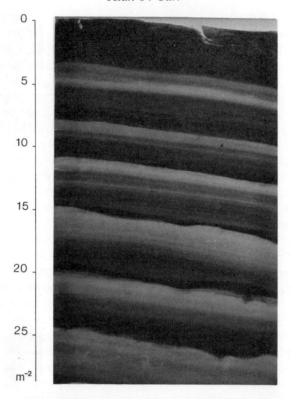

Fig. 6.2 X-Ray photograph of box-core showing cyclic sedimentation of sands, silt and mud near Port Talbot tidal harbour. The timescale of the sequences may be spring/neap tidal cycles, periods between successive dredging events, or longer periods

fine-grained sediments after that date. This approach may also prove valid for other metallic ions such as copper and nickel but with possibly less well defined operative dates. However, not only is the type of sediment restrictive in the applicability of the technique, but in addition there needs to be proximity to an industrial area and its pollutants.

A range of new dating methods from various disciplines has been developed throughout the post-war period, but these apply only in restricted environments. For example, little progress can be defined in areas of sediment accretion amongst non-cohesive sediments. The situation is even worse in oxidation zones above the watertable onshore, whilst areas subject to erosion suffer the loss of any form of tangible material record, as they always have done. In such a context the evidence provided by precise cartographic documentation is of particular value in the elucidation of a timescale in geomorphology.

There can be little doubt that while new techniques may be developed and existing methods may become more sophisticated, there will be a continuing need to use all the data sources that are available, one of which is the cartographic record.

Acknowledgements

The experimental work was carried out by the Physiographical Section of the (then) Nature Conservancy or, more recently, by part of the Sedimentation Group of the Institute of Oceanographic Sciences. The latter studies were funded by the Department of the Environment.

The Hydrographic Department, MOD (Navy), recomputed the 1852–53 tide levels for Chesil Beach on the author's behalf. In addition, the bulk of the 1974 hydrographic survey data, from which the 1859–1974 comparison (Fig. 6.1) was derived, is from the survey by Lt. Cmdr. J. Pugh on HMS Woodlark.

The ^{210}Pb dating of Swansea Bay cores was carried out for the Institute of Oceanographic Sciences by its sister organisation, the Institute for Marine Environmental Research. Both are part of the Natural Environment Research Council.

References

Blackley, M. W. L., and Carr, A. P. (1978). Swansea Bay project: Topic Report 2: Evidence for beach stability: photogrammatic and topographic measurements. *Institute of Oceanographic Sciences Report,* No. 51, 29 pp.

Blackley, M. W. L., Carr, A. P., and Gleason, R. (1972). Tracer experiments in the Taw-Torridge estuary with particular reference to Braunton Burrows NNR. *Unit of Coastal Sedimentation Report,* No. 1972/22, 28 pp.

Carr, A. P. (1962). Cartographic record and historical accuracy. *Geography,* **47,** 135–144.

Carr, A. P. (1965). Shingle spit and river mouth: short-term dynamics. *Trans. Inst. Br. Geog.,* **36,** 117–129.

Carr, A. P. (1969). The growth of Orford spit: cartographic and historical evidence from the sixteenth century. *Geog. J.,* **135,** 28–39.

Carr, A. P. (1970). The evolution of Orfordness, Suffolk, before 1600 AD: geomorphological evidence. *Z. Geomorph., N.S.,* **14,** 289–300.

Carr, A. P. (1971). Experiments on longshore transport and sorting of pebbles: Chesil Beach, England. *J. Sedim. Petrol.,* **41,** 1084–1104.

Carr, A. P. (1972). Aspects of spit development and decay: the estuary of the River Ore, Suffolk. *Field Studies,* **3,** 633–653.

Carr, A. P. (1975). Differential movement of coarse sediment particles. *Proc. 14th Conf. Cst. Engng., Copenhagen.* American Society of Civil Engineers, New York, **2,** 851–870.

Carr, A. P., and Blackley, M. W. L. (1977). Swansea Bay project: Topic Report 1, Part (b): Long-term changes in the coastline. *Institute of Oceanographic Sciences Report,* No. 42, 63 pp.

Carr, A. P., and Gleason, R. (1972). Chesil Beach, Dorset and the cartographic evidence of Sir John Coode. *Proc. Dorset Nat. Hist. Archaeol. Soc.,* **91,** 125–131 (Volume for 1971).

Coode, J. (1853). Description of the Chesil Bank, with remarks upon its origin, the causes which have contributed to its formation and upon the movement of shingle generally. *Minut. Proc. Inst. Civ. Engrs.,* **12,** 520–546.

de Boer, G. (1969). The historical variations of Spurn Point; the evidence of early maps. *Geog. J.,* **135,** 17–27.

Diver, C. (1933). The physiography of South Haven peninsula, Studland Heath, Dorset. *Geog. J.,* **81,** 404–427.

Gleason, R., Blackley, M. W. L., and Carr, A. P. (1975). Beach stability and particle size distribution, Start Bay. *J. Geol. Soc. Lond.,* **131,** 83–101.

Kidson, C., and Carr, A. P. (1960). Dune reclamation at Braunton Burrows, Devon. *Chart. Surv.,* **93,** 298–303.

Heathershaw, A. D., and Carr, A. P. (1977). Measurements of sediment transport rates using radioactive tracers. *Coastal Sediments '77.* Americal Society of Civil Engineers, Charleston, S. C., pp. 399–416.

Reyce (1618). *Breviary.* British Museum Harl. MSS 3873. Dedicated to Sir R. Crane, 9 February 1618.

Robbins, J. A., and Edgington, D. N. (1975). Determination of recent sedimentation rates in Lake Michigan using Pb–210 and Cs–137. *Geochim. Cosmochim. Acta*, **29**, 285–304.

Robinson, A. H. W. (1957). Marine surveying in Britain during the seventeenth and eighteenth centuries. *Geog. J.*, **123**, 449–456.

Royal Commission on Coast Erosion and Afforestation (1911). Vol. III, Pt. 1. Third (and Final) Report. HMSO, London. Evidence of Col. Hellard, pp. 43–44.

Tanner, W. F. (Ed.) (1978). *Standards for Measuring Shoreline Changes*. Coastal Research and Department of Geology. Tallahassee, Florida, 87 pp.

U.S. Army Coastal Engineering Research Center (1973). *Shore Protection Manual*, Department of the Army, Corps of Engineers, 3 vols.

Winterbotham, H. S. L. (Ed.) (1926). *Survey Computations to be Used in Conjunction with the Text Book of Topographical and Geographical Surveying*, HMSO, London, 3rd ed., p. 4.

Timescales in Geomorphology
Edited by R. A. Cullingford, D. A. Davidson and J. Lewin
© 1980 John Wiley & Sons Ltd

CHAPTER 7

Rates of geomorphological changes in proglacial areas

R. J. Price

Department of Geography,
University of Glasgow

Introduction

In comparison with many other landforms, those produced by glacial and fluvioglacial processes can be created and destroyed very rapidly. By examining changes in proglacial areas around the margins of existing glaciers by means of ground survey or sequential air photography it is possible to determine the timescales involved in the creation, modification, and destruction of glacial and fluvioglacial forms. Case studies of proglacial areas in Alaska, Yukon, and Iceland will be discussed and comparisons made with proglacial areas associated with Pleistocene glaciers and ice sheets.

It is possible to study proglacial areas in association with existing glaciers or as 'fossil' landscapes produced thousands of years ago by Pleistocene ice sheets and glaciers. However, it is extremely difficult to find any one analogue of Pleistocene proglacial environments around the margins of existing ice masses and the conclusions reached in this paper will form only a first approximation of some of the many environmental conditions which may have prevailed during the Pleistocene. This paper will concentrate on the rates of creation, change, and destruction of landforms rather than the mechanisms by which landforms are produced in proglacial areas.

The proglacial environment is characterized by very rapid changes when compared with other geomorphological systems. In temperate fluvial systems, for example, rates of erosion averaged over an entire drainage basin may be of the order of 3 cm per 1000 years, whereas in glacierized basins the rates of erosion can be of the order of 1 m per 1000 years, i.e. 30 times greater. In temperate fluvial systems flood discharges may occur once in every 2 or 3 years, whereas in proglacial areas flood discharges may occur several times in one ablation season.

Although this paper is concerned primarily with landforms, it should be noted that the proglacial environment is one in which there are rapid changes in climatological conditions both in time and over short distances and that soil-forming activity and vegetation colonization can take place rapidly during deglaciation. The total environment is characterized by rapid change and the geomorphological events described in this paper are only a small part of this dynamic environmental system.

For the purpose of this paper, the term 'proglacial area' is limited to the area which is about to be or has been covered by glacial ice, along with the narrow zone (1–2 km) beyond the maximum extent of an ice mass in which meltwater actively can result in significant landform modification (Fig. 7.1).

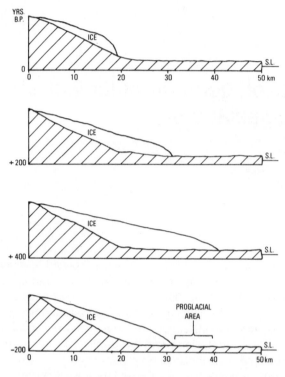

Fig. 7.1 A definition of 'proglacial area'

Landform Changes During Ice Advance

The rate of advance of existing ice fronts is well documented but the data are mainly confined to valley glaciers. Observations in Alaska, Yukon Territory, and Iceland suggest that valley glaciers advance at rates of between 10 and 50 m per year. There are no data for the rate of advance of the front of an existing temperate ice sheet.

Apart from changes in the location of the proglacial area, landforms resulting from an advance are difficult to evaluate because of their subsequent burial by ice and eventual modification during deglaciation. Advancing ice is believed to be capable of eroding hard rock at rates of between 1 mm per year (Goldthwait, 1974) and 3 mm per year (Boulton and Dent, 1974), whilst the rate of deposition of glacial till can be of the order of 1.5 cm per year. These figures are based on observations in South-east Iceland and the Glacier Bay area of Alaska, where the present climate is very moist and temperate. Goldthwait (1974) believes that 'till deposition is a very rapid process occupying a small fraction of glacial time in comparison with erosion, while fluvioglacial and ablation features may form in the last 1% of the total time of ice cover'. The most important stage in landform development occurs at the maximum of the last period of ice-front advance when push and dump moraines are formed along the ice front and may well survive the subsequent period of ice wastage and frontal retreat.

Surging Glaciers

Over the last decade the occurrence and significance of glacier surges have been more widely appreciated. It is now known that many glaciers experience short-term rapid increases in their rate of movement resulting in the folding of medial moraines, extensive development of crevasses, and the rapid forward movement of the ice margin. Such surges may last only a few months, although 2 or 3 years is not uncommon. Ice fronts may advance from 500 m to 10 km in one surge. In Iceland, the Bruarjökull ice front on the north side of Vatnajökull advanced 8 km in 5 months with a maximum rate of progress of 5 m per hour. It might be expected that a mass of ice 30–50 m thick extending over several kilometres might be capable of a great deal of geomorphological work. However, no push moraines were formed and much of the geomorphological work was related to marked increases in meltwater discharge and to the subsequent wastage of stagnant, debris-laden ice which existed at the end of the surge period. There are examples of push moraines with and without ice-cores (Johnson, 1972) being produced during the frontal advance of surging glaciers. As a result of the 1969 surge of the Donjek Glacier in the St. Elias mountains, the terminus was re-activated to produce an almost vertical, unstable ice face up to 30 m in height, below which there was an area of stagnant ice with a low angle slope. Johnson described several ice-cored and push moraines which developed along the margin as a result of the 1969 surge.

Clapperton (1975, p. 403) has concluded that 'the majority of surging glaciers, whether they are located in subpolar or temperate regimes, are much more highly charged with subglacially derived debris than most glaciers that do not surge'. He also pointed out (p. 404) that '. . . many of these glaciers have surged over the pre-deposited sediments of an outwash plain or of a fjord head and have basally incorporated considerable amounts of these materials in addition to tectonically deforming them into push moraines'.

It can be concluded, therefore, that although a glacial surge may represent the most dramatic change which takes place over a 2–3-year period, the glaciological activity is not matched by geomorphological changes of the same magnitude. Some push moraines may be developed and there may be an increase in the amount of meltwater discharged. However, it is likely that the most significant contribution of a glacial surge is the large amount of subglacial, englacial, and supraglacial debris which is quickly brought forward to the terminus and the extensive areas of stagnant ice which develop at the end of the surge period. It is the landforms which develop during the retreat phase after the surge has ended which are of most interest.

Normal Glacial Retreat

The rate of retreat of ice fronts is well documented in a wide variety of glacierized environments. Although we commonly refer to the retreat of an ice front in terms of the linear distance retreated during a given period, it must be remembered that frontal retreat results from a combination of downwasting of the ice surface and bottom melting (Fig. 7.2). The amount of debris on the wasting ice and the slope of both the ice surface and ground surface will all affect the rate of retreat.

In many glacierized areas, measurements of frontal retreat have been made for many years. A large number of glaciers have retreated at rates between 10 and 70 m per year. In Glacier Bay, in south-east Alaska, the record of retreat over the last 200 years is detailed (Fig. 7.3). Many of the glaciers in this area discharge into deep-water fjords which are tidal. The calving of icebergs results in very rapid rates of frontal retreat. For example, Muir Glacier is known to have retreated 9 km in 4 years (1903–07). Rapid

R. J. Price

Fig. 7.2 The effect of slope on the extent of frontal retreat

rates of ice wastage also occur over land areas in south-east Alaska. The Casement Glacier became land-ending in 1911 and by 1966 had retreated $4\frac{1}{2}$ km (Price, 1965). Profiles derived from photogrammetric maps (Fig. 7.4) made from aerial photography taken in 1948 and 1963 give a more detailed picture of the rate of downwastage of the Casement Glacier (Petrie and Price, 1966). For the zone 152–229 m above sea level on the snout just behind the ice front, the average annual rate of thinning was 10 m per year, which was reflected in a frontal retreat of about 50 m per year.

A similar pattern of ice wastage (Fig. 7.5) occurred at Breiðamerkurjökull, south-east Iceland, between 1890 and 1965. Over this period the broad piedmont ice lobe retreated between 3 and 4 km (Price, 1969). Within this period there were some marked variations in the annual average rates of retreat: 1890–1937, 12 m a^{-1}; 1937–45, 94 m a^{-1}; and 1945–65, 70 m a^{-1}. These rates of frontal retreat reflect rates of downwastage of the ice surface of between 5 and 8 m per year (Welch, 1967). During deglacierization it is therefore reasonable to expect that land will emerge from beneath ice at the rate of between 10 and 100 m per year depending upon local conditions. This is assuming that the ice margin is fairly well defined. Where stagnation has taken place along an ice front and extensive areas of debris-covered ice occur then masses of detached glacier ice may survive for several decades.

During rapid frontal retreat, a wide variety of landforms emerge from beneath the glacier or are developed along the ice margin or beyond it as a result of either glacial or fluvioglacial processes. The next section deals with the rates at which these landforms are believed to develop and change during the deglacierization period.

Ground Moraine

Most proglacial areas have an original cover of glacial deposits which may be partially or completely removed by subsequent fluvioglacial erosion. Ground moraine consists of two types of material: basal or lodgment till with a surface covering of ablation till. Along the margin of a retreating glacier which has a reasonable amount of debris in its basal layers and on its surface, the mixture of water, ice, and debris is continuously changing. Immediately adjacent to the ice edge the newly emerged ground is often very wet and 'porridge'-like. As surface and ground water drains away, the angular blocks of the ablation moraine stand above the compacted surface of the lodgment till. Boulton and Dent (1974) have shown that considerable changes can take place in the textural and structural characteristics of lodgment till within its first few years of exposure and that these changes are accompanied by increased concentrations of angular fragments on the surface as a result of the deflation of the finer particles. The surface form of newly exposed lodgment till is usually controlled either by the character of the surface upon which it has been deposited or by differential deposition beneath the ice. Streamlined forms varying in height from 0.5 to 2 m and several hundred metres in length are not uncommon in proglacial areas. Many of them are the result of the flow of subglacial till

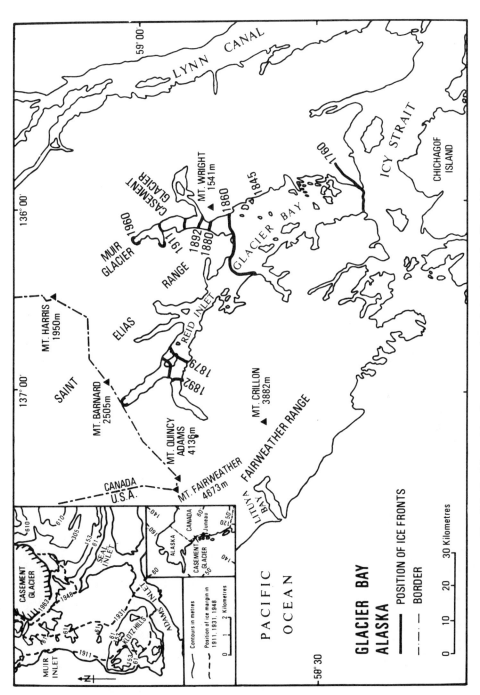

Fig. 7.3 Position of ice fronts at various dates in Glacier Bay, Alaska

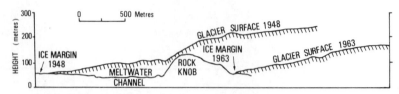

Fig. 7.4 Profiles of the surface of the Casement Glacier in 1948 and 1963

into cavities developed on the lee-side of large boulders beneath the ice. Very often the depressions between the ridges become meltwater routeways and much of the lodgement till is eroded. It is unlikely that fluted ground moraine will remain a distinctive type of landform if the ridges are less than 1 m high for much more than 50 years. Mass movement, soil formation, and vegetation colonization soon obliterate the distinctive surface form.

Moraine Ridges

As an ice-front retreats, ridges of till develop along the margin as a result of dumping of material off the glacier surface, or by squeezing of till from beneath the ice (Price, 1970). These moraines range from 1 to 5 m in height, have steep slopes (25–30°) and sometimes contain buried ice blocks. The fresh moraines with their uneven crest lines and steep slopes soon become altered by weathering and mass movements so that they have much gentler slopes (15–20°) and smooth crestlines. The fact that moraine ridges are generally transverse to the direction of ice movement and therefore to the direction of slope of the ice surface and of meltwater flow means that many ridges are destroyed by the development of the proglacial drainage system.

Meltwater Streams

The most rapid and the largest changes which take place in proglacial areas are the result of the establishment of the new drainage network which is required to cope with the large seasonal discharges associated with rapid ice wastage. Enormous volumes of meltwater are released at the height of the ablation season. The routes followed by these

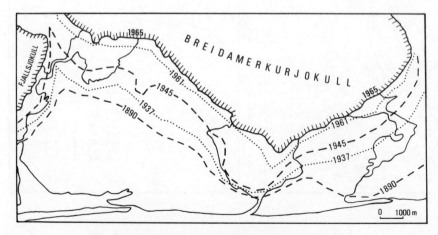

Fig. 7.5 Retreat of Breiðamerkurjökull 1890–1965

meltwaters are often determined by the form of the ground immediately adjacent to the
ice front and by irregularities in the form of upstanding rock knobs, moraine ridges, or
groups of kames and eskers.

The evolution of the proglacial drainage systems of the Casement Glacier since 1911
and of Breiðamerkurjökull since 1904 is well documented (Price, 1965; Price and
Howarth, 1970). In both locations the proglacial areas consist almost entirely of glacial
and fluvioglacial deposits and the coastline has never been more than 5 km from the ice
margin. Fairly direct routes of meltwater flow have been quickly established and equally
quickly abandoned.

In front of the Casement Glacier (Fig. 7.6) three large channels (10–30 m deep,
50–300 m wide) were established within 10–15 years of the glacier becoming land-
ending. The channels were probably initiated subglacially and esker systems at the head
of channels 7 and 9 represent a depositional phase of the same subglacial streams. These
direct routes of meltwater flow continued to function until 1940 when, as a direct result
of the ice wastage in the area north of Adams Inlet, channels 11 and 12 came into
operation. Channel 12 was abandoned in 1946 and channel 11 in 1948. By 1962,

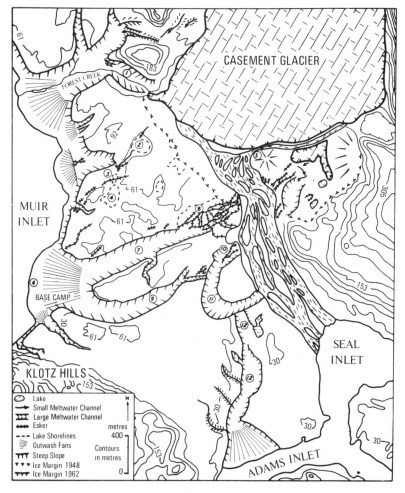

Fig. 7.6 The proglacial area of the Casement Glacier

virtually all of the meltwater from the Casement Glacier was flowing towards Adams Inlet and destroying many of the proglacial landforms produced between 1940 and 1960.

The proglacial drainage in front of Breiðamerkurjökull (Fig. 7.7) also saw many changes during its evolution. In this case, the pattern of drainage development was complicated by the development of four large proglacial lakes, the presence of extensive areas of buried stagnant ice and the occasional occurrence of large floods resulting from

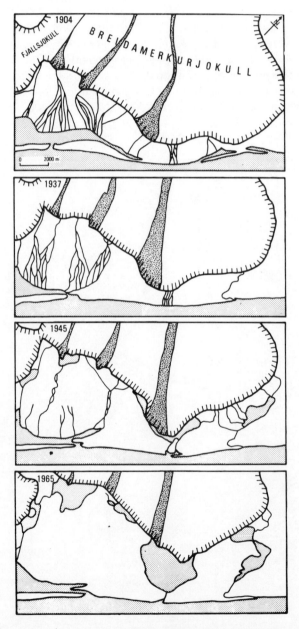

Fig. 7.7 The evolution of proglacial drainage at
Breiðamerkurjökull

the drainage of ice-dammed marginal lakes. In 1904, a great many streams issued from the ice front and followed braided courses to the coast. By the 1930s, the number of channels carrying meltwater beyond the oldest moraine had been reduced to seven and the effect of moraine ridges diverting meltwater flow parallel to the ice front can be clearly seen. By 1945, the large proglacial lakes, Stemmárlón, Jökulsárlón, Breiðárlón, and Fjallsárlón had begun to develop and, apart from drainage from these lakes, only one major meltwater stream flowed directly from the ice margin to the coast. Over the period 1945–65 the continued development of proglacial lakes concentrated all the proglacial drainage into three systems, each associated with a major river: Stemmá, Jökulsá, and Fjallsá.

Both of these case studies show just how rapidly proglacial drainage systems can change. The erosive capacity of meltwater streams in shallow channels which readily change course is enormous and many landforms created by glacial and fluvioglacial deposition are either completely destroyed or greatly modified within a decade of their formation.

Outwash Plains—Sandar

The largest landform produced during deglacierization is the sandur. Hundreds of square kilometres become progressively buried by the deposits of the proglacial meltwater streams. As these streams change their courses, the various outwash fans impinge upon one another until extensive areas are occupied by sands and gravels with low-angle surface slopes. The short-term changes which take place on these sandar result either from further accretion on their surfaces or local incision to produce terracing. If sandur development is active right up to the ice margin then it is possible for large masses of detached stagnant ice to become buried beneath the sandur surface. This ice may survive for 20–30 years, but in most cases it begins to melt out almost immediately with the result that the sandur surface above begins to collapse and kettle holes begin to form. Areas in front of Breiðamerkurjökull which are known not to have had kettle holes in 1945 were extensively kettled by 1961 (Price, 1969), whilst on one particular sandur it has been demonstrated, by means of photogrammetric measurement, that kettle holes 2–7 m deep developed between 1962 and 1965 and parts of the sandur surface were lowered by between 2 and 4 m (Price, 1971).

Areas of a sandur underlain by stagnant ice are subject to very rapid changes over a period of 5–15 years (Fig. 7.8). Large areas of the proximal parts of a sandur can be completely destroyed by the development of large numbers of kettle holes—what the dividing line is between kettled sandur (pitted outwash) and kame and kettle topography is a matter of debate. Once the buried ice has finally melted out, the steep-sided kettle holes and flat-topped ridges or plateaus which separate them begin to be modified by slumping and eventually smooth mounds and hollows develop which bear little resemblance to the initial form.

Eskers

Esker ridges are revealed by the retreat of an ice front at a rate roughly equal to the rate of horizontal retreat. However, many eskers which are produced by supraglacial and englacial streams (Price, 1966, 1969; Howarth, 1971) appear in the proglacial area with stagnant glacial ice beneath them (Fig. 7.9). Some of these eskers are lowered by between 10 and 20 m over a period of 15 years and rates of lowering as high as 3–13 m in one year have been recorded. Such rapid rates of lowering of an esker ridge without its complete destruction are remarkable. From the studies of ice-cored eskers in front of the

Casement Glacier and in front of Breiðamerkurjökull it seems likely that most eskers become reasonably stable forms, free of buried ice, within 20 years of their emergence from the ice.

Within the context of the three areas referred to in this paper, it seems that proglacial areas are likely to expand at the rate of between 10 and 100 m per year as an ice front retreats. Many landforms undergo rapid and significant changes during the first 20–50 years of their existence. As the ice front progressively gets further away from any given locality, landforms become more stable. This stability may occur roughly within 50 years or when the ice front is from 3–5 km distant. It is not surprising that this geomorphological stability roughly coincides with the beginning of rapid soil development and vegetation colonization.

Pleistocene Proglacial Changes

It is tempting to assume that the rates of proglacial change discussed above are very similar to those which took place during the fluctuations of the Pleistocene glaciers and

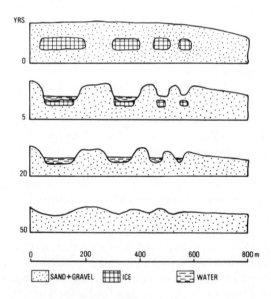

Fig. 7.8 The formation of kettle holes in a
sandur

ice sheets. There is only a limited amount of data with which to make comparisons. There are various estimates of the time required to allow the development of the Laurentide or Scandinavian ice sheets, ranging from 20,000 to 5000 years. In Britain we know that the Devensian ice sheet had not extended to the Glasgow area by 27,000 years bp (Rolfe, 1966), but that it had reached its maximum extent shortly after 18,000 years bp (Penny *et al.*, 1969). The carry of Ailsa Craig erratics to the southern side of Cardigan Bay (Fig. 7.10) suggests that there was a continuous ice stream from the Firth of Clyde to the southern shores of Cardigan Bay, a distance of *ca.* 400 km. Assuming that this ice front advanced over a period of 7000 years (25,000–18,000 years bp) the average annual rate of advance would have been about 60 m per year—a very reasonable figure in comparison with the behaviour of existing ice fronts.

Rates of retreat of the large Laurentide and Scandinavian ice sheets are well known. Along the southern edge of the Laurentide ice sheet in the early phases of ice wastage, rates of between 100 and 400 m per year were common whereas in Scandinavia they ranged between 50 and 100 m per year. In Britain the average rate of frontal retreat of the Irish Sea Glacier between 18,000 and 14,000 years bp was probably between 80 and 100 m per year.

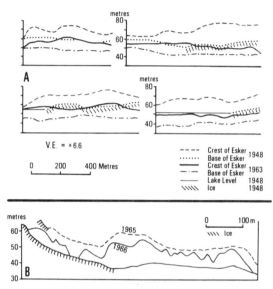

Fig. 7.9 Profiles of eskers at the Casement Glacier
(A) and at Breiðamerkurjökull (B)

On a more local scale the extent of the Loch Lomond Advance (Fig. 7.11) is now well known (Gray and Lowe, 1977). It is also believed that Scotland was completely ice free during the preceding period (the Allerød) and that the glaciers which formed the main ice cap in the western Grampians began as individual cirque glaciers. The actual date at which these glaciers began to form is not known but they did reach their maximum extent after 11,700 years bp. However, it is known that there was a sharp deterioration in the Scottish climate about 11,000 years bp (Bishop and Coope, 1977), so that the Loch Lomond Advance either was initiated by that climatic deterioration or at least greatly expanded by it.

The individual flow lines within the Lateglacial Grampian Ice Cap were never more than about 50 km in length. If one assumes a rate of glacier advance of 50 m per year then the main glaciers of the Loch Lomond Advance took about 1000 years to reach their maximum extent.

According to Bishop and Coope (1977), climate deterioration, as represented by a mean July temperature of 9 °C in south-west Scotland, ended about 10,000 years bp, after which there was rapid warming. However, Lowe and Walker (1976 and this volume, chapter 17) have obtained radiocarbon dates from the Moor of Rannoch which suggest that it was ice free by 10,200 bp or even earlier. At present, therefore, there is considerable uncertainty about the timing of the build-up and wastage of the Loch Lomond Advance glaciers. On the basis of known rates of wastage it would be feasible for those glaciers to have wasted away completely in less than 500 years. What is

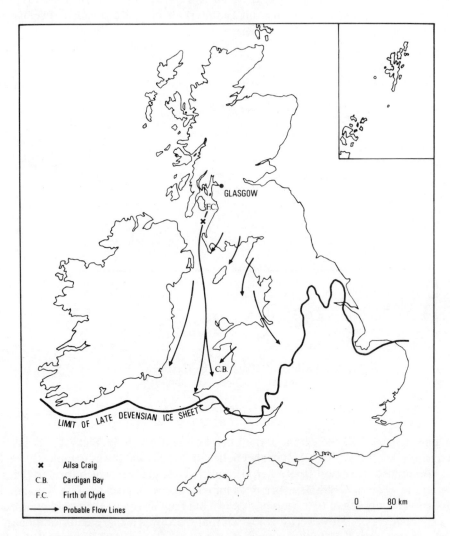

Fig. 7.10 The Late Devensian ice margin and selected flowlines

significant, however, is that during the period 14,000–10,000 years bp, Scotland saw radical and very rapid changes in climate and therefore in the type and rates of operation of geomorphological processes. In particular, it is possible that a complete sequence of periglacial, glacial, periglacial environments affected individual locations over a period as short as 1000 years.

It seems reasonable, therefore, to consider that the late Pleistocene proglacial areas were not very different from existing proglacial areas in Alaska, the Yukon, and Iceland in that they too expanded at rates of between 50 and 400 m per year. It is also probable that the major changes in the landforms and drainage patterns in these areas occurred during the first 50–100 years of their existence. In Britain there is a marked contrast in the freshness of glacial and fluvioglacial landforms inside and outside the limits of the Loch Lomond Advance. The landforms outside the limit have been extensively modified by periglacial processes. Recent work in the Glasgow area (Dickson *et al.*, 1976) has shown that even apparently undisturbed drumlins have been modified to the extent that

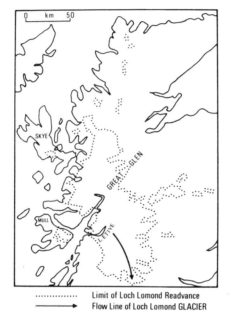

.... Limit of Loch Lomond Readvance
———▶ Flow Line of Loch Lomond GLACIER

Fig. 7.11 Limits of the Loch Lomond
Advance in the Scottish Highlands

4–5 m of till have moved down their lower slopes after 11,200 bp (Fig. 7.12). Even when we examine landforms formed by the most recent ice cover in Scotland we must remember that very considerable changes will have taken place as a result of post-glacial weathering and mass movement. All glacial and fluvioglacial landforms produced by Pleistocene glaciers and ice sheets are truly fossil. Regardless of whether the glacial or fluvioglacial processes which created those forms occurred under, in, on, or in front of the retreating Pleistocene ice mass, all the landforms were dramatically altered in their appearance and many were completely destroyed during the first 100 years of their existence. During the subsequent 10,000 years those glacial and fluvioglacial landforms which survived were even further modified. It is therefore not surprising that geomorphologists have differences of opinion about the origins and significance of landforms produced by Pleistocene glaciation.

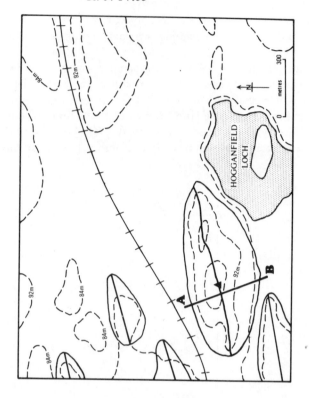

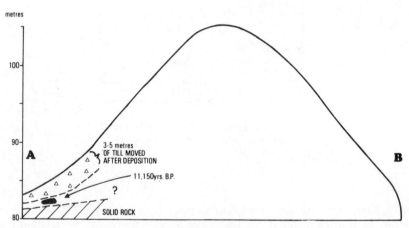

Fig. 7.12 A drumlin at Robroyston, Glasgow

References

Bishop, W. W., and Coope, G. R. (1977). Stratigraphical and faunal evidence for Lateglacial and
    early Flandrian environments in south-west Scotland. In *Studies in the Scottish Lateglacial
    Environment* (Ed. J. M. Gray and J. J. Lowe). Pergamon Press, Oxford, pp. 61–88.
Boulton, G., and Dent, G. (1974). The nature and rates of post-depositional changes in recently
    deposited till from south-east Iceland. *Geog. Annaler*, **56**, Ser A., 121–34.
Clapperton, C. M. (1975). The debris content of surging glaciers in Svalbard and Iceland. *J.
    Glaciol.*, **14**, 395–406.

Dickson, J. H., Jardine, W. G., and Price, R. J. (1976). Three late-Devensian sites in west central Scotland. *Nature, Lond.*, **262**, 43–44.

Goldthwait, R. P. (1974). Rates of formation of glacial features in Glacier Bay, Alaska. In *Glacial Geomorphology* (Ed. D. R. Coates). State University of New York, Binghamton, N.Y., pp. 163–185.

Gray, J. M., and Lowe, J. J. (Eds.) (1977). *Studies in the Scottish Lateglacial Environment*. Pergamon Press, Oxford, 197 pp.

Howarth, P. J. (1971). Investigations of two eskers at eastern Breiðamerkurjökull, Iceland. *J. Arct. Alp. Res.*, **3**, 305–318.

Johnson, P. G. (1972). The morphological effects of surges on the Donjek Glacier, St. Elias Mountains, Yukon. *J. Glaciol.*, **11**, 227–234.

Lowe, J. J., and Walker, M. J. (1976). Radiocarbon dates and deglaciation of Rannoch Moor, Scotland. *Nature, Lond.*, **264**, 632–633.

Penny, L. F., Coope, G. R., and Catt, J. A. (1969). Age and insect fauna of the Dimlington silts, East Yorkshire. *Nature, Lond.*, **224**, 65–67.

Petrie, G., and Price, R. J. (1966). Photogrammatric measurements of the ice wastage and morphological changes near the Casement Glacier, Alaska. *Can. J. Earth Sci.*, **3**, 827–840.

Price, R. J. (1965). The changing proglacial environment of the Casement Glacier, Glacier Bay, Alaska. *Trans. Inst. Br. Geog.*, **36**, 107–116.

Price, R. J. (1966). Eskers near the Casement Glacier, Alaska. *Geog. Annaler*, **48**, 111–125.

Price, R. J. (1969). Moraines, sandar, kames and eskers near Breiðamerkurjökull, Iceland. *Trans. Inst. Br. Geog.*, **46**, 17–43.

Price, R. J. (1970). Moraines at Fjallsjökull, Iceland. *J. Arct. Alp. Res.*, **2**, 27–42.

Price, R. J. (1971). The development and destruction of a sandur, Breiðamerkurjökull, Iceland. *J. Arct. Alp. Res.*, **3**, 225–237.

Price, R. J., and Howarth, P. J. (1970). The evolution of the drainage system (1904–1965) in front of Breiðamerkurjökull, Iceland, *Jökull*, **30**, 27–37.

Rolfe, W. D. I. (1966). Woolly rhinoceros from the Scottish Pleistocene. *Scott. J. Geol.*, **2**, 253–258.

Welch, R. (1967). *The Application of Aerial Photography to the Study of a Glacial Area: Breidamerkur, Iceland*. Unpublished Ph.D. Thesis, University of Glasgow.

Timescales in Geomorphology
Edited by R. A. Cullingford, D. A. Davidson, and J. Lewin
© John Wiley & Sons Ltd

CHAPTER 8

Lichenometry—Some recent applications

D. N. Mottershead

Department of Geography,
Portsmouth Polytechnic

Introduction

The use of lichenometry as a dating tool has not been widespread among British geomorphologists. Indeed, the bulk of the literature on the subject is to be found in Scandinavian and American geographical and geological journals, whilst the results of recent studies on lichen growth are to be found in the botanical literature. Accordingly, this volume offers an opportunity to present a consideration of the widely dispersed previous work and point towards trends in the development of the technique of lichenometry.

The basic principle of lichenometry is that lichens become larger with increasing age and, subject to certain caveats and assumptions, their size may be proportional to the age of the substrate on which they are growing. Depending on the degree of control over the determination of the lichen age–size relationship, various kinds of dating are possible. In an uncontrolled situation it is possible to distinguish between surfaces of different age, assigning relative ages to each (Bergström, 1954; Birkeland, 1973). At a more controlled level, Gregory (1976) has produced age–size relationships which yield minimum ages. More ambitious studies (Mottershead and White, 1972; Matthews, 1974, 1975; Mottershead and Collin, 1976) have attempted to produce precise dates for particular substrates.

The bulk of lichenometric applications in geomorphology have taken place in glacial environments and have been concerned with the problem of dating surfaces exposed by glacier recession (Andrews and Webber, 1964; Mottershead and Collin, 1976). Recently Gregory (1976) used lichenometry in the fluvial environment, relating channel performance to lichenometrically defined levels within the river channel. The possibility exists of extending this kind of study to coastal environments. Indeed, the author is currently investigating the feasibility of relating coastal erosion processes at different levels on a rocky shore to similarly defined lichen limits, which previous studies (Moyse and Nelson-Smith, 1963; Ferry and Sheard, 1969) have shown to be present in such locations. These more recent developments indicate that lichenometry may have more widespread application than has hitherto been appreciated.

It is the purpose of this paper to review briefly the principles upon which lichenometry is based, paying particular attention to some of the methodological and logistical problems involved. A specific study of glacier recession will then be presented as an example of the ways in which some of these problems may be overcome. Finally, the results of this study will be evaluated in terms of recent advances in the understanding of lichen behaviour and data analysis.

Lichenometry: Basic Principles and Assumptions

The basic principles underlying the lichenometric approach were put forward by Beschel (1950, 1961, 1973). Fundamental to any exercise in lichenometric dating is the establishment of the relationship between lichen size and lichen age.

There have been two approaches to this problem. The direct approach relies upon observation of individual lichens at repeated intervals of time over a period of several years in order to assess changes in lichen size. In this way the contemporary growth of a living lichen can be monitored. A second approach, and one hitherto more widely used since it permits extrapolation further back in time, is the indirect approach. This involves the recognition of substrates of different known ages, and the measurement of lichens growing upon them. The indirect method rests on a number of assumptions, of which the major ones may be identified as follows:

(i) That the largest lichens present are of the same age as the substrate. This has to be carefully evaluated. In a glacial environment, as Matthews (1973) and Griffey (1978) have shown, lichens may survive transport and subsequently be incorporated into morainic material. Thus the largest lichen may pre-date the surface on which it is found. Griffey, however, concludes that this would not have a significant effect on the total proglacial population. Alternatively, several mechanisms are known which may destroy a lichen cover, for example snowkill (Carroll, 1974), animal dung (Osborn and Taylor, 1975) and river floods (Gregory, 1976). In this case recolonization follows the destructive event, and the lichen cover will therefore be younger than the substrate.

(ii) That lichen colonization takes place immediately the substrate becomes exposed. This is impossible to verify directly in the case of lichens more than decades or centuries in age. Studies of contemporary colonization are not straightforward either, since initially lichens are of microscopic size. It seems inherently unlikely that there will be a great time lag between substrate exposure and lichen colonization and, in any case, the older the lichen the less significant in relation to its age will be such a time lag.

(iii) That the largest lichens are the oldest individuals growing under optimal conditions.

(iv) That smaller thalli present are either late colonizers or slow growers (Webber and Andrews, 1973). The growth rate will be lower in less favourable micro-environments, where the supply of moisture and nutrients may be limited.

(v) That growth of a particular lichen species within a region of essentially uniform macro-environment is a function of time, and therefore lichen size directly reflects age. It is a corollary of this argument that lichen growth rates vary from region to region, and the spatial validity of a particular age–size relationship must be carefully assessed.

(vi) That variation in local micro-environment which may affect lichen growth can be identified and taken account of.

(vii) That a sufficient number of substrates can be accurately dated by independent means, in order to provide a calibration of the lichen age–size relationship. To this end various techniques have been used, notably historical records, photographs and maps, dendrochronology and ^{14}C dating. The need for independent dating evidence means that there is always an overlap between the indirect lichenometric method and other dating techniques.

Within the constraints posed by these principles and assumptions, lichens may be sampled in order to establish the age–size relationship for the species and region concerned.

Data Collection

There are several aspects of data collection procedure which have a close bearing on the nature of the results obtained.

Choice of Species

The choice of species employed must be influenced in the first instance by the species locally available in sufficient abundance. A variety of species has been employed by different practitioners, although Webber and Andrews (1973) show that the yellow–green *Rhizocarpon* spp. emerged as a widely used clear favourite in a survey of over forty lichenometric studies. Osborn and Taylor (1975) in contrast use *Xanthoria elegans* on calcareous substrates in the Canadian Rockies. Gregory (1976) employs the more rapidly growing *Parmelia conspersa* and *Lecidea* sp. for the study of shorter term variations in fluvial processes. Where a variety of lichens is present, then species of differing growth rates can be employed over different timescales. Thus Reheis (1975) uses the more rapidly growing *Lecanora thompsonii* on younger surfaces in preference to *Rhizocarpon*. Similarly, Miller (1973a) uses *Rhizocarpon*, a slow-growing species in the arctic, for the oldest surfaces up to 5000 years old, and *Alectoria miniscula* up to 500 years.

Selection of Sample Sites

Within a chosen field area there will be lichens growing in a variety of habitats, differentiated by varying microtopography, lithology, aspect, and moisture availability. Whilst not all authors take account of these habitat factors, some studies have demonstrated their effect on lichen growth. Thus Gregory (1976) finds a difference in the growth rate of *Parmelia conspersa* between granitic and intrusive rocks (2.8 mm a^{-1}) and sandstones (2.6 mm a^{-1}). Recent experimental studies involving direct observation of lichen growth have indicated the influence of aspect (Armstrong, 1975, 1977a), availability of water (Armstrong, 1973, 1976) and water quality (Armstrong, 1977b). It is not clear how the influence of these factors, demonstrable in short-term studies, will affect long-term lichen growth. There is also the problem that historical studies may not yield sufficient data for multivariate analysis to permit the evaluation of such site factors. Given these constraints it is more feasible to overcome the problem by restricting sampling to sites of similar habitat characteristics.

Lichen Measurement

The attribute chosen to measure lichen size by the majority of authors is maximum diameter. This particular attribute is not greatly affected by lichen shape, and where the growth of a lichen may be irregular due to interference by adjacent individuals, a true maximum diameter can often be found. Recent suggestions by Woolhouse (1968) and Armstrong (1974) favour measurement of total lichen area. Maximum diameter can be readily assessed in the field with calipers, though more refined photographic techniques (e.g. Hooker and Brown, 1977) are being developed to measure area, particularly in the case of contemporary growth experiments. Griffey (1977) has put forward a simple field method for assessing the area of elliptical lichens. The use of the simpler diameter measurement has to date been favoured in most historical studies where large numbers of lichens may be sampled, often in awkward field situations, whereas the photographic technique may be more appropriate to controlled experiments where a large number of individual lichens are not required. The advantages of the respective parameters have to be balanced against the facility of acquiring the necessary data.

Lichen Sampling

Differences exist between authors on the number of lichens to be sampled at each site. Many authors (e.g. Webber and Andrews, 1973; Miller, 1973b; Karlén, 1973) cite the single largest lichen, arguing that this alone will be most closely representative of the age of the substrate. Others, however, have employed the mean of several (normally the five or ten) largest lichens (Stork, 1963; Mottershead and White, 1972; Matthews 1974, 1975). This latter school of thought is based on the premise that the single largest lichen may be in some way abnormal, perhaps for example having survived deposition from an active medial moraine, and therefore does not reflect substrate age. By measuring a small population of largest lichens discrepancies in the single largest lichen will be minimized.

The size of sample plot within which lichens are measured is of significance. Clearly, the larger the area searched, the greater is the probability of finding a larger 'largest lichen'. It is therefore desirable that the plot size be standardized. Various standards have been adopted by different authors. Thus, Beschel (1961) recommended a plot size of 100 m², whereas Stork employed 25 m² plots. Karlén (1973) recommends that a plot size of 400 m² is necessary in the Kebnekajse region of northern Sweden. The absolute area which it is necessary to search will depend on lichen abundance. More refined sampling methods (Mottershead and White, 1972; Matthews, 1974, 1975) have utilized multiple subplots in order to obtain a widespread distribution of standard-sized plots.

The desirability of standard sample plots may present problems when lichens have to be sampled on artificial surfaces such as old walls, mine tailings, or gravestones (e.g. Carrara and Andrews, 1973) in order to provide an age control. Their size and form may render it difficult to obtain a standard sample plot size. Accordingly, results from such limited areas may underestimate the largest lichen size.

The Age–Size Curve

From the measurements of lichen size on substrates of different age, an age–size relationship can be derived. Opinions differ as to the nature of lichen growth through time, and a variety of types of curve have been put forward to describe this.

According to Beschel (1950, 1973), 'At first there is a considerable period before the young lichen thallus becomes even macroscopically visible. Then a relative acceleration of growth rate occurs, which continues up to a certain diameter—lichen thalli generally have a circular outline—whereupon the diameter abruptly begins to grow very much more slowly, yet at a constant rate' (Fig. 8.1a). The nature of Beschel's field data is not stated, but it is clear that he used historical data (i.e. lichens from dated surfaces) rather than direct growth experiments. Other authors put forward growth curves of different shape. Andersen and Sollid (1971) show a simpler linear relationship (Fig. 8.1b). Gregory (1976) (Fig. 8.1c) draws a curve through the largest lichen of each age as representing optimal lichen growth, and shows a growth rate constant, then declining with age. Mottershead and White (1972) (Fig. 8.1d), fitting a curve to a scatter of points, produce a steadily declining growth rate.

Direct experimental measurements of lichen growth have to date been reported only over short timespans, the largest apparently over a 7-year period (Proctor, 1977). Both Armstrong (1973) and Proctor (1977) report declining growth rates through time over all but the earliest phase. Miller (1973a) (Fig. 8.1e) describes a sigmoid growth curve,

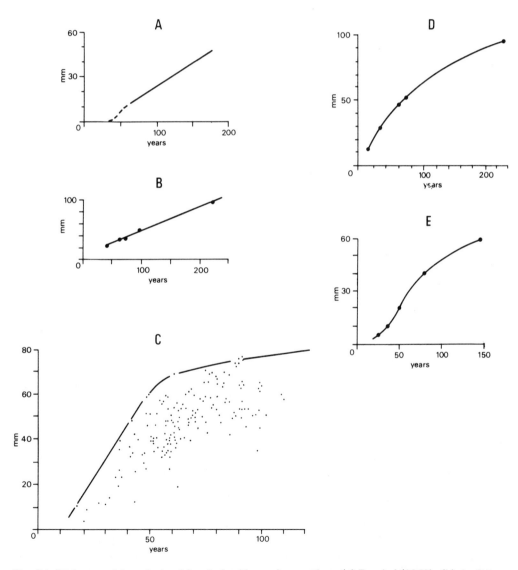

Fig. 8.1 Lichen age/size relationships derived by various authors (a) Beschel (1950); (b) Andersen and Sollid (1971); (c) Gregory (1976); (d) Mottershead and White (1972); (e) Miller (1973a)

first accelerating and later decelerating, from contemporary studies in the arctic.

Clearly, if lichen diameter growth varies at different stages of the lichen's growth, then care must be taken in deciding whether the portion of the curve derived relates to the early, mature, or later stage of lichen growth. The absolute timescale will vary too, both between species and in different environments. The form of a curve fitted to the age–size relationship is of great significance if it is to be used as a predictive device. In the absence of definitive studies of the long-term nature of lichen growth, this is clearly an area in which great care must be taken. The state of knowledge at the moment, however, does suggest that the assumption of a linear growth rate throughout the life of a lichen (King, 1971; Andersen and Sollid, 1971; Burrows, 1975) may not be valid. Accelerating, constant, and decelerating growth rates all appear to be possible at different stages in lichen growth, and indeed it is possible also that different lichen species possess growth curves which vary in form.

Significance and Range of the Age–Size Curve

The properties of the age–size curve need careful consideration before it is applied further. In addition to the shape of the curve, its significance will depend on the manner in which it is constructed. If single largest lichens are used, then there may be some justification for regarding the curve as representing lichen growth in optimal conditions, as Webber and Andrews (1973) do. This curve may be comparable to lichen growth curves derived from direct growth measurements. Where averages are employed, however, the age–size curve represents an empirical relationship between surface age and the size of a strictly defined lichen sample, and is not to be confused with a true growth curve. For this reason Matthews (1974) has described such empirical relationships as lichenometry curves.

The temporal and spatial significance of the age–size relationship needs comment. The temporal range is limited either by competition as plant succession takes place and lichens are replaced by dominant vascular plants, or in more open habitats by senescence in the lichens themselves. In temperate southern Norway below the tree line, the effective range of lichens would appear to be somewhere in excess of 250 years (Mottershead and White, 1972). In open tundra conditions, several authors have claimed that lichens may be identified up to several thousand years in age (Benedict, 1967; Karlén, 1973; Miller, 1973a).

The regional validity of the age–size curve is a property that no author has yet assessed in a definitive manner. If local micro-environmental influences can be assessed or eliminated, then it is assumed that the age–size curve reflects the regional macro-environmental conditions. In this context the different lichenometry curves produced by Karlén (1975) for the 'mountain' region and the 'pine forest' region in northern Sweden are of interest. As yet they appear to represent the only successful attempt to assess the effect of different environmental conditions within the same region. In many studies, the area sampled is highly restricted (to one glacier foreland, for example, an area of a few square kilometres) and regional validity is not a relevant issue. Miller and Andrews (1972) and Osborn and Taylor (1975) produce curves from sample sites distributed over distances in excess of 100 km, with seemingly reasonable results. On the other hand, attempts to extrapolate a curve from one region to another, as King (1971) has done from southern Scandinavia to Scotland, seem difficult to justify. In the absence of definitive investigations on this point, it is as well to exercise care over the regional extent to which a lichen age–size curve may be valid.

Lichenometric Dating of Moraines in Tunsbergdalen

Against this background of lichenometric practice, the use of the technique in a specific study of moraine surfaces will be examined. The work was carried out by the author and his collaborators in Tunsbergdalen, southern Norway, in order to investigate the recession of the glacier Tunsbergdalsbreen.

The basic technique was first outlined by Mottershead and White (1972), whilst certain elements were later elaborated (Mottershead and White, 1973) in response to critical comment (Worsley, 1973). A further study (Mottershead and Collin, 1976) contains a slightly more refined version. The main outlines of the approach will be re-stated here, prior to an evaluation of the results in the light of more recent lichenometric studies.

Control Surfaces

It proved possible to date, by independent methods, five surfaces which were then used as controls to calibrate the lichen age–size curve. Aerial photography permitted the identification of the 1957 ice margin, when the ice terminated upon a highly accidented rock surface along a line readily identifiable in the field. The 1937 position of the ice margin, on a similar surface, is mapped by Kick (1966) on the basis of terrestrial photographs. Prior to this time the glacier margin had been receding across an area of outwash gravels, reworking them into moraine ridges. Three of these moraines can be dated historically. Faegri's (1948) figures of annual recession, based on data whose collection was initiated and organised by J. Rekstad, indicate that the most probable age for the youngest moraine in the series is 1911 (Mottershead and Collin, 1976). Immediately prior to this date the ice margin had been almost constant for several years, whilst subsequently a rapid retreat is recorded. A photograph and surveys published by J. Rekstad permit the accurate reconstruction of the ice margin in September 1900, which is shown to be lying adjacent to a small moraine which was interpreted as having formed during the earlier part of that year. The oldest moraine in the series appears to date from a well-documented advance in the mid-eighteenth century. Rekstad (1901) quotes contemporary evidence which dates the maximum extent of the advance of several glaciers in the region, including Tunsbergdalsbreen as 1743, whilst Faegri (1934) has argued critically in respect of the nearby Nigardsbreen that retreat from this position did not begin until 1748. The latter date is accepted in the study as more closely reflecting the age of the proximal side of this moraine ridge, which would be available as a lichen substrate only as the ice receded.

Lichenometric Data

The lichen chosen for sampling was *Rhizocarpon geographicum*, L (D C), which was extremely abundant in the field area, providing an almost continuous cover at some sites. The attribute measured was the maximum thallus diameter, recorded by calipers to an accuracy of 0.05 mm. The abundance of this species and the author's reservations about use of the largest single lichen led to the measurement of the largest five lichens at each sample site.

The sample plot size was standardized at 25 m² and five such plots were sampled on each surface. The merits of this approach are two-fold. It permits a much broader spatial spread of sample surfaces, and at the same time allows sections of moraine subsequently modified by undercutting or slumping to be identified, since they would possess younger surfaces and consequently smaller lichens. Plots were sampled until five plots on each surface were obtained which yielded consistent results.

The Age–Size Curve

The age–size curve derived from Tunsbergdalen (Fig. 8.2) is based on the mean of the largest five lichens at the five most favourable sites. Each point therefore represents the mean value of 25 lichen diameters. The five points on the curve correspond to the five dated surfaces outlined above. It is an empirical relationship and may be used to interpolate age values for lichens on intermediate surfaces, provided that lichen size is

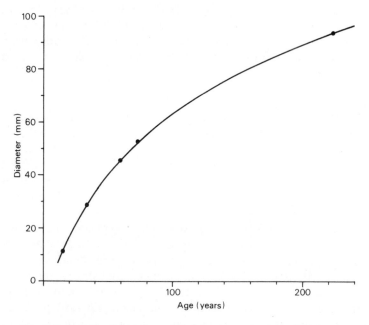

Fig. 8.2 Relationship between lichen size and age in Tunsbergdalen

determined in the same manner as on the control surfaces. Visual inspection shows that lichen size thus defined increases with age, rapidly at first, and then at a declining rate. This pattern suggests an exponentially declining growth rate and accordingly after log-transformation of the age data, a simple regression was carried out where y = age of substrate, x = lichen size and a, b and c are constants. A very good fit is obtained (Fig. 8.3), and the equation describing the transformed curve facilitates the prediction of the age of the unknown lichens (Table 8.1). Dates are thus obtained which are used to date the moraines to a specific year. Application of confidence limits estimates the statistical error associated with these dates. The recession of Tunsbergdalsbreen is then mapped in Fig. 8.4.

Validity of the Dates

Independent checks of the predicted dates, based on supporting evidence less precise than the age of the control surfaces, show in general that the dates are consistent with the historical record. The largest moraine ridge is dated at 1875, which accords well with the similar age of the largest moraine ridge historically observed in nearby Nigardsdalen. The pattern of recession of Tunsbergdalsbreen in the late 19th century as recorded by the lichenometrically predicted ages for the moraines, accords very well with weather

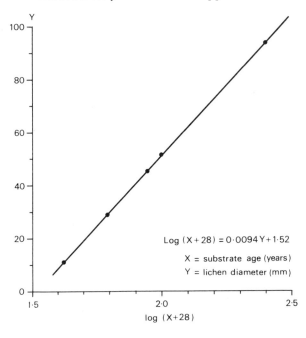

Fig. 8.3 The transformed lichenometric curve, Tunsbergdalen

records and glacier history in western Norway (Hoel and Werenskiold, 1962). Accordingly, reasonable confidence is placed upon the moraine dates in Tunsbergdalen.

Evaluation of the Tunsbergdalen Study

These results can now be considered in the light of recent developments to illustrate

Table 8.1 Lichen size and substrate age

Lichen size (1971) (mm)	Control dates	Predicted dates
93.4	1748	
82.5		1802 ± 2
76.4		1826 ± 2
69.4		1850 ± 2
65.1		1864 ± 2
60.9		1875 ± 2
54.5		1891 ± 2
53.2*		1895 ± 2
51.6	1900	
45.2	1911	
28.8	1937	
11.0	1957	

* Measured 1973.

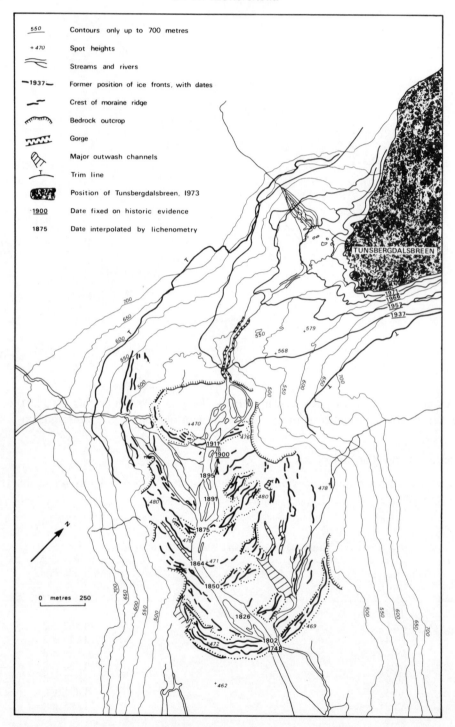

Fig. 8.4 Glacier recession in Tunsbergdalen, as shown by lichenometric dating of moraine ridges

possible shortcomings of the technique, as pointed out by its critics. These areas of doubt can be grouped as follows.

(i) The validity of the age–size relationship. Assuming that the control dates are adequately fixed, and the lichen size data are correctly collected, there remain two possible shortcomings in the form of the age–size curve. First, it may be argued that the curve is valid only if environmental conditions have remained constant throughout the period of lichen growth. This is unlikely to be the case in proximity to a receding glacier, for as the latter recedes from a specific location, changes in temperature and moisture availability can be expected to ensue. This potential shortcoming seems likely to have a greater validity where a functional growth curve is obtained, as opposed to a simple empirical relationship.

Secondly, the low number of control points used to support the age–size curve for Tunsbergdalen may be considered as less than adequate. Certainly there is a difference in approach between those studies which use an unavoidably small number of well controlled points, and other studies (e.g. Karlén, 1973) which employs a much larger number of less well controlled points. A balance has to be attained in this respect between the desired precision and available data.

Thirdly, there is the problem of the kind of curve to fit to the scatter of points. Whilst an exponential curve fits the Tunsbergdalen data extremely well, it would be equally possible subjectively to fit other kinds of curve through the same data points. Until more is known from experiment of the form of the age–size curve, this is a difficult problem to resolve.

(ii) It can be argued that the nature of the data does not justify the use of the correlation technique (Worsley, 1973). The use of lichen age, a form of cumulative data, creates autocorrelation yielding a spuriously high correlation coefficient and in consequence misleadingly narrow confidence bands. This point is dealt with in more detail by Matthews (1974). The authors of the Tunsbergdalen study for these reasons would not put too much emphasis on either the correlation coefficient or confidence limits, using the regression primarily to obtain a predictive relationship from the data.

These difficulties prompted Matthews (1974) to develop families of lichenometric curves. Using differing base data, either the largest one, five, or ten lichens per plot, from one, three, or five sites per surface, he constructed nine lichenometry curves by regression analysis, of the same form as employed in Tunsbergdalen. From these nine curves, based on different fractions of the total field data, nine predictions were derived. It was possible on this basis to quote a median, mean, and range of predicted ages for each unknown substrate. It is interesting to note that the closest approximation to the mean and median predicted dates was that derived from the five largest lichens for three sites on each surface, although the use of five lichens from five sites came a close second. The statistical analysis of lichenometric data was further developed in a later study (Matthews, 1975), in which the data used in the construction of multiple lichenometry curves were randomly selected from the total information available. The large number of age predictions so produced can be analysed to determine the reproducibility of results by this method. In a further development of this approach (Matthews, 1977), 300 lichenometry curves were employed, using a method of randomized extrapolation in order to test the age of a moraine beyond the range of the available data.

Thus, provided that sufficient field data are collected, it is possible to gain some measure of the consistency, and therefore reliability, of predicted ages. This kind of approach would appear to represent a significant amount of progress.

Conclusion

Lichenometric methods have been employed to span the time range between historically recorded events and ^{14}C dating. In the former case the timespans involved are normally measured in terms of decades or centuries, whilst the latter is more often applied to materials in excess of 1000 years old. The intermediate range is the one normally covered by lichenometric dating, and as such, lichenometric techniques may form a useful bridge between the two dating systems, especially when no other suitable techniques are available.

The reliability and precision of lichenometric dating will vary according to the assumptions made and the amount of field data available. Clearly, where lichens are more abundant, more elaborate sampling techniques can be employed, which may in turn lead to greater reliability in the age–size relationship. The degree of precision of predicted dates is a matter of some uncertainty, and is difficult to check. Since in practice any reasonably precise substrate ages are used in constructing the age–size curve, only less precise dates remain available for confirming the curve. In lichenometric dating, therefore, the age–size curves can normally be confirmed only in a general way. This should not, however, prevent the practitioner from striving for the most rigorous standard possible.

Perhaps the greatest asset of lichenometric techniques is that, in the absence of other dating systems, they can be used and permit some estimate to be made where no other is available. There are clear differences in precision between different published works, and the acceptance of lichenometric dates should be tempered with careful scrutiny of the means by which they were obtained. Clearly, some studies leave considerable room for scepticism, but there seems no reason at present why the more carefully controlled results should not be accepted.

Hence the author supports the optimistic view of Webber and Andrews (1973) that lichenometry does represent a valid technique, in contrast to the opinion of Jochimsen (1966, 1973). The latter author puts forward a totally negative view, emphasizing the shortcomings and weaknesses of the technique, after an apparently unsuccessful dating study which appears to rely on unstandardized sample sites. If one major area can be identified in which knowledge is most in need of advancement, it lies in a fuller understanding of the nature and pattern of lichen growth. To this end, improved measurement techniques (Foyer, 1973) and long-term growth studies, exemplified by Ten Brink (1973), appear to show the way forward.

Acknowledgements

Financial assistance toward the Tunsbergdalsbreen study was provided by Portsmouth Polytechnic, the 20th International Geographical Congress Fund of the Royal Society, the Gilchrist Educational Trust, the World Expeditionary Association, IBM, and the Green Shield Trading Stamp Company.

The diagrams were produced by the Cartographic Unit, Portsmouth Polytechnic.

References

Andersen, J. L., and Sollid, J. L. (1971). Glacial chronology and glacier geomorphology in the marginal zones of the glaciers Midtdalsbreen and Nigardsbreen, south Norway. *Norsk Geog. Tidsskr.*, **25**, 1–38.
Andrews, J. T., and Webber, P. J. (1964). A lichenometrical study of the northwestern margin of the Barnes Ice Cap: a geomorphological technique. *Geog. Bull.*, **22**, 80–104.

Armstrong, R. A. (1973). Seasonal growth and growth rate–colony size relationships in six species of saxicolous lichens. *New Phytol.*, **72**, 1023–1030.

Armstrong, R. A. (1974). Growth phase in the life of a lichen thallus. *New Phytol.*, **73**, 913–918.

Armstrong, R. A. (1975). The influence of aspect on the pattern of seasonal growth in the lichen *Parmelia glabratula ssp fuliginosa* (Fr. ex Duby) Laund. *New Phytol.*, **75**, 245–251.

Armstrong, R. A. (1976). The influence of the frequency of wetting and drying on the radial growth of three saxicolous lichens in the field. *New Phytol.*, **77**, 719–724.

Armstrong, R. A. (1977a). The response of lichen growth to transplantation to rock surfaces of different aspect. *New Phytol.*, **78**, 473–478.

Armstrong, R. A. (1977b). The response of lichen growth to addition of distilled water, rainwater, and water from a rock surface. *New Phytol.*, **79**, 373–376.

Benedict, J. B. (1967). Recent glacial history of an Alpine area in the Colorado Front Range, U.S.A. I. Establishing a lichen growth curve. *J. Glaciol.*, **6**, 817–832.

Bergström, E. (1954). Studies of the variations in size of Swedish glaciers in recent centuries. *Union Géodes. et Géophys. Int. Ass. Int. d'Hydrologie Publ.*, No. 39, pp. 356–366.

Beschel, R. E. (1950). Flechten als Altersmasstab rezenten Moränen. *Z. Gletscherkund Glazialgeol.*, **1**, 152–161 [for translation, see Beschel (1973)].

Beschel, R. E. (1961). Dating rock surfaces by lichen growth and its application to glaciology and physiography (lichenometry), In *Geology of the Arctic* (Ed. Raasch, G. O.). Proc. 1st Int. Symp. Arctic Geology, Alberta. Univ. Toronto Press, Toronto, Vol. 2, pp. 1044–1067.

Beschel, R E. (1973). Lichens as a measure of the age of recent moraines. *Arct. Alp. Res.*, **5**, 303–309 [translation of Beschel (1950)].

Birkeland, P. W. (1973). Use of relative age-dating methods in a stratigraphic study of rock glacier deposits, Mt. Sopris, Colorado. *Arct. Alp. Res.*, **5**, 401–416.

Burrows, C. J. (1975). Late Pleistocene and Holocene moraines of the Cameron Valley, Arrowsmith Range, Canterbury, New Zealand. *Arct. Alp. Res.*, **7**, 125–140.

Carrara, P. E., and Andrews, J. T. (1973). Problems and application of lichenometry to geomorphic studies, San Juan Mts., Colorado. *Arct. Alp. Res.*, **5**, 373–384.

Carroll, T. (1974). Relative dating techniques—a late Quaternary chronology, Arikaree Cirque, Colorado. *Geology*, **2**, 321–325.

Faegri, K. (1934). Über die Langenvariationen einigen Gletscher des Jostedalsbre und die dadurch bedingten Pflanzen sukzessionen. *Bergen Museum Årbok 1933*, No. 7 pp. 1–255.

Faegri, K. (1948). On the variations of western Norwegian glaciers during the last 200 years. *Union Géodes. et Géophys. Int. Ass. Gen. d'Oslo*, **II**, 1044–1062.

Ferry, B. W., and Sheard, J. W. (1969). Zonation of supralittoral lichens on rocky shores around the Dale peninsula, Pembrokeshire. *Field Studs.*, **3**(1), 41–67.

Foyer, M. B. (1973). Lichenometrical photography in the Kebnekaise Mountains, Swedish Lapland. *Arct. Alp. Res.*, **5**, 321–322.

Gregory, K. J. (1976). Lichens and the determination of river channel capacity. *Earth Surface Processes*, **1**, 273–285.

Griffey, N. J. (1977). A lichenometric survey of the Neoglacial end moraines of the Okstindan glaciers, north Norway, and comparisons with similar recent Scandinavian studies. *Norsk Geog. Tidsskr.*, **31**, 163–172.

Griffey, N. J. (1978). Lichen growth on supraglacial debris and its implications for lichenometric studies. *J. Glaciol.*, **20**, 163–172.

Hoel, A., and Werenskiold, W. (1962). Glaciers and snowfields in Norway. *Norsk Polarinst. Skr.*, **114**, 1–291.

Hooker, T. N., and Brown, D. H. (1977). A photographic method for accurately measuring the growth of crustose and foliose saxicolous lichens. *Lichenologist*, **9**, 65–75.

Jochimsen, M. (1966). Ist die Grösse des Flechten thallus wirklich ein brauchbarer Masstab zur Datierung von glazialmorphologischen Relikten? *Geog. Ann.*, **48A**, 157–164 [for translation, see Jochimsen (1973)].

Jochimsen, M. (1973). Does the size of lichen thalli really constitute a valid measure for dating glacial surfaces? *Arct. Alp. Res.*, **5**, 417–424 [translation of Jochimsen (1966)].

Karlén, W. (1973). Holocene glacier and climatic variations, Kebnekaise Mountains, Swedish Lapland. *Geog. Ann.*, **55A**, 29–63.

Karlén, W. (1975). Lichenometrisk datering i norra Skandinavien-Metodens tillförlitlighet och regionala tillämpning. *Naturgeografiska Institutionen Stockholms Universitet forskningsrapport*, **22**, 1–70.

Kick, W. (1966). Long term glacier variations measured by photogrammetry: a resurvey of Tunsbergdal after 24 years. *J. Glaciol.*, **6**, 3–18.

King, R. B. (1971). Boulder polygons and stripes in the Cairngorm Mountains, Scotland. *J. Glaciol.*, **10**, 375–386.

Matthews, J. A. (1973). Lichen growth on an active medial moraine, Jotunheimen, Norway. *J. Glaciol.*, **65**, 305–313.

Matthews, J. A. (1974). Families of lichenometric dating curves from the Storbreen gletschervorfeld, Jotunheimen, Norway. *Norsk Geog. Tidsskr.*, **28**, 215–235.

Matthews, J. A. (1975). Experiments on the reproducibility and reliability of lichenometric dates, Storbreen gletschervorfeld, Jotunheimen, Norway. *Norsk Geog. Tidsskr.*, **29**, 97–109.

Matthews, J. A. (1977). A lichenometric test of the 1750 end-moraine hypothesis: Storbreen gletschervorfeld, southern Norway. *Norsk Geog. Tidsskr.*, **31**, 129–136.

Miller, G. H. (1973a). Variations in Lichen growth from direct measurements: preliminary curves for *Alectoria miniscula* from eastern Baffin Island, N.W.T., Canada. *Arct. Alp. Res.*, **5**, 333–337.

Miller, G. H. (1973b). Late Quaternary glacial and climatic history of northern Cumberland Peninsula, Baffin Island, N.W.T., Canada. *Quat. Res.*, **3**, 561–583.

Miller, G. H., and Andrews, J. T. (1972). Quaternary history of northern Cumberland Peninsula, East Baffin Island, N.W.T., Canada, Part IV: preliminary lichen growth curve for *Rhizocarpon geographicum*. *Geol. Soc. Am. Bull.*, **83**, 1133–1138.

Mottershead, D. N., and Collin, R. L. (1976). A study of Flandrian glacier fluctuations in Tunsbergdalen, southern Norway. *Norsk Geog. Tidsskr.*, **56**, 413–436.

Mottershead, D. N., and White, I. D. (1972). The lichenometric dating of glacier recession, Tunsbergdalsbre, southern Norway. *Geog. Ann.*, **54A**, 47–52.

Mottershead, D. N., and White, I. D. (1973). Lichen growth in Tunsbergdal—a confirmation. *Geog. Ann.*, **55A**, 143–145.

Moyse, J., and Nelson-Smith, A. (1963). Zonation of animals and plants on rocky shores around Dale, Pembrokeshire. *Field Studs.*, **1**(5), 1–32.

Osborn, G. D., and Taylor, J. (1975). Lichenometry on calcareous substrates in the Canadian Rockies. *Quat. Res.*, **5**, 111–120.

Proctor, M. C. F. (1977). The growth curve of the crustose lichen. *Buellia canescens* (Dicks.) De Not. *New Phytol.*, **79**, 659–663.

Reheis, M. J. (1975). Source, transportation and deposition of debris in Arapaho Glacier, Front Range, Colorado, U.S.A. *J. Glaciol.*, **14**, 407–420.

Rekstad, J. (1901). Iagttagelser fra bræer i Sogn og Nordfjord. *Nor. Geol. Unders. Aarbog.*, **34** (3) 1–48.

Stork, A. (1963). Plant immigration in front of retreating glaciers, with examples from the Kebnekajse area, northern Sweden. *Geog. Ann.*, **45**, 1–22.

Ten Brink, N. W. (1973). Lichen growth rates in west Greenland. *Arct. Alp. Res.*, **5**, 323–331.

Webber, P. J., and Andrews, J. T. (1973). Lichenometry: a commentary. *Arct. Alp. Res.*, **5**, 295–302.

Woolhouse, H. W. (1968). The measurement of growth rates in lichens. *Lichenologist*, **4**, 32–33.

Worsley, P. (1973). An evaluation of the attempt to date the recession of Tunsbergdalsbreen, southern Norway, by lichenometry. *Geog. Ann.*, **55A**, 137–141.

Timescales in Geomorphology
Edited by R. A. Cullingford, D. A. Davidson, and J. Lewin
© 1980 John Wiley & Sons Ltd

CHAPTER 9

Caesium-137 and Lead-210: A review of the techniques and some applications in geomorphology

S. M. Wise

*Department of Geography,
University of London, King's College*

A wide range of radioactive dating techniques are now available, mostly applicable to timespans of the order of 10^3–10^8 years, and have been used increasingly in geomorphology, particularly in the study of the Pleistocene and early Holocene. However, these methods become very inaccurate when used on more recent material, because although in the long term radioactive material will decay at an exponential rate, the process is random in the short term. Hence over a period of time which is short relative to the half-life of the element, the inaccuracy involved can be very large.

In this paper some recently developed techniques involving caesium-137 and lead-210 will be discussed. These radionuclides have half-lives of 30 and 22 years, respectively (Pennington *et al.*, 1973, 1976) and are therefore more suitable for use over more recent timespans. Although the techniques differ, both in theory and in application, the results are complementary and can satisfy two particular objectives, namely (1) the accurate dating of lacustrine and marine sediments deposited during the last 100 years, and (2) the investigation of the movement of sediment in catchments and into lakes over a similar timescale.

The greatest potential of the techniques would seem to lie in the study of source areas of sediment, particularly that derived from soil erosion. This sort of information would be of use in the study of denudation rates, the development of three-dimensional hillslope and catchment erosion models, and the development of more sophisticated delivery ratios (Dickinson and Wall, 1977).

This paper first considers the manner in which the nuclides are formed, and their routing through the environment. A routing model is introduced for ^{137}Cs and the routing of ^{210}Pb is discussed. The methods are described and evaluated in the light of these routing models, and some potential applications in geomorphology are considered.

Formation and Routing of the Radionuclides

Caesium-137 is an artificially generated isotope, and is only produced in significant quantities as a result of a fission reaction. Thermonuclear weapon tests since 1954 have pushed radioactive products into the stratosphere, so that they are distributed over the globe. The distribution is not uniform, and for Cs-137 there are greater levels in the Northern Hemisphere, with a peak in mid-latitudes (Davis, 1963). The concentration in the air and in fallout also varies temporally and there were marked peaks in 1957–59, 1962–64 and 1971 (Ritchie *et al*., 1973) (see Fig. 9.5).

Lead-210 is a natural isotope, and forms part of the uranium-238 decay series (Krishnaswamy *et al*., 1971). An earlier member of this series is radium-226 which decays to ^{222}Rn. Since the latter is a gas, some of it diffuses into the atmosphere where it decays via a series of short-lived isotopes to give ^{210}Pb (Fig. 9.1.). Both ^{137}Cs and ^{210}Pb are washed out of the atmosphere by precipitation (Koide *et al*., 1972).

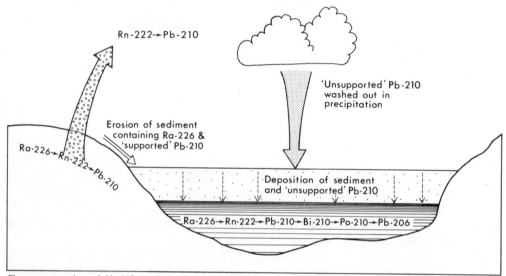

The concentration of Pb–210 in the lake sediment is shown systematically by the intensity of shading

Fig, 9.1 The formation of ^{210}Pb and its routes into lake sediments. The decay chain shown following ^{226}Ra is not complete—only the more long-lived isotopes are shown. Also, ^{226}Ra is not the origin of the chain, but the earlier members starting with ^{238}U have been omitted for clarity. With regard to the formation of supported ^{210}Pb, it does not matter whether an individual ^{226}Ra nuclide decays when it is in the lithosphere, or in the sediment. What is important is that the two nuclides are in secular equilibrium, and so the levels of each remain constant, in both rocks and sediment

The Routing of Caesium-137

The routing of fallout ^{137}Cs through the environment may be regarded as a cascading system (Chorley and Kennedy, 1971) in which the ^{137}Cs is deposited on one of four sub-systems, as shown in Fig. 9.2. The amount of ^{137}Cs deposited each year has been found to be related to the atmospheric concentration and mean annual rainfall. Davis (1963) found that the concentration varied with latitude, and that within a given latitudinal zone fallout was a linear function of annual rainfall. This is important, as fallout figures are available for only a few stations, but by using mean annual rainfall figures the ^{137}Cs input to the system at most locations can be estimated.

In humid temperate catchments, the majority of the ^{137}Cs will fall on to the vegetation cover (Fig. 9.2). Although the plants can absorb some ^{137}Cs the quantities are very small

Table 9.1 The rate of removal of caesium-137
from grass by rainfall

Source: Rogowski and Tamura (1970). Reproduced by permission of Pergamon Press

Time since deposition	% Washed off
6 weeks	55
3 months	65
5 months	72
12 months	93

(Davis, 1963). Both Middleton (1958) and van Wijk and Braams (1960) found that plant surfaces retained ^{137}Cs, but it was argued that it had been absorbed by soil particles on the leaves rather than by the plant. This material would eventually be washed from the leaves, a pattern observed by Rogowski and Tamura (1970). They sprayed a grass-covered plot with ^{137}Cs, and found that this was still being washed off the vegetation a year later (Table 9.1).

Hence the majority of the ^{137}Cs will find its way on to the soil surface, although with a lag of up to 12 months in some cases (Fig. 9.2). It has been reported many times in the literature that ^{137}Cs is adsorbed by clay and organic colloids within the soil, and is found largely within the top 30 cm of the profile (Davis, 1963; McHenry *et al.*, 1973).

Bolt *et al.* (1976) reported the following order of affinity of clays for monovalent cations: $Cs > Rb > K \approx NH_4 > Na > Li$. Sawhney (1966) observed that illite, mont-morillonite, and vermiculite all adsorbed ^{137}Cs even when saturated with potassium, while Tamura and Jacobs (1960) found that illite had a particularly high affinity for ^{137}Cs. This was attributed to the 10 Å spacing between the lattice layers. The saturation of montmorillonite and vermiculite with potassium decreased the inter-lattice spacing to 11.9 and 10 Å, respectively, and increased their uptake of ^{137}Cs by 20 and 200%, respectively. Bolt *et al.* (1976) also stressed the importance of the size of the hydrated ion, which allows it to occupy lattice edge and interlattice sites in 2:1 clays. This also explains the strength of the sorption, since once adsorbed the ^{137}Cs is virtually non-exchangeable (Davis, 1963). Lomenick and Tamura (1965) passed a variety of acids, bases, and oxidizing agents through lake sediment containing ^{137}Cs, but failed to remove more than 1% of the ^{137}Cs.

From the above discussion, it is hardly surprising that the amount of ^{137}Cs removed from the soil by plant roots (Fig. 9.2) is also negligible. Trace amounts are taken up, ingested by grazing animals, and transferred to man, through his consumption of milk and meat (Anderson, 1958). However, the quantities are so small that the Vegetation Store in Fig. 9.2 can safely be ignored.

On the other hand, rotting organic matter and humus can take up large quantities of ^{137}Cs, although it is not known if this is in an exchangeable form (Ritchie *et al.*, 1970). However, even if it is replaced by another cation, it is likely to be re-adsorbed by clay particles in the soil.

This adsorption of ^{137}Cs results in an exponential decrease in concentration with increasing depth below the soil surface. Beck (1966) combined the results of studies from several areas in the United States and concluded that '. . . fallout radioisotopes in the soil for longer than one month can be reasonably assumed to be distributed exponentially as

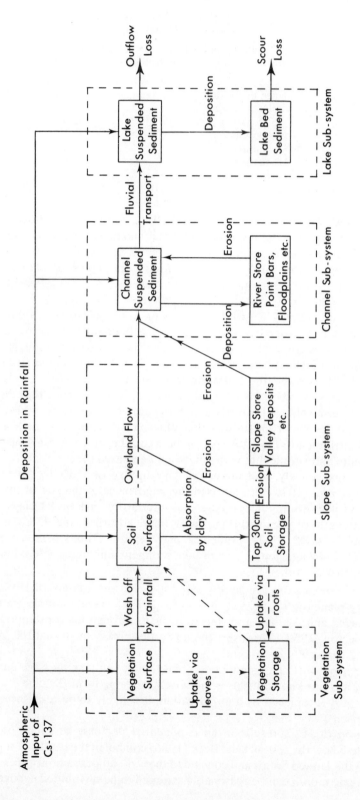

Fig. 9.2 A cascade model of the routing of ^{137}Cs through a catchment and into a lake

a function of depth with a relaxation length of approximately 3 cm'. This means that the top 10 cm of soil contains 63% of the ^{137}Cs. Similar results have been reported from the United Kingdom (Peirson and Salmon, 1959), Sweden (Löw and Edvardson, 1960), and India (Mishra and Sadasivan, 1972). Where soils have been ploughed, the distribution is uniform down to the plough layer (Ritchie and McHenry, 1973) (Fig. 9.3).

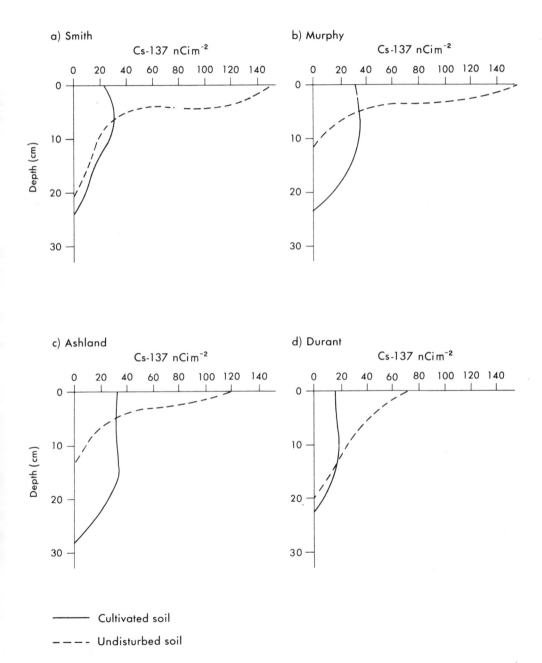

Fig. 9.3 Vertical distribution of fallout ^{137}Cs in cultivated and undisturbed soils in four North American catchments. Data from Ritchie and McHenry (1973)

The remainder of the routing model (Fig. 9.2) is largely concerned with the movement of ^{137}Cs in association with colloidal material. In terms of the Soil Store, this means the erosion of particles from the soil surface, and the translocation of colloids within the profile. The removal of ^{137}Cs from soils by soil erosion was studied by Rogowski and Tamura (1965, 1970). They applied ^{137}Cs to three small plots on a silt loam soil, one on bare soil and two under grass, by use of a spray. The plots were then left under natural rainfall conditions and the losses of soil and of ^{137}Cs were monitored at successive intervals over a period of 2 years. The investigation showed that the ^{137}Cs had been adsorbed by the soil, and then removed as the soil was eroded.

Figure 9.2 is an attempt to outline the more important routes taken by material which is eroded from the catchment slopes. With each of these routes there are two important factors to be considered: (1) the locations of both the sources of material and the routes, within the catchment; and (2) the appropriate timescales—the rates of operation and frequency of processes, and the time spent in the various stores. These factors are interrelated and they also depend on the processes operating and the nature of the material, whether it be soil or sediment. Both factors have been recently identified as major research themes (Wolman, 1977).

Material eroded from the slope will either be removed into the stream or redeposited in the Slope Store, according to the location of the source of the material, and the processes operating (Fig. 9.2). Rainsplash will move material only about a metre or so (Carson and Kirkby, 1972), leaving it in the Slope Store, whereas saturated overland flow is more likely to transport material off the slope altogether.

Moss and Walker (1978) have demonstrated the similarity between solid transport by flowing water on hillslopes and in channels. They showed how a series of erosional and depositional environments are formed with the changing hydraulic characteristics of the flow over a slope. Here, of course, particle size will play a large role in the processes of entrainment and deposition.

The time spent by material in store—either the Slope Store or River Store—will depend on the frequency of flows of sufficient magnitude to entrain it. The magnitude and frequency characteristics of streamflow have been studied in some detail (Leopold *et al.* 1964), but much less has been done on overland flow (Pearce, 1976).

Thus the routing of ^{137}Cs from catchment slopes via the stream system into a lake is complex, both in time and space. The ^{137}Cs which reaches the lake will either be deposited on the lake bed or be lost over the outflow. Since ^{137}Cs is mostly adsorbed by very fine particles, loss over the outflow is a distinct possibility, especially in small lakes.

The only routes not discussed are the direct input of ^{137}Cs into streams and lakes in rainfall. In both cases, the ^{137}Cs will be adsorbed by fine sediment, either in the water or on the bed, and be routed through the system as described (Armstrong and Gloyna, 1969).

The Routing of Lead-210

In the case of ^{210}Pb it is not yet possible to develop a routing model since so little is understood of its behaviour in the environment. However, there is an important distinction to be drawn between two different routes by which ^{210}Pb reaches lake sediments (Fig. 9.1).

As mentioned earlier, [226]Ra decays to give [222]Rn, which is a gas. Some of this diffuses into the atmosphere, and rapidly decays to [210]Pb. The half-life of [222]Rn is only 3.8 days (Cuninghame, 1964) and much of it will decay within the lithosphere to produce [210]Pb. Since the other intermediate nuclides are even shorter lived, the amount of ^{210}Pb formed in this way depends on the amount of ^{226}Ra present, since this is a long-lived isotope (half-life 1620 years). Evidently any sediment reaching the lake will contain some ^{226}Ra and ^{210}Pb, and this is called the 'supported' ^{210}Pb (Koide *et al.*, 1972). In contrast to this, the atmospheric ^{210}Pb is called the 'unsupported' or 'excess' ^{210}Pb and it is this which is of interest here.

It is known that unsupported ^{210}Pb falling onto lakes and oceans is incorporated into the accumulating sediment. However, very little is known about the fate of ^{210}Pb which lands on the catchment slopes. The available evidence suggests that very little of it reaches the lake, although it is not clear why this should be so.

Table 9.2 shows some figures from Krishnaswamy *et al.* (1971) on ^{210}Pb fallout rates and the ^{210}Pb content of some lake sediments. The figures suggest that the majority of the ^{210}Pb in the lakes has come from fallout, though without knowing the rate of loss at the outflow this is very tentative.

Table 9.2 Fallout of lead-210—input from rain
and content in sediment for four lakes

Source: Krishnaswamy *et al.* (1971)

Lake	^{210}Pb fallout (d.p.m. cm^{-2})	Total activity in lake sediment (d.p.m. cm^{-2})
Lake Pavin	36	26
Lake Pavin	⩾32	26
Lake Leman	13	15
Lake Tansa	45	50

A core from the lake near Wadhurst, in Sussex, which the author is studying, was found to have a very low unsupported ^{210}Pb content, despite high ^{137}Cs levels (see Fig. 9.6). The suggested explanation is that the ^{210}Pb, falling onto the lake surface, has been 'diluted' by the amount of lead-free sediment accumulating.

The importance of this is that since the annual deposition of ^{210}Pb from the atmosphere appears to be relatively constant (Crozaz *et al.*, 1964), it can reasonably be assumed that the rate of supply of unsupported ^{210}Pb to the sediment surface is constant. (Inputs of unsupported ^{210}Pb by erosion from catchment slopes would be expected to cause variations in the annual rate of supply.)

The Use of Caesium-137 in Sediment Tracing

The fact that ^{137}Cs is adsorbed by clay and organic matter, and can be measured relatively easily and accurately (McHenry *et al.*, 1973), immediately suggests its use as a tracer. This can most easily be done on catchment slopes, where the input can be estimated fairly simply. By measuring the amount of ^{137}Cs in the soil at a point any loss or gain can be identified, indicating sediment removal or build-up, respectively.

This approach has been tested on three American watersheds by Ritchie *et al.* (1974). Samples of soil were taken from beneath each major land-use type and an average ^{137}Cs content calculated in each case. Total fallout was considered to be equal to the concentration in the soil under an oak–hickory wood, where soil removal was assumed to be negligible. The rate of soil erosion under the other land-use types was estimated using the Universal Soil Loss Equation (Wischmeier and Smith, 1965) and plotted against the loss of ^{137}Cs since 1954 (Fig. 9.4).

These figures were combined with data from the literature on small-plot studies, using fallout radionuclides ^{137}Cs, ^{90}Sr, and ^{85}Sr and the following regression equation was obtained:

$$Y = 1.6\,X^{0.68} \qquad r = 0.95 \qquad (1)$$

where

Y = radionuclide loss as a percentage of input;
X = soil erosion (Mg hm^{-2} a^{-1}).

An *F*-test showed that the regression was significant at the 1% level.

Despite these impressive results, there are some difficulties associated with this method. Firstly, there is the problem of relating the movement of the colloidal matter, with ^{137}Cs attached, to the process of soil erosion. It has been suggested that since clay and organic matter bind soil aggregates together, their removal is necessary before erosion can take place (Bryan, 1968), but this is only a necessary rather than a sufficient condition. Hence it is possible for colloidal material to be removed, leaving coarser particles behind, and eroded material is commonly richer in fine particles than the parent soil (Carson and Kirkby, 1972).

There are also problems in interpreting equation 1 since soil loss is given as an annual rate whilst radionuclide loss is expressed as the total loss since 1954.

These problems can partly be overcome by the collection of more data in order to validate the method and calibrate it for a variety of soils and climatic regimes (Ritchie *et*

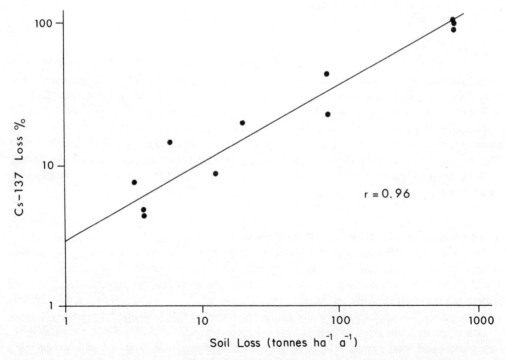

Fig. 9.4 Graph to show the relationship between soil erosion and loss of ^{137}Cs from three American catchments. Data from Ritchie *et al.* (1974)

al., 1974). Where this is possible, the method has great potential for the rapid estimation of soil erosion rates. The technique needs no special equipment and, even more important, it gives an estimate of soil erosion over several years (i.e. since 1954). This is a timescale which is more appropriate to studies of hillslope processes than monitoring methods such as the use of small plots.

Where small plots are used, these give a detailed picture of soil erosion over time, and here the ^{137}Cs method could be used to extend these results both in time, back to 1954, and in space, since a large number of points can be sampled.

Even if proper calibration is not possible, the measurement of the ^{137}Cs content of soil may still indicate areas of erosion and deposition on slopes, and give relative rather than absolute rates. Since the measurement can be done at a point (or over a small area of up to *ca.* 10 m²) it should be possible to study variations in erosion and deposition over a slope or within a catchment. Perhaps the greatest potential for this sort of technique is in the study of source areas of sediment (Wolman, 1977) and of sediment routing on hillslopes.

The Estimation of Sedimentation Rates

Lead-210 has been used to estimate rates of sedimentation in both lacustrine and marine sediments (Koide *et al.*, 1973). As noted earlier, unsupported ^{210}Pb is incorporated into sediments which are being deposited in water (Fig. 9.1). Since ^{210}Pb is radioactive it obeys the exponential decay law

$$P_t = P_0 e^{-\lambda t} \qquad (2)$$

where
- P_t = number of atoms of ^{210}Pb at time t;
- P_0 = number of atoms of ^{210}Pb in original material;
- λ = decay constant;
- t = time since the decay began (usually in years).

Thus the amount of unsupported ^{210}Pb in the sediment will decline with depth.

The 'supported' [210]Pb also decays, but the amount in the sediment is maintained at a constant level by the decay of [226]Ra in the sediment. This supported activity has to be measured in a sediment core, usually by measuring the [226]Ra activity, and subtracted from the total ^{210}Pb activity to give the unsupported [210]Pb (Pennington *et al.*, 1976, and Fig. 9.7). As the unsupported ^{210}Pb decays, the supported activity becomes relatively more important until it makes the measurement of the unsupported activity inaccurate. This places a limit of 100–120 years on the method (Pennington *et al.*, 1976).

In order to calculate an age–depth curve from the unsupported ^{210}Pb levels, it has to be assumed that the supply of ^{210}Pb to the sediment is constant. If it is also assumed that the sedimentation rate is constant (Robbins and Edgington, 1975; Krishnaswamy *et al.*, 1971), the concentration of unsupported ^{210}Pb per unit weight of sediment will decline exponentially with depth:

$$C_t = C_0 e^{-\lambda t} \qquad (3)$$

where
- C_t = unsupported ^{210}Pb concentration at time t years since incorporation into sediment, in picocuries per gram (pCi g^{-1});
- C_0 = unsupported ^{210}Pb concentration at time of incorporation into sediment (taken as the concentration in the surface layers of sediment) (pCi g^{-1});
- λ = decay constant = 0.03114.

Since the sedimentation rate has been assumed to be constant, we have

$$t = \frac{z}{S}$$

where   (4)

 z = depth from surface of sediment (cm);
 S = annual sedimentation rate (cm a^{-1}).

and so the expression for the relationship between the age and the ^{210}Pb concentration at depth is

$$t = \frac{1}{\lambda} \ln\left(\frac{C_0}{C_z}\right)$$ (5)

Robbins and Edgington (1975) give a more complete forumulation allowing for the effect of changing water content down the profile. However, the assumption of a constant sedimentation rate cannot always be satisfied, and this not only invalidates equation 4 but also the assumption that C_0 is constant. Appleby and Oldfield (1978) propose an alternative approach, assuming only that the rate of supply of ^{210}Pb to the sediment surface is constant, and prove that this necessitates using the integrated unsupported ^{210}Pb activity below a given depth, rather than the concentration at that depth:

$$t = \frac{1}{\lambda} \ln\left(\frac{A_0}{A_z}\right)$$ (6)

where

 A_z = total unsupported ^{210}Pb beneath sediment of depth z (pCi);
 A_0 = total unsupported ^{210}Pb in sediment column (pCi).

They applied both equations 5 and 6 to data from the New Guinea Highlands and Lough Erne in Northern Ireland and found that equation 6 [The Constant Rate of Supply (CRS) model] produced results which were more consistent internally, and gave better agreement with independent dating evidence (Oldfield et al., 1978). Another advantage of the CRS method is that the rate of sedimentation at different depths can be calculated from

$$r = \frac{\lambda A_z}{C_z}$$ (7)

where
 r = dry mass sedimentation rate (g cm^{-2} a^{-1}).

Table 9.3 gives some results from the literature using ^{210}Pb (based on equation 5 in all cases) compared with other methods, and shows that in most cases the agreement is fair. Using essentially the same technique, ^{210}Pb measurements have also been used to give marine sedimentation rates (Koide et al., 1972) and rates of accumulation of snow both on polar ice sheets (Goldberg, 1963; Crozaz et al., 1964) and on temperate glaciers (Windom, 1969).

However, there are still problems with the method. The first is the possibility of diffusion of ^{210}Pb within the sediment column. Until more is known about the mechanism of the absorption of ^{210}Pb by sediment, and its behaviour in the chemical environment of lacustrine and marine sediments, this cannot be discounted as a source of error.

The other difficulty is that not enough is known about the routing of ^{210}Pb through the environment. If large quantities of ^{210}Pb find their way to a lake or the sea via the

Table 9.3 Sedimentation rates calculated using lead-210 and caesium-137, compared with results using other methods

Lake or Reservoir	Sedimentation rate (cm a^{-1})								Source
	^{137}Cs	^{210}Pb	Survey	Palaeo-magnetism	^{55}Fe	River sediment	Pollen analysis	^{14}C	
Blelham Tarn	0.4–0.6	0.5							Pennington *et al.* (1976)
	0.8–1.1	1.0							Pennington *et al.* (1976)
	0.3–0.6	0.4							Pennington *et al.* (1976)
Lake Michigan	0.04	0.10							Robbins and Edgington (1975)
	0.28	0.28							Robbins and Edgington (1975)
	0.05	0.07							Robbins and Edgington (1975)
	0.08	0.07							Robbins and Edgington (1975)
	0.11	0.13							Robbins and Edgington (1975)
	0.07	0.08							Robbins and Edgington (1975)
	0.05	0.08							Robbins and Edgington (1975)
Lake Leman	0.4	12.5							Krishnaswamy *et al.* (1971)
Lake Tansa	4.0	≥2.0							Krishnaswamy *et al.* (1971)
Mule Creek B	10.0		10.4						Ritchie *et al.* (1973)
	11.4		12.5						Ritchie *et al.* (1973)
Tortugas	20.0		22.5						Ritchie *et al.* (1973)
Arroyo	10.8		10.0						Ritchie *et al.* (1973)
Frye Creek	12.1		12.5						Ritchie *et al.* (1973)
Powerline	<1.0		<1.0						Ritchie *et al.* (1973)
Lake Windermere	0.3–0.4			0.2					Pennington *et al.* (1973)
Lake Pavin	0.13	0.13			0.2				Krishnaswamy *et al.* (1971)
Lake Leman	0.12	0.12			0.1				Krishnaswamy *et al.* (1971)
Lake Tahoe	0.10	0.10				0.13		0.012	Koide *et al.* (1973)
Lake Mendota	0.58	0.58					0.62	0.45	Bartleson and Lee (1972)

a) Annual fallout of Caesium-137

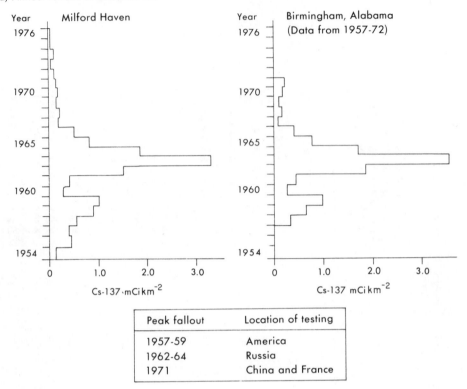

Peak fallout	Location of testing
1957-59	America
1962-64	Russia
1971	China and France

b) Vertical distribution of Cs-137 in lake sediment

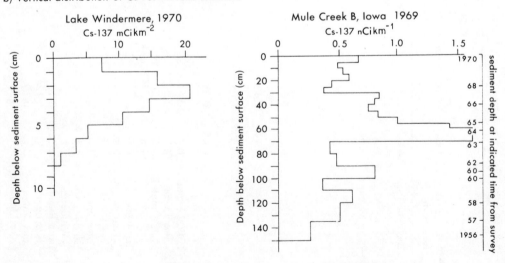

Fig. 9.5 Fallout of ^{137}Cs since 1954 and ^{137}Cs concentrations in lake sediments in the U.S.A. and Great Britain. Data for G.B. from R. S. Cambray (personal communication); data for U.S.A. From McHenry *et al*. (1973)

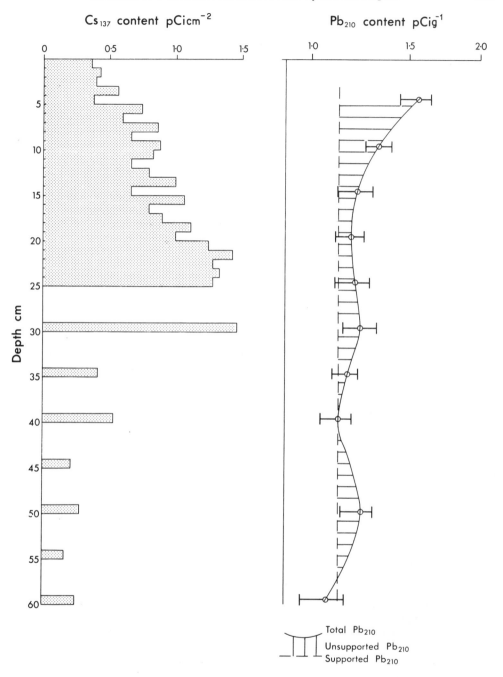

Fig. 9.6 Caesium-137 and lead-210 profiles for Wadhurst Park lake, Sussex. The lake (TQ 635280) is an artificial one, constructed about 100 years ago. It has a surface area of 1.04 km^2 and a catchment of 12.1 km^2, and its maximum depth is approximately 3.0 m. The ^{137}Cs core gives a sedimentation rate of 1.5–2.0 cm a^{-1}. The unsupported ^{210}Pb content of the sediment is low, making age calculations less accurate, but results obtained using the C.R.S. model of Appleby and Oldfield (1978) give very good agreement with the ^{137}Cs results (F. Oldfield, pers. comm.). However more work is needed before any firm conclusions can be drawn

catchment soils or vegetation, then the total amount of ^{210}Pb delivered to the sediment surface each year is less likely to be constant. As shown earlier, the available evidence indicates that very little ^{210}Pb in lakes is derived this way, but the data are by no means unequivocal.

Caesium-137 has also been used in lake sediments to give estimates of sedimentation rates. As mentioned earlier, the fallout rate of ^{137}Cs has varied since 1954 (Fig. 9.5) with a particularly marked peak between 1962 and 1964 (Ritchie *et al.*, 1973). This peak has been found in a large number of lake cores from all over the world. The examples given here are from the UK and the USA (Figs. 9.5 and 9.6). The data from Mule Creek B (Fig. 9.5) show the level of the sediment surface as measured by survey methods, and demonstrate that the peak in ^{137}Cs concentrations does occur in the 1963 level. Thus it is possible to estimate the mean rate of sedimentation in the core since 1963. Table 9.3 shows some results produced using this method, together with results from other methods where these are available for comparison. The agreement is good in most cases, especially between the ^{137}Cs and the ^{210}Pb results.

The problems with this technique are essentially the same as for ^{210}Pb, namely diffusion and routing. It is possible to detect the presence of downward diffusion of ^{137}Cs since its lower limit in the sediment should correspond to the 1954 sediment layer. Table 9.4 shows some figures calculated from published profiles (McHenry *et al.*, 1973; Pennington *et al.*, 1973) and indicates that in all but two cases ^{137}Cs is found below the 1954 sediment layer. Pennington *et al.* (1973, 1976) argue that the clearly structured distribution of ^{137}Cs in the cores suggests that very little vertical mixing has taken place, and attribute the downward movement of the nuclide to faunal activity or possibly chemical diffusion. Hence, although some ^{137}Cs is relocated within the core, the position of the main peak is unlikely to be affected.

Table 9.4 Maximum penetration of caesium-137 compared with depth of 1954 layer in lake sediments

Lake	Depth of 1954 layer (cm)	Maximum depth of ^{137}Cs (cm)
Mule Creek B*	173	150
Ashland*	173	80
Creighton*	140	150
Tviet Pond*	80	150
Sardis*	27	40
Esthwaite†	16	24
Blelham Tarn†	11	15
Windermere†	6	10
Ennerdale†	3.5	9
Wastwater†	2	5

* Source: McHenry *et al*. (1973).
† Source: Pennington *et al*. (1973).

The other problem is the relative contribution to the lake of ^{137}Cs derived directly from fallout, and by erosion from the catchment (Fig. 9.2). The concentration of ^{137}Cs in the former will change as the atmospheric concentration changes, preserving this pattern in the lake sediment. However, the catchment soils will accumulate fallout, so that the concentration in eroded material will generally increase with time (until radioactive decay offsets the input from fallout). If the ^{137}Cs content of a lake core is much greater than could be accounted for by fallout, the remainder has presumably been derived from the catchment, and this may be a problem.

This is the case in the American lakes studied by McHenry *et al.* (1973) and also in Wadhurst Park Lake which the author has investigated. In the latter the cumulative fallout level is 8.2 pCi cm^{-2} while the lake core contains at least 37 pCi cm^{-2} (Fig. 9.6). Hence only 22% of the ^{137}Cs has come from fallout, while the bulk (78%) must have come from the catchment.

It is instructive to break the ^{137}Cs content down in this way for each year, to study the changing contributions from fallout and erosion, and this has been done for Mule Creek B and for Wadhurst Park (Fig. 9.7). In the case of Wadhurst Park a constant rate of sedimentation of 2 cm a^{-1} (calculated from the ^{137}Cs peak) has been assumed to divide

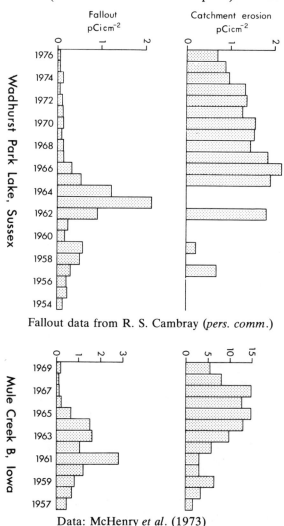

Fig. 9.7 Relative contribution of fallout and catchment erosion to the ^{137}Cs content of lacustrine sediment. The figures were constructed using data on fallout and on the ^{137}Cs content of the lake cores concerned. The catchment erosion contribution was calculated as the difference between the fallout concentration and the sediment concentration for each year

the sediment column into annual increments. For Mule Creek B this was done using the surveyed depths of sediment (Fig. 9.5). The columns labelled Catchment Erosion in Fig. 9.7 represent the difference between the ^{137}Cs in the sediment and the fallout concentration for each year.

Several interesting points emerge from Fig. 9.7. The Mule Creek B data show a lag of 2–4 years between the fallout peak and the peak concentration in material eroded from the catchment. The ^{137}Cs measurements are unfortunately not available for this 1963 period in the Wadhurst Park core but this does show how the concentration of ^{137}Cs coming off the catchment falls much more slowly after 1963 than the fallout levels do. Not until 1973 do the concentration levels fall below 1 pCi cm^{-2}.

The implication in both cases is that a lag of several years is operating between material entering the system as fallout onto the soil (Fig. 9.2) and its delivery to the lake. This is fortunate from the point of view of interpreting ^{137}Cs profiles, since the 1963 fallout peak will not be swamped by high concentration inputs from the catchment, even in catchments which are fairly small (Mule Creek B is 2.4 km^2 and Wadhurst Park 12.1 km^2). Thus, although more work is needed on the routing of ^{137}Cs through the environment and on its behaviour in a sediment column, the method appears to have considerable potential in the estimation of lake sedimentation rates. There is also the intriguing possibility of using ^{137}Cs measurements to study the length of time which it takes material to move through catchments of different sizes and in different climatic regions.

Some Applications in Geomorphology

These techniques provide a means of estimating relatively recent sedimentation rates. Lead-210 in particular, going back about 100 years, can be used to supplement ^{14}C, which is inaccurate over this timescale. In fact, Pennington et al. (1976) have already made use of this range of available timespans in their study of Blelham Tarn, in the Lake District. Some applications in geomorphology include the following:

(a) Estimation of denudation rates: by making suitable allowances for trap efficiency, etc. (Gottschalk, 1948; Brune, 1953), a sedimentation rate can be converted into a denudation rate for the lake catchment (Young, 1958; Langbein and Schumm, 1958). Lead-210 in particular, when interpreted by the method of Appleby and Oldfield (1978), can give details of changes in rates during the last 100 years, a period when it may be possible to relate these to documented changes in land-use and settlement in the catchment.

(b) Dating of sediment horizons: changes in sediment texture, chemical content, and pollen content within lake cores can be interpreted in terms of changes in the lake catchment. Mackereth (1966) has shown how the chemical content of lake sediments can be used to infer changes in the rate of removal of catchment soils. These studies benefit from an ability to date the major changes which occur, and again ^{210}Pb and ^{137}Cs can be used for this purpose on recent sediments.

However, perhaps the greatest potential for these methods lies in their use when combined with ^{137}Cs measurements within the catchment. The ^{137}Cs content of soils and sediments within the catchment could be used to indicate the source areas of the material which reaches the lake. This information would be useful in showing which areas were being actively eroded so that a more meaningful denudation rate could be calculated from the lake sedimentation rate. By studying the patterns of erosion and deposition it might also be possible to develop a more sophisticated approach to the problem of linking slope erosion rates with downstream sediment loads, other than a simple delivery ratio (Dickinson and Wall, 1977).

Conclusion

In this paper an attempt has been made to show that a routing model for ^{137}Cs is not only necessary as a background for the description of the techniques, but also draws attention to areas where further work is needed. This is also true in the case of Pb-210 where the lack of knowledge about its behaviour in the environment is one of the great limitations on the method. This knowledge would not only aid in the use of the technique for estimating sedimentation rates, but could lead to other applications. Although the techniques described can be used separately, their greatest potential probably lies in being used together in the study of sediment movement within catchments. Some applications of the methods in geomorphology have been suggested, but only field testing will show whether these are practical. Finally, one advantage that all the techniques have is that they are appropriate to a timescale of 10^1–10^2 years, which is intermediate between short-term (10^0–10^1 years) process studies and long-term (10^3–10^8 years) dating techniques.

Acknowledgements

This work was carried out as part of research funded by a NERC Studentship. The ^{210}Pb and ^{137}Cs measurements from Wadhurst Park Lake were financed by grants from the Central Research Fund of the University of London and the Geography Department of King's College, respectively. I am grateful to Mr. J. D. Eakins who provided the ^{210}Pb profile, and to Mr. R. S. Cambray, AERE, Harwell, for, providing data for Figs. 9.5 and 9.7. I acknowledge approval to reproduce this information from the United Kingdom Atomic Energy Authority (UKAEA), who retain the copyright. Thanks are also due to Mr. Fox for permission to take the lake core, the Drawing Office at King's College for the illustrations, Dr. J. B. Thornes and Prof. F. Oldfield who criticized earlier drafts of the paper, and Dr. D. Brunsden for help and encouragement.

References

Anderson, E. C. (1958). Radioactivity of people and milk: 1957. *Science*, **128**, 882–886.

Appleby, P. G., and Oldfield, F. (1978). The calculation of lead-210 dates assuming a constant rate of supply of unsupported ^{210}Pb to the sediment. *Catena*, **5**, 1–8.

Armstrong, N. E., and Gloyna, E. F. (1969). Mathematical models for the dispersion of radionuclides in aquatic systems. In *Symposium on Radioecology* (Eds. D. J. Nelson and F. C. Evans). USAEC Doc. Conf. 670503, pp. 329–335.

Beck, H. L. (1966). Environmental gamma radiation from deposited fission products 1960–1964. *Health Phys.*, **12**, 313–322.

Bolt, G. H., Bruggenwert, M. G. M., and Kamphorst, A. (1976). Adsorption of cations by soil. In *Soil Chemistry A: Basic Elements* (Eds. G. H. Bolt and M. G. M. Bruggenwert). Elsevier, Amsterdam.

Bortleson, G., and Lee, G. F. (1972). Recent sedimentary history of Lake Mendota, Wisconsin. *Envir. Sci. Technol.*, **6**, 799–808.

Brune, G. M. (1953). Trap efficiency of reservoirs. *Trans. Am. Geophys. Union*, **34**, 407–418.

Bryan, R. B. (1968). The development, use and efficiency of indices of soil erodibility. *Geoderma*, **2**, 5–26.

Carson, M. A., and Kirkby, M. J. (1972). *Hillslope: Form and Process*. Cambridge University Press, Cambridge.

Chorley, R. J., and Kennedy, B. A. (1971). *Physical Geography: A Systems Approach*. Prentice-Hall, London.

Crozaz, G., Picciotto, E., and DeBruek, W. (1964). Antarctic snow chronology with Pb-210. *J. Geophys. Res.*, **69**, 2597–2604.

Cuninghame, J. G. (1964). *Introduction to the Atomic Nucleus*. Elsevier, Amsterdam.

Davis, J. J. (1963). Cesium and its relationship to potassium in ecology. In *Radioecology* (Eds. V. Schultz and A. W. Klement, Jr.). Reinhold, New York.

Dickinson, W. T., and Wall G. J. (1977). The relationship between source area erosion and sediment yield. *Symposium of Paris 1977*, International Association of Scientific Hydrology Publ. No. 122.

Goldberg, E. D. (1963). Geochronology with ^{210}Pb, in *Radioactive Dating Symposium, IAEA, Athens, Nov. 1962*, IAEA, Vienna, pp. 121–131.

Gottschalk, L. C. (1948). Analysis and use of reservoir sedimentation data. *Fed. Interagency Sed. Conf. Proc. 1948*, Washington, D. C., pp. 131–138.

Koide, M., Soutar, A., and Goldberg, E. D. (1972). Marine geochronology with ^{210}Pb. *Earth Planet. Sci. Lett.*, **14**, 442–446.

Koide, M., Brulard, K. W., and Goldberg, E. D. (1973). Th-288/Th232 and Pb-210 geochronologies in marine and lake sediments. *Geochim Cosmochim. Acta*, **37**, 1171–1187.

Krishnaswamy, S., Martin, J. M., and Meybeck, M. (1971). Geochronology of lake sediments. *Earth Planet. Sci. Lett.*, **11**, 407–414.

Langbein, W. B., and Schumm, S. A. (1958). Yield of sediment in relation to mean annual precipitation. *Trans. Am. Geophys. Union,* **30**, 1076–1084.

Leopold, L. B., Wolman, M. G., and Miller, J. P. (1964). *Fluvial Processes in Geomorphology*. Freeman, San Francisco.

Lomenick, T. F., and Tamura, T. (1965). Naturally occurring fixation of cesium-137 on sediments of Lacustrine origin. *Proc. Soil Sci. Soc. Am.*, **29**, 383–387.

Löw, K., and Edvardson, K. (1960). Content of caesium-137 and (zirconium + niobium)-95 in Swedish soils. *Nature, Lond.*, **187**, 736–738.

Mackereth, F. J. H. (1966). Some chemical observations on post-glacial lake sediments. *Phil. Trans. R. Soc.*, **B250**, 165–213.

McHenry, J. R., Ritchie, J. C., and Gill, A. C. (1973). Accumulation of fallout cesium-137 in soils and sediments in selected watersheds. *Water Resourc Res..* **9**, 676–686.

Middleton, L. J. (1958). Absorption and translocation of strontium and caesium by plants from foliar sprays. *Nature, Lond.*, **181**, 1300–1303.

Mishra, U. C., and Sadasivan, S. (1972). Fallout radioactivity in Indian soils. *Health Phys.*, **23**, 55–62.

Moss, A. J., and Walker, P. H. (1978). Particle transport by continental water flows in relation to erosion, deposition, soils and human activities. *Sed. Geol.*, **20**, 81–139.

Oldfield, F., Appleby, P. G., and Battarbee, R. W. (1978). Alternative ^{210}Pb dating: results from the New Guinea Highlands and Lough Erne. *Nature, Lond.*, **271**, 339–342.

Pearce, A. J. (1976). Magnitude and frequency of erosion by Hortonian overland flow. *J. Geol.*, **84**, 65–80.

Peirson, D. H., and Salmon, L. (1959). Gamma radiation from deposited fallout. *Nature, Lond.*, **184**, 1678–1679.

Pennington, W., Cambray, R. S., and Fisher, E. M. (1973). Observations on lake sediments using fallout ^{137}Cs as a tracer. *Nature, Lond.*, **242**, 324–326.

Pennington, W., Cambray, R. S., Eakins, J. D., and Harkness, D. D. (1976). Radionuclide dating of the recent sediments of Blelham Tarn. *Freshwater Biol.* **6**, 317–331.

Ritchie, J. C., Clebsch, E. E. C., and Rudolph, W. K. (1970). Distribution of fallout and natural gamma radionuclides in litter, humus and surface mineral soil layers under natural vegetation in the Great Smoky Mountains, North Carolina–Tennessee. *Health Phys.*, **18**, 479–489.

Ritchie, J. C., and McHenry, J. R. (1973). Vertical distribution of fallout cesium-137 in cultivated soils. *Radiation Data and Reports*, **12**, 727–728.

Ritchie, J. C., McHenry, J. R., and Gill, A. C. (1973). Dating recent reservoir sediments. *Limnol. Oceanog.*, **18**, 254–263.

Ritchie, J. C., Spraberry, J. A., and McHenry, J. R. (1974). Estimating soil erosion from the redistribution of fallout ^{137}Cs. *Proc. Soil. Sci. Soc. Am.*, **38**, 137–139.

Robbins, J. A., and Edgington, D. N. (1975). Determination of recent sedimentation rates in Lake Michigan using Pb-210 and Cs-137. *Geochim. Cosmochim. Acta*, **39**, 285–304.

Rogowski, A. S., and Tamura, T. (1965). Movement of cesium-137 by runoff, erosion and infiltration on the alluvial Captina silt loam. *Health Phys.*, **11**, 1333–1340.

Rogowski, A. S., and Tamura, T. (1970). Erosional behaviour of cesium-137. *Health Phys.*, **18**, 467–477.

Sawhney, B. L. (1966). Kinetics of cesium sorption by clay minerals. *Proc. Soil Sci. Soc. Am.*, **30**, 565–569.

Tamura, T., and Jacobs, D. G. (1960). Structural implications in cesium sorption. *Health Phys.*, **2**, 391–398.

van Wijk, H. J., and Braams, R. (1960). Incorporation of caesium-137 from nuclear debris into the biosphere. *Nature, Lond.*, **188**, 951–952.

Windom, H. L. (1969). Atmospheric dust records in permanent snowfields: implications to marine sedimentation. *Geol. Soc. Am. Bull.*, **80**, 761–782.

Wischmeier, W. H., and Smith, D. D. (1965). Rainfall-erosion losses from cropland east of the Rocky Mountains. *USDA Handbook 282*, U.S. Dept. of Agriculture, Washington.

Wolman, M. G. (1977). Changing needs and opportunities in the sediment field. *Water Resour. Res.*, **13**, 50–54.

Young, A. (1958). A record of the rate of erosion on Millstone Grit. *Proc. Yorks. Geol. Soc.*, **31**, 149–156.

SECTION II

Medium Timescales (*ca.* 10^3 to 10^4 Years)

Timescales in Geomorphology
Edited by R. A. Cullingford, D. A. Davidson, and J. Lewin
© 1980 John Wiley & Sons Ltd

CHAPTER 10

Holocene alluvial sequences:
Problems of dating and correlation

Karl W. Butzer

Departments of Anthropology and Geography,
University of Chicago

Background

Geomorphology as a discipline derives from the intellectual ferment of the earth sciences during the late eighteenth and early nineteenth centuries. Initially, geomorphology represented a qualitative and often deductive search to identify modern processes that might serve to explain the origin of geological strata. It subsequently emerged as a subfield of geology and physical geography devoted to description and analysis of landforms. The geological legacy has remained pervasive, not only in the persistent concern with sequential events and related processes, but also through the many field procedures, laboratory techniques, and general perspectives that geomorphologists continued to share with geologists in general. The long tradition of denudation cycles and structural histories could be viewed as a counterpart to the geologists' interest in identifying stratigraphic complexes. On a finer scale, the development of historical geomorphology (not to be confused with the approach of W. M. Davis) went hand in hand with refinements in glacial geology, as part of the increasingly diverse contributions to an understanding of the Quaternary era. The most recent penchant for detailed micro-studies, increasingly quantitative and inductive, is once again shared with a wide range of specialized earth science subfields.

These links between geomorphology and the broader earth science tradition are logical as well as indispensible, but they have also been detrimental in that this tradition has generally been a conservative one. A half century elapsed between Charpentier and Agassiz on the one hand, and achievement of a majority view that Pleistocene glaciation had been extensive on the other. Similarly, Wegener's hypothesis of continental drift was derided for 50 years prior to the latter-day enthronement of plate tectonics. Geomorphologists, in their turn, failed to respond to the challenge to integrate their research in the evolving field of geography. They had almost no part in as logical an offshoot as soil science, which consequently developed in response to agricultural interests. Accelerated soil erosion, a pre-eminently geomorphological problem, was ignored by geomorphologists until after World War II. Hydrology owes its origins to engineering interests, with geomorphologists still assuming the role of consumers rather than innovators. The great upsurge of interest in environmental quality and management that began a decade ago found American geomorphology, on the whole, painfully unprepared to contribute a self-evident range of expertise.

The conservatism of geomorphology is also apparent in the lagging development of realistic temporal frameworks. The persistent misconception that 'denudation chronology' can be equated with Davisian cycles 'dated' by landform geometries underscores the continuing ignorance of many geomorphologists as to what timescales really are. The historical geomorphologist, in the strict sense, aspires to establish both relative and chronometric sequences of verifiable events.

The perspective of relative scale is critical. 'Polyglacialism' was firmly established by Penck and Brückner in 1911, in part on the basis of a complex sequence of glacio-fluvial 'terraces'. A subsequent generation of geomorphologists simply assumed that alluvial units corresponded to glacial–interglacial cycles. Functional floodplains were ascribed to the sum total of 'post-glacial' time, and most geological mapping services even now continue to equate such floodplains with 'Holocene'. A complex suite of distinct 'post-glacial' environments had been demonstrated for temperate Europe on palynological grounds, within a decade of Penck and Brückner's Alpine study. Yet geomorphologists chose to continue to work with the much coarser traditional timescales of the earth sciences.

New Perspectives in Historical Geomorphology

A revolution in historical geomorphology was eventually made possible by the successful application of sedimentological techniques, by advances in isotopic dating, and by collaborative geo-archaeological efforts.

Multiple morpho-stratigraphic units of Holocene age were occasionally identified by field studies during the 1920s and 1930s, but they were often ascribed to non-cyclic channel shifts and little significance was attached to them. It is to the credit of Bryan (1941) and Hack (1942) that two alluvial cycles were specifically recognized and linked with mid- to late-Holocene settlement phases in the American Southwest. A similar interest in relatively small-scale, short-term events intricately related to human occupance can subsequently be discerned in other areas, for example in the Mediterranean Basin, Germany, and Britain. Archaeological associations, particularly potsherds or buried structures, were commonly employed to provide *maximum* possible ages, i.e. a deposit can be no older than the youngest sherds that were incorporated during transport. Such attention to detail is characteristic of most geo-archaeological work, and it can be safely said that the involvement of geomorphologists in archaeological research has contributed substantially to refinement of timescales, not only in fluvial, but also in cave, littoral, and eolian contexts. Despite this increasing awareness of temporal and spatial complexity, the traditional tendency to oversimplification has been persistent. For example, Vita-Finzi (1969) and Bintliff (1975) stress a single alluviation phase during the Holocene in the Mediterranean Basin and Greece, respectively. But it appears that, overall, geo-archaeological efforts in historical geomorphology have gathered sufficient momentum to set and maintain new standards of sophistication.

Archaeological dating, while useful and often essential, proved of limited help for stratigraphic discrimination in the Holocene record in many areas or time ranges. Pottery dating, even in areas with adequate seriation and firm links to historical chronologies, requires either large samples or diagnostic types that are seldom found in sedimentary contexts. Lithic artifacts in 'pre-pottery' deposits are still more equivocal, and even where, for example, a specialized projectile point does have specific temporal implications, supposed dating ranges tend to be uncertain or unreasonably broad. A fundamental problem, too, is that archaeologists have commonly sought dating controls for their assemblages in geological sequences, while geomorphologists have frequently attempted to date their sequences by archaeological inclusions. The two approaches are inter-dependent and complementary, but both require independent chronometric aids.

Until the advent of isotopic dating, absolute time controls were essentially lacking for prehistoric settings. Radiocarbon (^{14}C) dating had a truly revolutionary impact for microstratigraphy and geomorphological interpretation in the 5000–40,000 year time range. The problems of such radiometric work, in terms of inherent methodology and of application, need no enumeration here. Despite persistent geochemical and sampling problems, geomorphological sequences have become rather more refined and detailed, while countless stratigraphic errors, often gross, have been eliminated. It is safe to say that in almost all morpho-stratigraphic work, the ^{14}C assays are correct more often than the field assessments. A particularly impressive example of the impact of ^{14}C dating is Haynes' (1968) revision of the alluvial chronology of the southwestern USA, showing the existence of five depositional hemicycles during the last 10,000 years, with a degree of temporal overlap between regions and even different valleys. Although other dating techniques, such as pottery thermoluminescence, obsidian hydration, or potassium–argon isotopic decay have been used in some situations, none has yet proved of similar, almost universal utility.

Geomorphological sequences are also intrinsically informative. Early work, even when correctly identifying alluvial cycles, paid scant attention to sediment variability or interpretation. Such variability may be 'normal' but it is never uninformative, and no two depositional hemicycles are identical. The tools to provide objective analysis and identification of facies sequences and palaeosols were initially derived from soil science, then applied to the rapidly growing field of sedimentology (critical in petroleum exploration), and more recently augmented by the experience gained from small-scale, contemporary process studies. A range of particle-size analyses, and morphometric, geochemical, and other techniques now provide the opportunity for identifying the fine details of alluvial aggradation (Gladfelter, 1977).

Contemporary short-term, small-scale changes, when properly measured, temporally analysed, and applied, have great potential for accurate interpretation and calibration (Thornes and Brunsden, 1977; this volume, Section I). However, few process geomor-phologists have acquired the requisite expertise in geochronology and palaeoclimatology to deal with complex landscape periodicities. In fact, the blanket dismissal by Thornes and Brunsden (1977) of 'traditional' analytical work would appear to reflect a lack of familiarity with, or comprehension of, the better examples of historical geomorphology, as well as an inability to distinguish clearly between large- and small-scale features or events. Substantive disciplinary progress is possible only through informed dialogue between the practitioners of various specialities such as is attempted in this volume.

Basic Problems in Historical Alluvial Geomorphology

Recent advances in historical geomorphology have primarily served to delineate a number of critical and persistent problems. These include the identification of successive phases of local cyclic events, their internal dating and external correlation, and their causation. Chronometric controls, consideration of complex geomorphic systems (rather than of single processes), and evaluation of multiple variables are all essential. In the case of Holocene alluvial sequences the specific issues can be briefly enumerated as follows.

Internal Dating

Alluvial deposits record only a fraction of an alluvial cycle (Butzer, 1976a), possibly a long period of slow, net accumulation with many equilibria, possibly a brief period of disrupted equilibrium with rapid mobilization and aggradation of valley floor sediment (Baker, 1977). Suitable samples for ^{14}C dating are commonly limited and the range of statistical or contaminant error between any two assays may exceed the true age span of an entire sedimentary body. As a result, radiometric dating tends to be spotty, and frequently is based on fortuitous samples of differing materials from widely separated areas, sometimes not even from the same drainage. Yet dissection may begin downstream (or along a higher order stream) centuries earlier than it does upstream (or in a low-order valley), where dynamic equilibrium may still persist. In this way the drainage-wide selection of ^{14}C samples that commonly is indispensible for even a rudimentary dating framework may introduce unwelcome error. It is consequently not surprising that the temporal components of Holocene alluvial cycles remain imperfectly understood, even in the best studied stream systems.

Intraregional Correlation

Fundamental to the establishment of regionally valid alluvial sequences is close attention to morpho-stratigraphic detail: relative sets of longitudinal gradients, vertical and lateral patterning of facies, disconformities or soils, and relationships between stream sediments, colluvia, and slope forms. Given a reasonable number of chronometric cross-checks, adjacent stream systems of intermediate order and comparable lithologies may allow for gross correlation and the identification of landscape periodicities with regional validity. A judicious combination of local detailed studies and broader reconnaissance is essential to such goals.

Regional Delimitation

Alluvial histories, like those of other environmental components, tend to be areally circumscribed. Sufficient field exploration will normally allow an appropriate definition of the region in which alluvial sequences are comparable. This in turn may coincide, for example, with a bedrock or terrain type, an ecozone, or a prehistoric culture area. Such spatial resolution is critical for assessment of various potential causative factors.

Causation

Given adequate temporal and spatial controls, it may be possible to consider the potential role of climatic change, human activities, or a host of other environmental variables, singly or interactively, in affecting ground cover, runoff volumes and periodicities, and sediment supply and mobilization. If the basic causes are isolated, then the timescales of landscape periodicities can be properly interpreted and, in turn, refined.

In effect, alluvial histories can only be explicated by holistic research projects that pay due attention to scale and multivariate interactions. Both the problems and realizations can be usefully illustrated by a selection of examples from different macro-environments at different latitudes on three continents. These studies have been deliberately chosen from areas where the author has some degree of field familiarity and can claim methodological comparability. The references cited provide the indispensible details for what can be no more than synopses.

The Upper Danube Basin, Central Europe

The floodplains of central Europe are extensively veneered by flood silts and related colluvium of Mediaeval date, with more localized, earlier wash, mainly of the late Bronze or early Iron Age (Butzer, 1974a). These deposits (haugh loams) reflect accelerated runoff in the wake of intensive human occupation, including cultivation of upland loess soils, grazing on valley-margin slopes, and finally large-scale clearance and frequently abortive cultivation of irregular terrain prone to sheet, gully, and rill erosion. Haugh loam mantles have tended to obscure complex suites of alluvial bedload facies, resulting from reworking of late Pleistocene gravels, primarily during the last 5 millennia (Schirmer, 1977).

A representative example of this Holocene dynamism in a temperate, mesic environment is provided by the Reichenhall Basin of the Saalach River in Bavaria (Brunnacker *et al.*, 1976). During mid-Atlantic times the Saalach still meandered in a channel incised only 4 m into an intact body of glaciofluvial gravels of terminal Pleistocene age. Then channel shortening led to 20 m of downcutting. Pollen diagrams from the silts and peats that subsequently accumulated in the new channels, as well as in the abandoned meanders, record the Atlantic-Subboreal transition and, in one core, the base of the Subatlantic. The former is dated *ca.* 4750–4450 bp in the general area, suggesting dramatic incision shortly after 5000 bp (all 'before present' dates represent uncalibrated ^{14}C years). Subsequently, gravel and colluvial rubble were aggraded by tributary fans while 10 m of silt and clay rapidly buried a growing forest on the Saalach floodplain. This phase of sedimentation is linked to a late Bronze (Urnfield) cemetery and attributed to widespread deforestation *ca.* 1300 BC. After a period of stabilization, 2–3 m of coarse valley-margin fans and floodplain silts accumulated between AD 150 and 700. Minor downcutting (by 1 m) in late Mediaeval times was followed by building up of the modern floodplain with local, marginal fans.

This case study from the intermediate-order Saalach is complemented by work on the high-order Danube between Linz and Vienna (Fink, 1977). Here five major alluvial bodies are recognized, as dated by ^{14}C and dendrochronology on logs or *in situ* stumps. After 5–10 m of end-Pleistocene dissection, a comparably thick fill aggraded *ca.* 9800–8100 bp, followed by a similar cut-and-fill cycle with alluviation *ca.* 7600–5100 bp. Both early Holocene alluvia are at similar elevations to the last Pleistocene glaciofluvial terrace, whereas later fills generally form one or two lower terraces. The next alluvial body is dated *ca.* 4500–3000 bp, with two further, minor fills between 2700 bp and AD 850. Accumulation of the modern floodplain began a little before AD 1400.

There is a reasonable degree of regional correlation along the Danube and its tributary systems, but details vary, in part due to variations in valley geometry, with downcutting along one stretch accompanied by local fan development at suitable points further downstream (Fink, 1977; Brunnacker *et al.*, 1976). The underlying readjustments in discharge, channel and valley gradient, as well as sediment yield, appear to reflect environmental inputs more complex than those of the standard Holocene pollen zones. The crude ^{14}C frameworks suggest that intervals of downcutting may have averaged somewhat less than 5 centuries in duration, with aggradation and eventual dynamic equilibrium lasting 500–2500 years. Dendrochronological results are more precise (Becker, 1977), showing that Holocene phases of fluvial 'activation' in central Europe seldom exceeded a few centuries, but that fluvial systems continued to readjust in response to the initial triggering impetus for as much as several millennia.

The role of human occupance deserves close attention. Along the drier margins of the mixed deciduous forests of central Europe, prehistoric agricultural settlement had the effect of favouring a subclimax vegetation with reduced arboreal cover, lowered watertables, accelerated runoff, increased peak discharge, and reduced base flow. It has been usual to play down the potential impact of early Neolithic settlement, let alone of Mesolithic activities, in temperate Europe. However, Dimbleby (1976) presents a case for a less deductive approach, and Brunnacker (1971) has shown that soils in the proximity of Lepenski Vir, in the Iron Gate stretch of the Danube, were intensively disturbed by local settlement *ca.* 7300–6300 bp. A series of detailed local soil and molluscan studies along the interfingering forest–steppe boundary in Czechoslovakia show no disturbance prior to the late Atlantic (Smolíková and Ložek, 1973; Ložek, 1975, 1976). Local deforestation is first evident on a local scale during the 5th millennium bp.

Widespread deforestation with rapidly expanding cultivation began with the late Bronze Age (late Subboreal), leading to a fundamental change of biota during the Hallstatt–La Tène period (early Subatlantic, last millennium BC). Later, during Mediaeval times, slopes of as much as 8° were brought under cultivation, with reworking of most soils and permanent establishment of steppic biota. This evidence suggests that cut-and-fill cycles after 3500 bp will have been significantly affected, if not controlled, by human activities, as in the case of the colluvial mantles or fans with late Bronze Age sherds found on footslopes or floodplains from the Iron Gate to the Lower Rhine and Weser. On the other hand, the major and universal phase of fluvial readjustment shortly after 5000 bp is difficult to relate to human activities, and significant alluviation in northwestern Lower Austria began 4850 bp, at a time when this area was not yet settled (Peschke, 1977; Fink, 1978).

It would appear that central European stream behaviour during early and mid-Holocene times included both minor channel readjustments and major floodplain changes, the latter in response to environmental oscillations lasting no more than a few centuries and perhaps too brief to show up in conventional biotic records. During the later Holocene such fluctuations in stream dynamism appear to become more common and, in areas of intensive settlement, their overall impact was magnified and linked to considerably more generalized environmental changes. It nonetheless remains uncertain whether human activities triggered the cut-and-fill cycles after 3500 bp, rather than merely creating fragile ecosystems that responded dramatically to relatively minor climatic stimuli.

The Prairie Peninsula, Illinois

The central European cases outlined here suggest that Holocene environmental changes at several different timescales had a variable impact on geomorphic and vegetational patterns. The true complexity of differential scales is better illustrated along the margins of the Prairie Peninsula in the American Midwest, a continental environment with maximum precipitation in spring and late summer. Palynological and faunal evidence from Minnesota, Illinois, and Missouri (Wood and McMillan, 1976; Wright, 1976; King and Allen, 1977; King, 1977) shows that the grassland belt of AD 1800 was created at the expense of woodland shortly after 9000 bp, with maximum aridity during the 8th millennium bp, and partial forest recolonization of the prairie margin 6500–4500 bp.

The history of the lower Illinois River is presently understood in a similarly generalized way, with evidence for at least 15 m of bed-load aggradation *ca*. 8000–5500 bp, stabilization of a braided-river floodplain by 5000 bp, then evolution into a high-sinuosity river with flood silt accretion, modified by several phases of channel simplification during the last 3 millennia (Butzer, 1977). The more complex details of repeated geomorphic change can be discerned in the better exposed, minor tributary streams and at the Koster archaeological site in southwestern Greene County.

The Koster sequence, as based on deep excavations, bore profiles, conventional drainage basin studies, and calibrated by a good array of ^{14}C dates on charcoal (Butzer, 1977), begins with evidence for moderately active erosion of loessic slopes and colluvial accretion *ca*. 9700–8500 bp. Maximum geomorphic activity, accompanied by 50 cm per century net footslope deposition *ca*. 8000 bp, was followed by a degree of slope stability 7700–5500 bp, with renewed soil erosion until 5000 bp. Then dynamic equilibrium allowed deep soils to develop until cut-and-fill cycles were inaugurated *ca*. 100 BC and again AD 750. These late cycles involved initial gullying, followed by rapid loess fan accretion, and ultimately stabilization with soil development. Erosion in response to Anglo–American settlement has been prominent since AD 1830. Contemporary observations indicate that active slope stripping or gullying is linked with forest decimation, arguing that the period 9700–5000 bp was generally drier than today, with two incisive dry spells during late Holocene time. Similarities with the behaviour of the Illinois River are apparent, and there is also good correspondence with changes in the level of Lake Michigan (Larsen, 1979): the lake was generally low but fluctuating prior to a very high level 5000–3000 bp, since which it has oscillated strongly about its recent mean. Some of the short-term oscillations ($\times 10^2$ years) that are superimposed upon the long-term trends ($\times 10^3$ years) of Lake Michigan cannot yet be identified in the geomorphic record.

These examples from the Prairie Peninsula show that the critical thresholds for stream behaviour are lower than those for discernible regional vegetation change, even though rapid and significant changes in local groundcover were directly implicated in the cut-and-fill cycles. Only the gross configuration of the alluvial sequences is related to long-term trends spanning several millennia; the critical impulses that cumulatively effect major floodplain change appear seldom to have exceeded a century or two. Changes in land use patterns are immaterial for interpretation of the Illinois record prior to AD 1800, although very local, but at times intensive disturbance of Indian site proximity may have caused minor variations in sediment transfer rates.

The Mediterranean Basin

The evidence for alluvial sequences in the semiarid, subtropical Mediterranean Basin has already been reviewed by Vita-Finzi (1969) and Butzer (1974a, 1975), with recent noteworthy contributions by Bintliff (1976), Büdel (1977), and Davidson (this volume, Chapter 11). Available data suggest that complex alluvial sequences, of the kind described from central Europe and Illinois, are either uncommon or poorly developed. There are, instead, widespread colluvial deposits, frequently grading into heterogeneous alluvial fills that, judging by archaeological associations, postdate the apex of intensive Roman land use. In the course of the author's work in different parts of Spain it became apparent that such 'post-Classical' deposits are limited to areas of intensive Roman agriculture or to the periphery of larger Roman settlements; colluvia or alluvial fills in other regions are much more recent, and can be linked to post-Mediaeval deforestation and agricultural expansion into marginal environments, or to over-exploitation of fragile ecozones. Wherever found and whatever its age, 'post-Classical' detritus is the most conspicuous geomorphic feature in the Holocene landscape, even though no pollen profiles record drastic environmental change during the last two millennia. These facts, in combination with the variable age of initial geomorphic activation between the third and twentieth centuries AD, leave little doubt that the 'post-Classical' deposits were primarily a response to human activities.

The geomorphic record of human interference is not limited to the last 1500 years. In various sectors of earlier intensive settlement, both late Bronze Age and classical Greek, there are many instances where colluviation, alluviation, or rapid coastal siltation in deltaic regions can be firmly dated in the 1500–3500 bp time range.

The Mediterranean Basin record is therefore distinct from those of central Europe and the Prairie Peninsula. Early to mid-Holocene alluvial sequences may yet be deciphered from some river systems. But the dominant pattern is one of accelerated soil erosion in response to human misuse of the land—beginning locally during the late Bronze Age and becoming more universal after the economic decline of the Roman Empire. Climatic impulses may have favoured such geomorphic activation, but the variable timing, and the unprecedented extent and scope of these slope and valley changes within the Holocene record, remain inconceivable without a pre-eminently cultural impetus.

The Egyptian Desert

With a hyperarid climate, most of the Sahara displays very little geomorphic dynamism. The only sector of the Egyptian Sahara that exposes an informative, Holocene alluvial record is the Eastern Desert where wadi valleys 'drain' the Red Sea Hills to the Nile (Butzer and Hansen, 1968; Butzer, 1974b, 1979). Approximate dating is provided by a limited number of ^{14}C dates and archaeological associations.

Sandy alluvial fills with basal gravels accumulated after *ca*. 11,000 bp, coeval with Nile aggradation, although well developed calcareous root tubules and snail proliferations indicate abundant desert vegetation. Building up of the nilotic floodplain continued until *ca*. 6000 bp but geomorphic activity in the desert wadis gave way to soil development some two millennia earlier. The resulting 30–100 cm cambic horizons record partial decalcification, rubefaction, and kaolinitic clay formation, indicating a fair amount of biochemical weathering that implies a period of repeated, gentle rains. Following an interval of wadi dissection, sheets of coarse piedmont colluvium were activated through much of the Eastern Desert, sweeping down into the gravelly sands filling the lower wadis, where such local alluvia interdigitate with nilotic flood silts aggraded during the 5th and 4th millennia BC. It can be shown that both the early and mid-Holocene wadi fills, as far south as the Egyptian–Sudanese border, were deposited while the Nile floodplain was desiccated, i.e. during the winter half year, in response to rains of westerly rather than monsoonal origin. A last phase of wadi activation is recorded by fine-grained alluvia in the larger wadis, and dated to the 11th century AD. In more recent times the localized heavy rains that appear to occur about once a century only suffice to transfer detritus for short distances along isolated wadi reaches.

The Omo–Rudolf Basin, East Africa

The Lower Omo Basin, at the northern end of Lake Rudolf, provides the best Holocene alluvial sequence in East Africa. The record includes deltaic and alluvial formations of the Omo River that reflect regional conditions over a large montane drainage system with a long summer rainy season, as well as local piedmont alluvial fans and terraces that reflect changes at generally lower elevations with short spring and autumn rainy seasons (Butzer, 1971a, 1976b, 1980; Butzer *et al.*, 1969, 1972).

During the terminal Pleistocene, Lake Rudolf was at a relatively low level, the Omo River cut down its channel by at least 15 m, while exposed alluvial surfaces were calcified, with local salt hydration of buried gravel and patination of surface lag. At the beginning of the Holocene, Lake Rudolf expanded rapidly and fluctuated between 60 and 85 m above its present level *ca.* 9800–7000 bp, judging by a representative suite of Holocene ^{14}C shell dates. Along the piedmont margins, associated lake beds may be interbedded with limonitic detrital units ranging in texture from silts to cobble gravels; such deposits grade laterally into stream terraces with as much as 12 m of fine alluvium. Shortly after 7000 bp the lake shrank rapidly to approximately its present dimensions, and the Omo River was entrenched by 40 m, piedmont streams by 8 m and more. A new transgression was under way 6600 bp and the lake fluctuated at +65 to +75 m from 6200 bp until 4000 bp, with development of shallow alluvial terraces on the piedmonts. A temporary regression of unknown amplitude was followed by transgression to +75 m *ca.* 3250 bp, at which time Lake Rudolf was last linked to the Nile Basin across a shallow divide.

After a rapid drop of level and downcutting by the Omo and various piedmont streams, Lake Rudolf fluctuated between +20 and +50 m about 4000–3500 and 3000–2500 bp; this stage includes fluviolacustrine deposits along the Lower Omo River as well as extensive lateral alluvial terraces or fans, at least 5 m thick, ranging from sandy silts to gravels. During the last 2500 years the lake fluctuated rapidly between 15 m above and 5 m below its present level, dropping 20 m between 1897 and 1955; adjustment of the lateral streams has been limited to fill-dissection, averaging 3–5 m along the Omo floodplain margins and across the piedmont alluvia. The major oscillations since the twelfth century AD had a mean amplitude of about 150 years.

Particularly striking about the Omo–Rudolf record is the amplitude and rate of hydrological and geomorphic changes that were clearly linked and apparently synchronous throughout the basin. Alluviation was evidently related to moister anomalies, dissection to drier trends. The rapidity of these changes and their replication through large parts of tropical Africa preclude a significant human impact.

The Interior and the Cape Coast of South Africa

The Vaal–Orange Basin of South Africa provides a low-relief erosional landscape with a subtropical, semiarid climate, characterized by summer rains. Shallow alluvial fills are well developed and extensively exposed by gullying or through channel shortening and incision. Radiometric controls are a major problem since suitable sample material is rare. The resulting dating framework is poor, despite corroboration from spring sequences along the interfluves (Butzer, 1974c; Butzer *et al.*, 1973, 1978, 1979).

Early Holocene downcutting was followed by 5–10 m of flood silt aggradation, capped by a vertisol that records seasonally wet floodplain surfaces with meandering streams. Broadly dated *ca.* 4500–1300 bp, this alluvial fill remained undissected in many lower order drainage basins until a century or two ago and, in the Vaal headwaters, some tributaries still retain marshy, meandering floodplains. Elsewhere, in large streams prone to high peak discharge, the Holocene fill is subdivided: temporary downcutting *ca.* 2600–2250 bp was followed by accretion of a smaller body of sandier alluvium that lacks the characteristic vertisol.

This evidence for wetter floodplains and reduced discharge seasonality implies a more equable climate, particularly during the 4th millennium bp. Parallel sequences are provided by organic spring deposits, expanded lakes in closed depressions, accelerated karstic spring discharge, and soil formation. Since subsequent dissection and gullying through much of the basin began at least 800 years ago, it predates local intrusion of Bantu and Afrikaner pastoralists and farmers. Nonetheless, overgrazing, fencing, and deliberate burning have favoured range deterioration during the last century and thus accelerated erosional processes already under way. There appears to be no alluvial record of the moister conditions indicated by karst springs and local lacustrine beds *ca.* 9700–6500 bp.

The mesic woodlands of the southern Cape Province have an analogous Holocene alluvial record, despite a significantly different Pleistocene trajectory (Butzer and Helgren, 1972; Butzer *et al.*, 1978b).

During the early Holocene, coastal dunes, related to the glacio-eustatic transgression, invaded areas well inland, while slope erosion brought thick colluvial deposits into the valleys. Humic or weak podsolic soils temporarily stabilized the dune fields during part of the 8th millennium bp. General slope stability was only established *ca.* 4200 bp, after which slow organic accumulations, including local palmetto peats, indicate ponded stream beds with high watertables. Renewed downcutting *ca.* 1000 bp was followed by rapid aggradation of sands along steeper stream channels. Fresh gullying during the last two centuries was accompanied by reactivation of the coastal dunes, probably in response to Afrikaner pastoral activities and burning, and more recent deforestation. Pollen profiles and faunal changes bear out these interpretations, with a predominantly open vegetation during the early Holocene, and forest establishment during the mid-Holocene.

The comparative simplicity of the South African alluvial record may reflect higher geomorphic thresholds or a lower degree of resolution, or both. In fact, occasional, minor erosional shoulders cut into various fills suggest readjustments of stream gradient that did not produce tangible, primary deposits.

Conclusions and Prospects

The alluvial sequences outlined here serve to underscore the basic problems of internal dating, intraregional correlation, regional delimitation, and causation discussed earlier. It is apparent that each sequence is complex, that events of both greater and lesser wavelength must be distinguished, and explanations can only be offered and evaluated within a broader context of palaeoenvironmental indicators. Each of the areas discussed has a unique record. Some areas were moister during the early Holocene, others during the mid-Holocene; some areas were geomorphologically uneventful during the early Holocene, others during the middle or late Holocene. Those generalists prone to searching for hemispheric or even global parallels and periodicities will be disappointed and, hopefully, cautioned. Simplistic, long-range correlations are more likely to be wrong than right because dating is only approximate, multiple short-term changes are difficult to pin-point with accuracy, and directions of change may well differ in different regions. Periodicities that are real and hemispheric or global in scale are unlikely to be truly synchronous because specific geomorphic thresholds are defined by several variables and can be expected to vary both spatially and temporally.

The alluvial cycles identified in this paper reflect complex ecological readjustments that involve channel and floodplain geometry, rainfall seasonality, intensity, and periodicity, as well as runoff patterns, ground cover, and sediment calibre and amount. The critical, immediate variables are ground cover, runoff, and sediment supply. But the ultimate variables are climate and human activity. Climatic variation during the course of Holocene time has not been of the same scale that demarcated glacials and interglacials or that delineated the fluctuations of the deep-sea isotope curves. But it has sufficed to affect geomorphic trends repeatedly and significantly.

These Holocene events provide as yet little appreciated information on environmental interactions that would not only help elucidate the details of Holocene palaeoclimatology, but could provide useful models for more effective interpretation of gross Pleistocene changes. They further offer critical contextual information for prehistoric settlement trajectories. Last, but not least, they provide a challenging geo-archaeological opportunity to examine the spatial and temporal dimensions of human interference in complex ecosystems.

References

Baker, V. R. (1977). Stream channel response to floods, with examples from central Texas. *Bull. Geol. Soc. Am.*, **88**, 1057–1071.

Becker, B., and Frenzel, B. (1977). Paläoökologische Befunde zur Geschichte postglazialer Flussauen im südlichen Mitteleuropa. *Erdwiss. Forschung*, **13**, 43–61.

Bintliff, J. (1975). Mediterranean alluviation: new evidence from archeology. *Proc. Prehist. Soc.*, **41**, 78–84.

Bintliff, J. (1976). The Plain of Macedon and the Neolithic site of Nea Nikomedeia. *Proc. Prehist. Soc.*, **42**, 241–262.

Brunnacker, K. (1971). Geologisch–pedologische Untersuchungen in Lepenski Vir am Eisernen Tor. *Fundamenta*, **A–3**, 20–32.

Brunnacker, K. (1977). Das Holozän im Binnenland—die geologische Gegenwart. *Geol. Rundschau*, **66**, 755–770.

Brunnacker, K., Freundlich, J., Menke, M., and Schmeidl, H. (1976). Das Jungholozän im Reichenhaller Becken. *Eiszeitalter Gegenwart*, **27**, 159–173.

Bryan, K. (1941). Pre-Columbian agriculture in the Southwest as conditioned by periods of alluviation. *Ann. Assoc. Am. Geog.*, **31**, 219–242.

Büdel, J. (1977). *Klima Geomorphologie*, Bornträger, Berlin.

Butzer, K. W. (1971a). Recent history of an Ethiopian delta: the Omo River and the level of Lake Rudolf. *Univ. Chicago Geog. Dept. Res. Pap.*, **136**, 1–184.

Butzer, K. W. (1971b). Fine alluvial fills of the Orange and Vaal Basins, South Africa. *Proc. Assoc. Am. Geog.*, **3**, 42–49.

Butzer, K. W. (1974a). Accelerated soil erosion, in *Perspectives on Environment* (Eds. I. Manners and M. W. Mikesell). Association of American Geographers, Washington, D.C. pp. 57–78.

Butzer, K. W. (1974b). Modern Egyptian pottery clays and Predynastic buff ware. *J. Near East. Stud.*, **33**, 377–382.

Butzer, K. W. (1974c). Geology of the Cornelia beds. *Mem. Nat. Mus. Bloemfontein*, **9**, 7–32.

Butzer, K. W. (1975). Pleistocene littoral–sedimentary cycles of the Mediterranean Basin: a Mallorquin view, in *After the Australopithecines* (Eds, K. W. Butzer and G. L. Isaac). Mouton, The Hague, pp. 25–71.

Butzer, K. W. (1976a). *Geomorphology from the Earth*, Harper and Row, London and New York.

Butzer, K. W. (1976b). The Mursi, Nkalabong and Kibish Formations, Lower Omo Basin, Southwest Ethiopia, in *Earliest Man and Environments in the Lake Rudolf Basin* (Eds. Y. Coppens, F. C. Howell, G. L. Isaac, and R. E. F. Leakey). University of Chicago Press, Chicago, pp. 12–23.

Butzer, K. W. (1977). Geomorphology of the Lower Illinois Valley as a spatial–temporal context for the Koster Archaic site. *Illinois State Mus. Rep. Invest.*, **34**, 1–60.

Butzer, K. W. (1979). Pleistocene history of the Nile Valley in Egypt and Lower Nubia, in *The Sahara and the Nile* (Eds. M. A. J. Williams and H. Faure). Balkema, Rotterdam, pp. 248–276.

Butzer, K. W. (1980). The Holocene lake plain north of Lake Rudolf, East Africa. *Phys. Geog.*, **1**, in press.

Butzer, K. W., and Hansen, C. L. (1968). *Desert and River in Nubia*, University of Wisconsin Press, Madison, Wisc.

Butzer, K. W., and Helgren, D. M. (1972). Late Cenozoic evolution of the Cape Coast between Knysna and Cape St. Francis, South Africa. *Quat. Res.*, **2**, 143–169.

Butzer, K. W., Brown, F. H., and Thurber, D. L. (1969). Horizontal sediments of the Lower Omo Basin: the Kibish Formation. *Quaternaria*, **11**, 15–30.

Butzer, K. W., Isaac, G. L., Richardson, J. L., and Washbourn-Kamau, C. K. (1972). Radiocarbon dating of East African lake levels. *Science*, **175**, 1069–1076.

Butzer, K. W., Helgren, D. M., Fock, G. J., and Stuckenrath, R. (1973). Alluvial terraces of the Lower Vaal River, South Africa: a re-appraisal and re-investigation. *J. Geol.*, **81**, 341–362.

Butzer, K. W., Fock, G. J., Scott, L., and Stuckenrath, R. (1979). Dating of rock art: contextual analysis of South African rock engravings. *Science*, **203**, 1201–1214.

Butzer, K. W., Stuckenrath, R., Bruzewicz, A. J., and Helgren, D. M. (1978). Late Cenozoic paleoclimates of the Gaap Escarpment, Kalahari margin, South Africa. *Quat. Res.*, **10**, 310–339.

Dimbleby, G. W. (1976). Climate, soil and man. *Phil. Trans. R. Soc. Lond.*, **B275**, 197–208.

Fink, J. (1977). Jüngste Schotterakkumulationen im österreichischen Donauabschnitt. *Erdwiss. Forchung*, **13**, 190–211.

Gladfelter, B. G. (1977). Geoarcheology: the geomorphologist and archaeology. *Am. Antiq.*, **42**, 519–538.

Hack, J. (1942). The changing physical environment of the Hopi Indians of Arizona. *Harvard Univ. Peabody Mus. Arch. Ethnol. Pap.*, **35**, 1–85.

Haynes, C. V. (1968). Geochronology of late Quaternary alluvium, in *Means of Correlation of Quaternary Successions* (Eds. R. B. Morrison and H. E. Wright). University of Utah Press, Salt Lake City, pp. 591–631.

King, J. E. (1977). Vegetational history of the Prairie Peninsula, U.S.A. *X INQUA Congress (Birmingham, 1977), Abstracts*, p. 242.

King, J. E. and W. H. Allen (1977). A Holocene vegetation record from the Mississippi River Valley, southeastern Missouri. *Quat. Res.*, **8**, 307–323.

Larsen, C. E. (1979). Southern Lake Michigan: a case for Holocene lake level fluctuations. *Illinois State Geol. Survey Circular*, in press.

Ložek, V. (1975). Zur Problematik der landschaftsgeschichtlichen Entwicklung in verschiedenen Höhenstufen der Westkarpaten während des Holozäns. *Biul. Geol.*, **19**, 79–92.

Ložek, V. (1976). Zur Geschichte der Bodenerosion in den mitteleuropäischen Lösslandschaften während des Holozäns. *Strat. Newsl.*, **5**, 44–54.

Peschke, P. (1977). Zur Vegetations- und Besiedlungsgeschichte des Waldviertels (Niederöster-reich). *Mitt. Komm. Quartärforschung, Öster. Akad. Wiss.*, **2**, 1–84.

Schirmer, W. (1977). Holocene development of Middle European valley floors. *X INQUA Congress (Birmingham, 1977), Abstracts*, p. 402.

Smolíková, L., and Ložek, V. (1973). Der Bodenkomplex von Velký Hubenov als Beispiel einer retrograden Bodenentwicklung im Laufe der Nacheiszeit. *Čas. Mineral. Geol.*, **18**, 365–377.

Thornes, J. B., and D. Brunsden (1977). *Geomorphology and Time*. Methuen, London.

Vita-Finzi, C. (1969). *The Mediterranean Valleys*. Cambridge University Press, Cambridge.

Wood, W. R., and McMillan, R. B. (1976). *Prehistoric Man and his Environments: a Case Study in the Ozark Highland*. Academic Press, New York.

Wright, H. E. (1976). The dynamic nature of Holocene vegetation. *Quat. Res.*, **6**, 581–596.

Timescales in Geomorphology
Edited by R. A. Cullingford, D. A. Davidson, and J. Lewin
©1980 John Wiley & Sons Ltd.

CHAPTER 11

Erosion in Greece during the first and second millennia BC

Donald A. Davidson

Department of Geography,
University of Strathclyde

As timescales expand and if, as a further complication, they become separated from the present, the difficulties of reconstructing and explaining the geomorphic record become very apparent. This paper illustrates the problems which are associated with establishing and interpreting the erosional record of Greece during the 1st and 2nd millennia BC. If a detailed erosional chronology can be established, then factors which induced soil erosion can be postulated. For example, if a phase of erosion was a synchronous event throughout Greece, then emphasis might be given to climatic change in causing such erosion. In contrast, the effects of man's activities might be stressed if there was spatial and temporal correlation between these activities and the acceleration of erosion. Of course, it is possible for climatic change, the activities of man, and a host of other factors to have resulted in various phases of erosion in the past.

Despite the fragmentary record of erosion, there is much archaeological and historical evidence to establish a chronological framework within the 2nd and 1st millennia BC. Before this period, there were flourishing Neolithic communities from *ca.* 6500 to *ca.* 3000 BC when the Early Bronze Age began and continued until *ca.* 2000 BC. Thus the start of the 2nd millennium BC coincides with the opening of the Middle Bronze Age, which is best expressed in Crete by the construction of the first palace complexes, the foci of Minoan communities of which Knossos is the best known site (Fig. 11.1). All the characteristics of an organized urban society began to emerge and the Minoans reached their cultural peak on Crete during the second palace period (1700–1450 BC), though their influence was not restricted to Crete. On Santorini (Thera), for example, there was a Minoan community evidenced by the archaeological site near Akrotiri. This site was buried by pumice and volcanic dust (tephra) from a gigantic volcanic explosion. The destruction of Minoan Crete in *ca.* 1470 BC coincides with the eruption of the Santorini volcano, but the detailed chronology of such events has been the subject of much controversy. One widely held view is that the tsunamis and earthquakes associated with the eruption caused much devastation on Crete and neighbouring islands. Yet human causes for the decline of Minoan Crete are also possible; the Mycenaeans, for example, were on the ascendancy and they may have attacked the Minoans. Thus, in the middle of the 2nd millennium BC the centre of gravity moved from Crete to the southern Greek mainland.

The rise of Mycenae (Fig. 11.1) from about 1600 BC marks the beginning of the Late

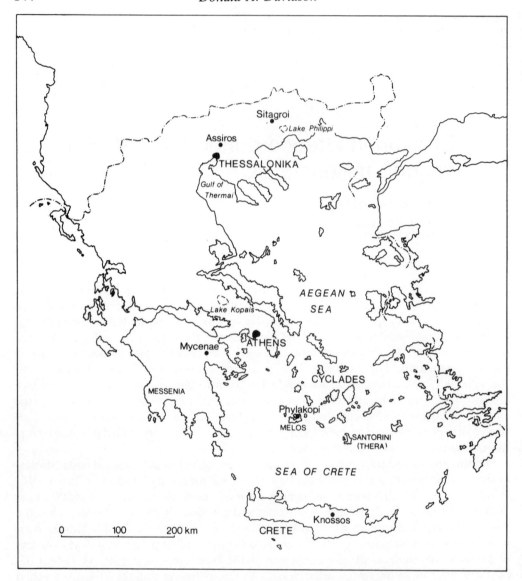

Fig. 11.1 Location map showing sites mentioned in text

Bronze Age and Mycenae soon became the political centre of southern Greece. The Mycenaean world gradually ended around 1200–1100 BC, probably as a result of interstate wars (Warren, 1975), concluding the Bronze Age and commencing the Dark Ages. Comparatively little is known about the period from 1100 to 750 BC but the archaeological and written record becomes fuller again after this time. An intricate history of expanding and warring tribes gradually led to the evolution of the city states of the Classical Period. The peak of Greek political influence as well as the time of Greece's greatest achievements in science, art, literature, and philosophy occurred in the Hellenistic period which is taken to begin at the death of Alexander (325 BC) and ends with the conquest of the Greek world by the Romans in the 1st century BC.

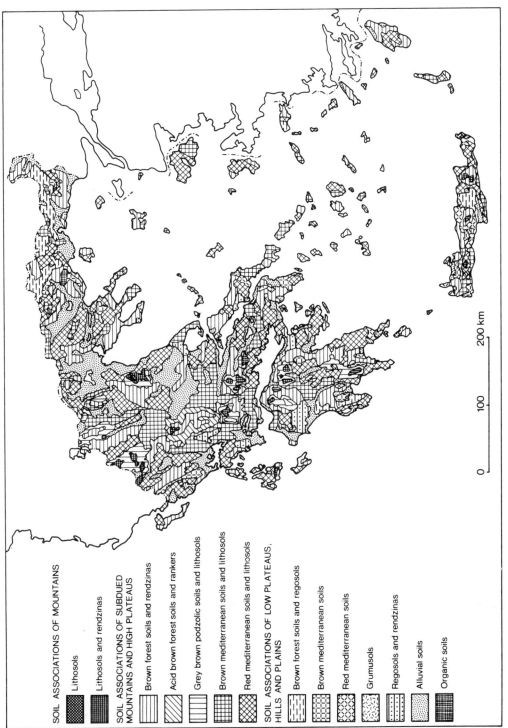

Fig. 11.2 Soil map of Greece (extract from *Soil Map of Europe*. 1:2,500,000, FAO, 1966)

SOIL ASSOCIATIONS OF MOUNTAINS

Lithosols

Lithosols and rendzinas

SOIL ASSOCIATIONS OF SUBDUED
MOUNTAINS AND HIGH PLATEAUS

Brown forest soils and rendzinas

Acid brown forest soils and rankers

Grey brown podzolic soils and lithosols

Brown mediterranean soils and lithosols

Red mediterranean soils and lithosols

SOIL ASSOCIATIONS OF LOW PLATEAUS,
HILLS AND PLAINS

Brown forest soils and regosols

Brown mediterranean soils

Red mediterranean soils

Grumusols

Regosols and rendzinas

Alluvial soils

Organic soils

0   100   200 km

The Background to Soil Erosion in Greece

The effects of erosion are clear in many areas of Greece today, expressed in terms of slopes dominated by lithosols and by extensive areas of alluvium in valley floors. However, it would be wrong to suggest that Greece only has lithosols and alluvial soils. Fig. 11.2 shows the distribution of soils in Greece and, as can be seen, there are spatially distinct occurrences of red and brown mediterranean soils, though these often occur in association with lithosols. The red and brown mediterranean soils are generally accepted as being relict and in Italy, for example, appear to have formed during the last interglacial (Heilmann, 1972). The clear inference is that the magnitude of soil erosion varies spatially.

The history of soil erosion has been largely approached by the study of alluvial sequences. The pioneering work on the subject was carried out by Vita-Finzi (1969), who examined alluvial sequences not only in Greece, but also in other Mediterranean countries. He identified two major periods of valley fill, an 'Older Fill', exemplified by the Red Beds in Greece containing Mousterian and Upper Palaeolithic artefacts, and a 'Younger Fill' with sherds ranging from the 2nd–3rd centuries AD to virtually the present. It is this later deposit which is of particular relevance to the present discussion since, according to Vita-Finzi, a period of net channel erosion from *ca.* 8000 BC until post-Roman times was followed by net channel deposition until incision occurred in the last few decades. This Younger Fill, consisting usually of stratified sands and silts but often containing rounded and sub-rounded gravel and stones, has been observed in many areas of Greece (Vita-Finzi, 1969; Davidson, 1971; Davidson *et al.*, 1976; Bintliff, 1976, 1977).

There has been much debate over the causes of such aggradation and all writers stress the difficulties involved in attempting to identify specific causal factors. Climatic, eustatic, isostatic, and vegetational changes, as well as the spread of man's influence through forest clearance and the rise of animal husbandry, are frequently mentioned. In many ways the task of explaining changes in drainage basins over a period of 2000 years seems extremely difficult, given the problems in trying to account for erosional patterns for the last 100 years (Cooke and Reeves, 1976) or for present day processes in a semi-arid area of Spain (Thornes, 1976). Indeed, it is very difficult to postulate the response of a river to a change in an environmental factor, a problem recently discussed by Allchin *et al.* (1978). Progress can only be made if a detailed chronology can be established for sedimentation, tectonic events, changes in climate, base level, and vegetation as well as for the spread of man's activities. Vita-Finzi (1969) was impressed by the apparent synchroneity in the initiation of the Younger Fill throughout the Mediterranean and this led him to suggest the importance of climatic change in inducing this deposition, though he also stressed the accessory role of man and other factors. Allchin *et al.* (1978), though very aware of the associated problems, use the same argument to suggest climatic change as the prime underlying cause of the terrace sequence in the Great Indian Desert. In the Mediterranean basin, since Vita-Finzi's (1969) initial study, more dates for the Younger Fill have become available and in more recent publications he describes a negative correlation between age and latitude (Vita-Finzi, 1973, 1976). He accounts for such diachronism by describing the southward lag resultant upon a progressive displacement of the circulation pattern.

An alternative interpretation is to view the variability in age of the Younger Fill as the result of local factors, and, in particular, the role of man is stressed (Butzer, 1974). There are written records which indicate that certain areas were much more forested in Classical times; deforestation and the spread of goats and sheep led to accelerated erosion, a fact observed by Classical writers such as Pausanias, Herodotus, Strabo, and Aristotle (Kraft *et al.*, 1975). Butzer (1974, p.66) quotes from the commentary of Plato (Critias, iii, D–E) in the fourth century BC:

'In consequence of the successive violent deluges . . . there has been a constant movement of soil away from high elevations; and, owing to the shelving relief of the coast, this soil, instead of laying down alluvium as it does elsewhere, has been perpetually deposited in the deep sea around the periphery of the country or, in other words, lost . . . All the rich, soft soil has molted away, leaving a country of skin and bones (so that rainfall) is allowed to flow over the denuded surface (directly) into the sea . . .'

Although this quotation gives emphasis to the effect of extreme rainfall events on erosion, elesewhere Plato relates this soil erosion to deforestation (Butzer, 1974). The debate over soil erosion in Greece and indeed in the whole Mediterranean basin has come to be dominated by two rival explanations—climatic and anthropogenic. Before these views are discussed, it is instructive to examine and exemplify the geomorphic techniques which are used to investigate soil erosion over a timescale of 2000 years.

Problems of Dating Sediments

The geomorphic investigation of soil erosion in Greece during the 1st and 2nd millennia BC is restricted to the residual sediments in the form of river, hillslope, and coastal deposits. River terraces have proved to be the prime focus for study, but many problems are encountered in trying to date former alluvial periods, a topic discussed by Butzer (this volume, chapter 10). The burial of datable buildings such as at Olympia clearly gives a maximum age whilst a datable feature on top of alluvium as with some tells in northern Greece provides a minimum age. Sherds of diagnostic type can often be found in alluvial sections and clearly the deposition of such material took place at some unknown time after the date of the youngest pottery. Great care has to be exerted in the interpretation of pottery evidence from alluvial sections. For example, the great abundance of Classical sherds in alluvium is often observed. Such frequency could be the result of large numbers of widely distributed Classical sites rather than the sudden acceleration of erosion in post-Classical times. Broad patterns of sedimentation can be elucidated based on sherd evidence, but more detailed investigation demands radio-carbon dates. Again, serious difficulties are encountered since instances of preserved organic matter in alluvial sections are infrequent. A team which has assembled a number of radiocarbon dates is that of J.C. Kraft and colleagues (Kraft *et al.*, 1975). Their studies were in coastal localities and the fossil records from their sites aided the interpretation of former environmental conditions. The dating of hillslope deposits poses the same problems as those encountered with alluvium, but an additional major difficulty is the lack of hillslope deposits which exhibit a sedimentary sequence. Again, the preservation of organic matter in sections is rare and, in addition, as will be illustrated for a section on Melos, difficulties arise over the interpretation of the organic material. Sedimentation of particular coastal embayments has been investigated using written records; for example, Bintliff (1976) uses Classical sources to re-interpret the evolution of the plain of western Macedonia, whilst Kraft and Aschenbrenner (1977) use historical evidence for their reconstruction of the Methoni embayment in the Peloponnese. The difficulties involved in using such evidence need no emphasis.

From this brief summary of problems associated with dating sediments, it is clear that the geomorphic evidence for elucidating the erosional record of Greece in the 1st and 2nd millennia is very fragmentary. Some of these problems can be illustrated by considering selected sites in Macedonia, Melos, and Santorini.

Macedonia

Many prehistoric sites known as tells occur in this area of Greece. These sites, ranging in age from the middle Neolithic times to the Bronze Age and later in several instances, were built up by people living more or less continuously in the same settlement for up to 3000 years. In the plain of Drama 18 sites are known; despite the density of such tells, little impact seems to have been made on the natural woodland until post-Classical times (Greig and Turner, 1974). In detail the geomorphic setting of these tells varies. For example, Fig. 11.3 illustrates the situation of Assiros tell (site 1) which has been

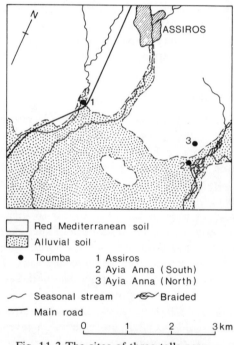

Red Mediterranean soil
Alluvial soil
• Toumba   1 Assiros
            2 Ayia Anna (South)
            3 Ayia Anna (North)
Seasonal stream   Braided
Main road

Fig. 11.3 The sites of three tells near
Assiros in the Langadas basin

excavated in recent years by K. Wardle. This tell, in the Langadas basin to the north-east of Thessalonika (Fig. 11.1), was occupied from *ca.* 2000 to 900 BC (Wardle, personal communication). The tell is situated where a gently sloping sequence of Tertiary clays, marls, sands, and gravels become mantled with more recent alluvium. The Greek Soil Survey has described a profile about 2 km to the west of the Assiros tell; they class it as a red mediterranean soil. At a profile a further kilometre to the west, they describe a grumosol (vertisol), again on the Tertiary parent material. Present day erosion of the red mediterranean profile is classed by the Survey as strong, whilst the grumosol is suffering only from slight erosion. To the immediate east of the tell the alluvial cover is very thin; the effect of ploughing is to bring the Tertiary material to the surface. Pottery dating to the end of last century or early in this century was found in alluvial sections along stream courses, indicating that alluviation continued to within 80 years of the present. Unfortunately, no evidence could be obtained from the Langadas basin to show when the recent alluvial aggradation began.

A tell which does offer some information on the sequence of alluviation is at Sitagroi in the plain of Drama (Fig. 11.1), a site which was excavated by A.C. Renfrew in the late 1960s. It was possible at this tell to link the sequence of wash deposits from the site with an alluvial sequence (Davidson, 1976). Fig. 11.4 is a generalized interpretation of the

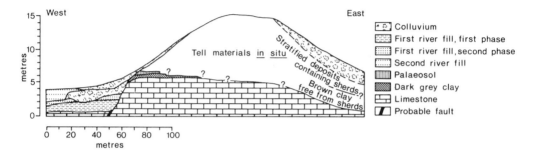

Fig. 11.4 Stratigraphy on the flanks of the Sitagroi tell in the Plain of Drama (from Davidson, 1976, p. 261. Reproduced by permission of Duckworths)

stratigraphy on the flanks of the tell. The alluvial sequence is associated with the River Angitis which flows incised in the alluvium at a distance of about 300 m to the south west of the tell. The initial valley was probably fault guided. The first river fill is represented by sands and gravels and a clay deposit. During part of this first river fill the tell would have been occupied (5400–2200 BC). Following abandonment of the site, erosion of the tell led to the deposition of the colluvial material containing sherds of all phases of occupation. This material must then have been trimmed by the river. The resultant colluvial terrace was then buried by the next phase of deposition which corresponds to Vita-Finzi's Younger Fill, since Classical sherds can be found in this material. The final phase which can be postulated from the stratigraphy shown in Fig. 11.4 is a very recent colluvial deposit, probably the result of the site being ploughed for the first time. Thus the stratigraphy at this site indicates an alluvial phase which was in existence during the 3rd–5th millennia BC in addition to the Younger Fill phase. The inference is that individual drainage basins in Greece will have varied markedly in their alluvial histories and thus the correlation of alluvial phases must be approached with great care. Another interesting result from the Sitagroi project was that it was possible to make some quantitative estimates of the extent to which the tell had been eroded since its abandonment in 2200 BC. Measurements of the amount of remaining colluvial material indicated that the fomer summit area was a minimum of 0.49 ha compared with 0.25 ha today; the former slope of the tell was at least 18° compared with 15° today. Such figures indicate the magnitude of erosion of unconsolidated material since the start of the 1st millennium BC (Davidson, 1976). Indeed, all the tells in eastern Macedonia have been very much degraded. Some are being actively undercut by rivers. For example, a rescue excavation is in progress at the site at Kastanas on the river Axios, which is seriously eroding the tell. This site, which was first occupied in the Early Bronze Age, is on the floodplain of the Axios. Again, the inference is of extensive alluvial deposits prior to the Bronze Age, but confirmation of the stratigraphy below the site must await further excavation.

Donald A. Davidson

In north-east Greece there are many occurrences of alluvium containing Classical sherds which indicate a late or post-Classical age for the extensive aggradation. This view accords with Vita-Finzi's Younger Fill. No evidence has been obtained in Macedonia to assist with more precise dating of the initiation of this aggradation. It is possible that erosion of the Sitagroi tell was underway during the 1st millennium BC, but any inference about general landscape erosion from this single observation would be very dangerous.

The best evidence for sedimentation comes from coastal localities. Bintliff (1976) has reviewed the evidence for the growth of the plain at the head of the Thermaic Gulf, west of Thessalonika (Fig. 11.1). In the 6th millennium BC most of the present day plain was part of the Thermaic Gulf with limited deposition by the main rivers, Aliakmon, Moglenitsa, Axios, and Gallikos. Not a great deal of change in the extent of the gulf is envisaged until about the fifth century BC. From this time until the fifth century AD, marked reduction took place in the size of the gulf owing to rapid sedimentation, which implies a change in rate of sediment supply, or a eustatic or tectonic change.

Melos and Santorini

The Cyclades are the group of islands to the south-east of the mainland and between the Aegean Sea and the Sea of Crete (Fig. 11.1). From 1974 until 1978 A.C. Renfrew directed the excavation of the site of Phylakopi on Melos. This town, which was first occupied in the Early Bronze Age, came strongly under Minoan influence and finally into the Mycenaean orbit. Geomorphological work was carried out on the island by C. M. K. Tasker and the author in collaboration with the archaeological project. A preliminary report of this work has been published (Davidson *et al.* 1976) and a full report is in press (Davidson and Tasker, in press). For present purposes, particular attention is directed towards an erosional chronology. In contrast to the plainlands or lower slopes of north-eastern Greece, erosion of Melian hillslopes is very apparent. These slopes are characterized by the virtual absence of a soil cover— lithosols are prevalent over much of the island. On many parts of the island, terraces have been constructed, a response in part to the clear need for soil and water conservation. The obvious need is to try to date the initiation of such erosion.

In many of the valleys, there is a sharp discontinuity between the rocky hillslopes and the extensive fill in the valley floor, a characteristic also noted by Russell (1954) for lower valleys in western Anatolia. On Melos examination of the stratigraphy of this fill revealed frequent occurrences of Classical and later sherds. At one site a small building dating to *ca.* 300–0 BC was found to be buried by alluvium. In other words, extensive alluviation was under way by late-Classical times, again conforming to Vita-Finzi's Younger Fill. Without doubt this was the main period of aggradation, but it is possible that such processes were well under way before Classical times. Evidence for this was obtained from two localities.

A colluvial embayment is present to the immediate south of Phylakopi. By good fortune a well had been sunk into this material and examination of the sherds in section proved possible (Fig. 11.5a). A total of 3.25 m were exposed; the lower 0.5 m only contained sherds of Late Bronze Age date (*ca.* 1500–1100 BC), whilst the upper 2.75 m had both Classical and Late Bronze Age sherds. This stratigraphic section neatly demonstrates the difficulties involved in dating sedimentary phases using pottery evidence. The fact that the lower 0.5 m contains no Classical sherds whilst Classical sherds are very common today on the surrounding slopes suggests that the lower deposit was formed before Classical times.

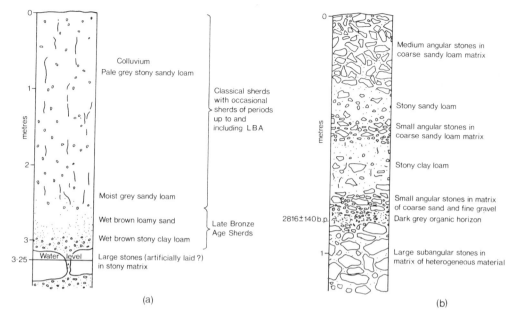

Fig. 11.5 Stratigraphy at two sites on Melos: (a) the well section and (b) the hillslope section (adapted from Davidson *et al.*, 1976, pp. 225 and 226. Reproduced by permission of Academic Press)

Another site provided similar evidence. An exposure at the side of a dry stream channel in the upper reaches of the Phylakopi valley revealed a sequence of coarse hillslope deposits on top of a dark organic band, which in turn overlies alluvial deposits (Fig. 11.5b). The radicarbon date for the organic band was 2816 ± 140 bp (SRR–793), which after calibration is equivalent to a date in calendar years of 1050 ± 150 BC. This implies (taking a range of two standard deviations) at the 95% significance level that the date lies between 1350 and 750 BC. This organic matter was sealed by the arrival of colluvium from the slope behind the site and the assumption, albeit open to debate, is that the onset of colluviation is indicated by the radiocarbon date. It is possible that there was a distinct time gap between the formation of the organic matter and the arrival of the colluvium, but it is difficult to visualize how an old organic surface could have been preserved for some time in this particular site before the deposition of the colluvium.

The well section and the radiocarbon site both suggest that hillslope degradation on Melos was probably underway by the end of the Bronze Age and accelerated in the 1st millennium BC. The magnitude and extent of the erosion are problematic and the other major difficulty is to assess the effect of man's activities during the Bronze Age in accelerating this erosion. It is tempting to visualize the effects of Bronze Age activities culminating in the deterioration of the landscape and there is the additional possibility that such soil degradation and coastal sedimentation may have hastened the decline of the Bronze Age economy. However, such a suggestion can only remain as an untested hypothesis, given the lack of a detailed erosional chronology and the absence of information about land use practices. The political and economic changes of the Bronze Age in Greece must also be considered in such a proposal.

The island of Santorini (Thera), about 80 km to the south-east of Melos, also had a flourishing Minoan society, best expressed in a site near the village of Akrotiri (Fig. 11.6), but this society came to an abrupt end with the cataclysmic eruption of the volcano

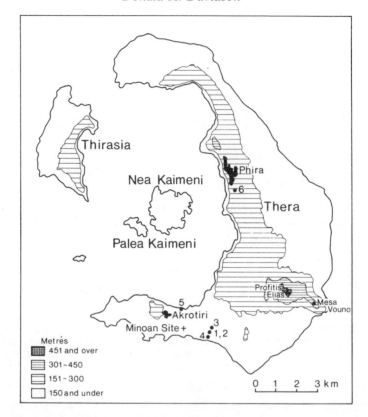

Fig. 11.6 Santorini (Thera) and the location of the sites where
the Minoan soil was sampled. Exposures 1, 2 and 3: sections at
base of ravines in the deeply eroded area to the east of the
archaeological site near Akrotiri. Exposure 4: section near base
of cliff on coast to the east of the archaeological site. Exposure 5:
section at side of footpath down to the small harbour to the
immediate north of the village of Akrotiri. Exposure 6: section
near base of Phira quarry to the immediate south of Phira (from
Davidson, 1978, p. 243. Reproduced by permission of *Nature*)

in *ca*. 1470 BC (Luce, 1876). At this time major earthquakes were succeeded by the
eruption of pumice and tephra and then the subsidence of the central part of the island to
form the caldera.

The site near Akrotiri is mantled with a few centimetres of fine pellety pumice which is
overlain by coarse pumice and then tephra. The thickness of the pumice and tephra
varies over the island; in the Phira quarries in the central part of the island these deposits
have a maximum depth of about 30 m. The effect of the pumice was to bury the soils as
they existed in Minoan times. In order to investigate these palaeopedological conditions,
a search was made for exposures which exhibited material immediately below the
diagnostic fine pellety pumice. A major difficulty was the lack of sections which displayed
this material and any general interpretation must be made with care given the paucity of
sites. Nevertheless, some exposures were found and their locations are shown in Fig.
11.6. Exposures of the same stratigraphic sequence were also sought in the east-central
part of Thera, but without success. The only other types of sites encountered were on
steep hillslopes; for example, on the east side of Mesa Vouno, with slopes of the order of

Table 11.1 Soil analytical data

Exposure	Sampling depth (cm)	Colour	Particle size (μm)				Organic matter (% of < 2 mm)	Cation-exchange capacity (mequiv. per 100 g)
			>2000	(2000–63) sand	(63–2) silt	(<2) clay		
1	5	7.5YR3/2	41	49	9	1	0.1	5
2	5	7.5YR3/2	16	71	12	2	0.1	6
3	5	10YR4/3	23	63	12	2	0.4	7
3	13	10YR4/2	20	65	13	2	0.1	8
4	5	7.5YR3/2	34	62	3	1	0.1	5
5	5	7.5YR3/2	18	72	9	1	0.1	5
5	38	7.5YR3/2	16	74	9	2	0.1	6
6	5	10YR5/3	22	66	11	1	0.1	9
6	38	10YR4/3	5	83	12	1	0.1	10
7	—	2.5Y5/2	37	60	3	1	0.1	9
8	—	2.5Y5/6	24	58	16	3	0.3	3

Exposures 1–6 inclusive refer to material from the Minoan level whilst exposures 7 and 8 are from present tephra-derived soils. The sampling depth is measured from the base of the fine pellety pumice. (From Davidson, 1978, p. 243. Reproduced by permission of *Nature*.)

25–30°, pumice, presumably from the Minoan eruption, directly overlies in places either the bedrock of marbles and phyllitic schists or a rubbly drift derived from these rocks. The implication is that the surface of these steep hillslopes in Minoan times was characterized either by the absence of soil or by the presence of a thin, rubble-derived soil.

The material immediately below the fine pellety layer of pumice was carefully examined in the field in order to establish if any former soil horizons could be identified. The material was loose, varying from a stony gravel to a sand, and in most cases colour differentiation was not apparent, though a slight contrast was evident in exposure 3 (Table 11.1). The suggestion is that there are no distinct buried soil profiles. To obtain further evidence about the Minoan soil, samples from the exposures were analysed for particle size, organic matter, and cation-exchange capacity and the results are given in Table 11.1. Two samples of present day topsoil derived from tephra are included to permit comparison.

The outstanding feature about all the particle size data is the coarse nature of the material—dominantly sands with only small quantities of silt and almost no clay. The organic contents are all negligible; the only slight suggestion of a former horizon with some organic matter is at exposure 3. The organic content figures should be seen in relation to the very slight amounts for present day soils. Cation-exchange capacity is a useful general indicator of soil fertility and, again, the results for both the Minoan and present day soils are low.

On the lower areas of the island the Minoan level overlies a small sequence of welded tuffs and slightly welded pumice flow deposits (Pichler and Friedrich, 1976). These ignimbrites would have been the parent material of the Minoan soil. As noted, a characteristic of the material below the fine pellety pumice level is its loose nature. Such disaggregation may have resulted from the weathering of the ignimbrites, but this needs to be examined by mineralogical analysis. Overall the Minoan soil can be interpreted as some type of inceptisol without even a cambic horizon (Butzer, personal communication). The similarity between the Minoan soil and the present xeroandepts on the tephra is thus apparent. Jassoglou and Nobeli (1972) have also noted a similarity between Bronze Age soils and those of today in Messenia.

Evidence for well developed and fertile soils on Santorini at the time of the Minoan eruption cannot be presented. Instead the evidence at best is that only poorly developed soils existed in the lower areas of southern and central Santorini at *ca*. 1500 BC. In terms of particle size and cation-exchange capacity these palaeosols are similar to those derived today from the tephra. The organic content of these Bronze Age soils was very low or non-existent, though remains of trees have been reported from the Minoan level (Luce, 1969). On the steep slopes of the higher areas, there would have been either bare rock surfaces or poorly developed soils on rock rubble.

Recent geological work suggests that there was a period of around 15,000 years without volcanic activity which preceded the late Minoan outburst (Pichler and Friedrich, 1976). Such a long period would have resulted in well developed soils, but such evidence is not present in the palaeopedological record. One explanation is that these soils, if they did exist, had been subjected to major erosion and general deterioration by the time of the eruption. Such erosion is suggested by the irregular nature of the unconformity at the base of the fine pellety pumice as exposed in the extensive Phira quarries. In addition, the similarity between present day tephra-derived soils and the Minoan-level soil has already been described: on Santorini today soils are being very actively eroded, this being reflected most clearly in the material blown by wind and deposited against walls. Despite the 3500 years since the cataclysm, soils today are poorly developed and their character is largely resultant upon erosional processes and underlying geology.

The similarity between Minoan and present day tephra-derived soils has been described, but major difficulties arise when the timescale of soil deterioration in Minoan times is discussed. Such a problem has to be resolved before factors inducing soil erosion can be examined. The island prior to the eruption must have been subjected to major earthquakes resulting in soil conditions highly susceptible to erosion. A few major storms could have caused major soil erosion over a few months just before the eruption. However, the fact that no buried soil was found which exhibited any characteristics of a reasonable soil, suggests that soil deterioration was underway well before *ca*. 1470 BC. The suggestion is that the Minoans, in their later years on Santorini, were causing erosion. In other words, as on Melos, the spread of agriculture and the herding of animals could have led to the acceleration of erosion. But such increasing land use difficulties were completely crowned by the volcanic event of *ca*. 1470 BC which devastated and transformed the island.

Discussion

In summary, the view that extensive channel aggradation took place in Greece from late-Classical times until almost the present is supported. In addition, an earlier alluvial deposit was observed on the flanks of the Sitagroi tell, hillslope erosion on Melos was probably underway by 1000 BC and degraded soils existed on Santorini by 1470 BC. Supporting evidence of a more intricate erosional/aggradational chronology than previously envisaged for the Mediterranean basin can be obtained from other studies, a viewpoint also adopted by Butzer (this volume, Chapter 10). A study of Van Zuidam (1975) in the Zaragoza area of Spain has also indicated that the Younger Fill began to be deposited at an earlier time—from *ca*. 700 BC to 100 AD with a maximum between 500 and 100 BC. He relates such geomorphic changes to human activity. Harvey (1978) also concludes from a study of dissected alluvial fans in south east Spain that erosional and depositional phases during the Holocene are primarily the result of man-induced vegetation and land use changes. In Italy Judson (1963) identified two periods of deposition in Sicily (post-eighth century BC to 325 BC and in the mediaeval period) separated by an erosional phase, whilst in southern Etruria he observed that one fill phase began no earlier than late-Roman times and continued into the mediaeval period. These results from Etruria have recently been supported by Potter (1976). As far as archaeological studies are concerned, the prime need is to determine the magnitude and chronology of such erosion. As already stated, the soil map for Greece (Fig. 11.2) indicates the magnitude and spatial variability of erosion; the extent of erosion is even more dramatic when soils are mapped at the local scale (Davidson and Tasker, in press). The more difficult and controversial issue is the explanation of erosion and sedimentation. As already indicated, there seems to be some evidence that landscape change was underway in Melos and Santorini during the 1st and 2nd millennia BC, a consequence possibly of man's activities. Support for this view can be obtained from other palaeoenvironmental evidence.

Greig and Turner (1974) have investigated the old lake of Philippi in the northeast of Greece (Fig. 11.1). Their pollen spectrum covers the Neolithic and part of the Early Bronze Age. They suggest that during the period *ca*. 6500–2500 BC the local area was a mixed oak forest with oak on heavier soils, elm and lime on damper land, and some hazel and ash in more open glades. The pollen record for the remainder of the Bronze Age at this site shows an increase in maquis vegetation, indicating the spread of grazing. Clear evidence for vegetation change caused by human activity was found for the period 1900–1360 BC. Oak forest was still dominant but there was a distinct rise of olive pollen, indicating cultivation. In the following period (1360–1000 BC) there was a drop in olive pollen, which again increased during 1000–550 BC. The vegetation from 550 BC to 0 BC appears similar to the periods 2500–1900 and 1360–1000 BC. So the picture which emerges from the locality is that during the 2nd millennium BC, man was gradually exerting his influence on the forest cover, but he seems to have had little overall impact until post-Classical times. The chronology of deforestation established by Greig and Turner (1974) in this northern locality is in marked contrast to the pattern which they derived from a site at Lake Kopais in central Greece (Fig. 11.1) and from the Peloponnese (Wright, 1972).

In these localities, the palynological evidence is that the forest was probably substantially reduced by the Bronze Age. Greig and Turner (1974) suggest that the plains would have been very similar to the treeless landscape of today, with perhaps only the hills remaining well wooded. Thus the Bronze Age soils of the plains in the centre and south of Greece would have been similar to those of today, whilst in the north forest soils would still have been in existence. Such spatial differences in Greek soils during the Bronze Age can in part be explained by the evolving pattern of settlement and agriculture. The growth and spread of population during the Bronze Age came from the south. Climatic and soil differences within Greece are also relevant, but it seems that a major climatic change cannot account for the patterns of vegetational change. Wright (1968) stresses that no variation in the pollen record for this period can be attributed with any confidence to major climatic change, a conclusion also supported by Greig and Turner (1974) and Turner and Greig (1975).

Similar results have also been obtained by Jassoglou and Nobeli (1972), who worked as soil scientists on the Messenia project. By examination of profile morphology they were able to demonstrate the magnitude and spatial variability of human activity on soils. Polygenetic profiles were identified and Jassoglou and Nobeli noted the similarity between present day alfisols (relict in origin) and buried soils, which led them to suggest that pedogenetic phases during the last few thousand years were distinguished by a general constancy of climate and vegetation. The effect of erosion has been to degrade the alfisols to relict B_t or C horizons or bedrock exposed at the surface. Similar results have been obtained by Dennell and Webley (1974) for southern Bulgaria. For example, they suggest that the present day cinnomonic forest soils and the diluvial sandy soils in the Nova Zagora area were in existence in the 6th millennium BC. They also identify a secondary phase of smolnitza formation during the Early Bronze Age. This formation appears to have been associated with erosion and deposition which caused a major change in the land resource base at this time.

A recurring difficulty in any attempt to account for changes in rates of erosion and deposition is that the pattern of erosion has to be determined from the sedimentological record and there are many interrelated factors which can result in these changes. This means that there are many problems in trying to isolate the effect of hillslope erosion on alluviation. For coastal localities, Kraft (1972) specifies seven variables which might affect coastal stability, *viz.* eustatic change, tectonic change of coastal plain-sediment basin, regional climatic change, cyclic storm track shift, local change in supply of sediments, sediment compaction with time, and tectonic change of eroding area. Another general difficulty is encountered in trying to reconstruct erosional processes; it is in this area that research on present day processes in the Mediterranean basin offers some help. Unfortunately, there are few such studies and none in Greece. Work by Thornes (1976) in Spain indicates the geomorphic importance of the more extreme events, but more research is required to be able to postulate models of soil and sediment movement within drainage basins.

The inference from this summary of problems could be that the difficulties over finding sites and about interpretation are so great that little can ever be established about Greece during the 1st and 2nd millennia BC. Such a view would be unduly pessimistic. The work by Kraft and his colleagues illustrates the value of detailed geological study in reconstructing palaeogeographic conditions. Indeed, the need is for far more such studies so that regional patterns may be suggested on the basis of numerous local investigations. Another fruitful method of approach is for geomorphologists to increase their coopera-tion with archaeological excavations. As described, there are some palaeoenvironmental data available from pollen studies, but little is known about the genesis of Greek soils. In Italy, for example, Heilmann (1972) has investigated the formation of red soils in the lower Crati basin. He identified three phases of soil development primarily on the basis of micromorphological evidence and he relates the most recent phase to deforestation and resultant erosion in historical times. An allied avenue for further research is to determine the magnitude of erosion through its effect on surface sherd distribution following the approach of Rick (1976).

In terms of models from other timescales being appropriate to this study of geomorphic change over 2000 years, detailed investigations for a 100-year period seem the most useful. In particular, the models of arroyo formation developed by Cooke and Reeves (1976, p. 188) have clear applications to any geomorphic interpretation of Greek landscape development in the 1st and 2nd millennia BC. The large number of significant relationships between variables and resultant arroyo formation demonstrates the weak-ness of any argument which only stresses one factor in causing erosion.

In summary, this paper has tried to demonstrate that the onset of aggradation was not a synchronous event in post-Classical times. Instead, there is evidence from Melos, Santorini, and the pollen and pedological records, as well as from the geological work of Kraft (personal communication), that at certain sites erosion was underway during the Bronze Age, a trend which continued in the following periods. Although support has been given to the view of the anthropogenic factor in inducing erosion during the 1st and 2nd millennia BC, the lesson of the arroyo models is clear—the need for a multiple working hypothesis is essential. At present the evidence is fragmentary and only when more extensive and detailed palaeoenvironmental data are available can explanatory models of geomorphic change be offered for Greece in the 1st and 2nd millennia BC.

Acknowledgements

I am very grateful to Karl Butzer and to Claudio Vita-Finzi for comments on a draft of this paper.

References

Allchin, B., Goudie, A., and Hegde, K. (1978). *The Prehistory and Palaeogeography of the Great Indian Desert*. Academic Press, London.
Bintliff, J. L. (1976). The plain of western Macedonia and the Neolithic site of Nea Nikomedeia. *Proc. Prehist. Soc.*, **42**, 241–62.

Bintliff, J. L. (1977). Natural environment and human settlement in prehistoric Greece (2 volumes). *British Archaeological Report Supplementary Series*, 28.

Butzer, K. W. (1974). Accelerated soil erosion: a problem of man–land relationships, in *Perspectives on Environment* (Eds. I. R. Manners and M. W. Mikesell). Association of American Geographers, Washington, D.C., pp. 57–77.

Cooke, R. U., and Reeves, R. W. (1976). *Arroyos and Environmental Change in the American South-West.* Clarendon Press, Oxford.

Davidson, D. A. (1971). Geomorphology and prehistoric settlement of the plain of Drama. *Rev. Geomorph. Dyn.*, **20**, 22–26.

Davidson, D. A. (1976) Processes of tell formation and erosion, in *Geoarchaeology* (Eds. D. A. Davidson and M. L. Shackley). Duckworths, London, pp. 255–265.

Davidson, D. A. (1978). Soils on Santorini at *ca.* 1500 BC, *Nature, Lond.*, **272**, 243–244.

Davidson, D. A., Renfrew, A. C., and Tasker, C. M. K. (1976). Erosion and prehistory in Melos: a preliminary note. *J. Arch. Sci.*, **3**, 219–227.

Davidson, D. A., and Tasker, C. M. K. (in press). The geomorphic evolution of Melos during the late Holocene, in *An Island Policy* (Eds. A. C. Renfrew and M. Wagstaff). Cambridge University Press, Cambridge.

Dennell, R. W., and Webley, D. (1974). Prehistoric settlement and land use in southern Bulgaria, in *Palaeoeconomy* (Ed. E. S. Higgs). Cambridge University Press, Cambridge, pp. 97–109.

Greig, J. R. H., and Turner, J. (1974) Some pollen diagrams from Greece and their archaeological significance. *J. Arch. Sci.*, **1**, 177–194.

Harvey, A. M. (1978) Dissected alluvial fans in southeast Spain. *Catena*, **5**, 177–211.

Heilman, P. G. F. (1972). *On the Formation of Red Soils in the Lower Crati Basin (S. Italy).* International Institute for Aerial Survey and Earth Sciences, Enschede.

Jassoglou, N. J., and Nobeli, C. (1972). Soil studies, in *The Minnesota Messenia Expedition: Reconstructing a Bronze Age Regional Environment* (Eds. W. A. McDonald and G. R. Rapp). University of Minnesota Press, Minneapolis, pp. 171–176.

Judson, S. (1963) Erosion and deposition of Italian stream valleys during historic time. *Science*, **140**, 898–899.

Kraft, J. C. (1972) A reconnaissance of the geology of the sandy coastal areas of eastern Greece and the Peloponnese, *Technical Report No. 9, College of Marine Studies.* University of Delaware, Newark.

Kraft, J. C., and Aschenbrenner, S. E. (1977). Palaeogeographic reconstructions in the Methoni embayment in Greece. *J. Field Arch.*, **4**, 19–44.

Kraft, J. C., Rapp, G., and Aschenbrenner, S. E. (1975). Late Holocene palaeogeography of the coastal plain of the Gulf of Messenia, Greece, and its relationships to archaeological settings and coastal change. *Geol. Soc. Am. Bull.*, **86**, 1191–1208.

Luce, J. V. (1969). *The End of Atlantis.* Thames and Hudson, London.

Luce, J. V. (1976). Thera and the devastation of Minoan Crete: a new interpretation of the evidence. *Am. J. Arch.*, **80**, 9–16.

Pichler, H., and Friedrich, W. (1976). Radiocarbon dates of Santorini volcanics. *Nature, Lond.*, **262**, 373–374.

Potter, T. W. (1976) Valleys and settlements: some new evidence. *World Arch.*, **8**, 207–219.

Rick, J. W. (1976). Downslope movement and archaeological intrasite spatial analysis. *Am. Antiq.*, **41**, 133–144.

Russell, R. J. (1954). Alluvial morphology of Anatolean rivers. *Assoc. Am. Geog. Annals.*, **44**, 363–391.

Thornes, J. B. (1976). Semi-arid erosional systems. *L.S.E. Geog. Pap.*, **7**.

Turner, J., and Greig, J. R. A. (1975). Some Holocene pollen diagrams from Greece. *Rev. Palaeobot. Palynol.*, **20**, 171–204.

Van Zuidam, R. A. (1975). Geomorphology and archaeology: evidences of interrelation at historical sites in the Zaragoza region, Spain. *Z. Geomorph., N. F.*, **19**, 319–328.

Vita-Finzi, C. (1969). *The Mediterranean Valleys.* Cambridge University Press, Cambridge.

Vita-Finzi, C. (1973). *Recent Earth History.* Macmillan, London.

Vita-Finzi, C. (1976). Diachronism in Old World alluvial sequences. *Nature, Lond.*, **263**, 218–219.

Warren, P. (1975) *The Aegean Civilizations.* Elsevier, Amsterdam.

Wright, H. E. (1968) Climatic change in Mycenaen Greece. *Antiquity*, **42**, 123–127.

Wright, H. E. (1972) Vegetation history, in *The Minnesota Messenia Expedition: Reconstructing a Bronze Age Regional Environment* (Eds. W. A. McDonald and G. R. Rapp). University of Minnesota Press, Minneapolis, pp. 188–199.

Timescales in Geomorphology
Edited by R. A. Cullingford, D. A. Davidson, and J. Lewin

CHAPTER 12

Channel changes in a lowland river catchment over the last 13,000 years

J. Rose

Department of Geography,
Birkbeck College, University of London

C. Turner

Department of Earth Sciences, Open University, and Sub-Department of Quaternary Research,
Cambridge University

G. R. Coope

Department of Geological Sciences,
Birmingham University

and M. D. Bryan

Birmingham City Museum

Introduction

This paper describes the form and development of the channel of the River Gipping in Suffolk, England, over the past 13,000 years. During this period the channel of this lowland river has changed from a relatively stable condition in the early and middle parts of the Windermere Interstadial (Coope and Pennington, 1977) to an unstable condition in the later part of this interstadial and the whole of Younger Dryas time. It has remained stable throughout most of the Flandrian. During the period of channel stability, bed-load transport was limited and the river was confined between walls of cohesive bed material. In contrast, during the period of instability bed-load transport was dominant and the channel pattern ranged from deep, large-scale discontinuous gullies to meanders, and then to braids. The channel instability is attributed to a period of high, short-lived discharges caused by seasonal snow-melt, and the changes from erosion to deposition and meandering to braiding are related to the relative magnitudes of the peak discharges and the available sediment supplied to the channel from the adjacent hillside slopes. It is suggested that these changes clearly demonstrate the importance of short-lived, climatically induced changes of energy input into a given fluvial system.

The study is based on the analysis of sediments and landforms from a gravel pit

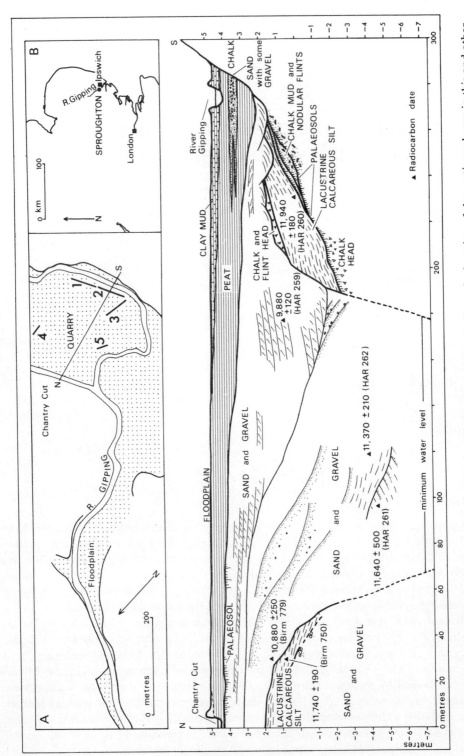

Fig. 12.1   Schematic representation of the stratigraphy at Sproughton. Inset A shows the location of the sections shown in this and other figures. Inset B shows the location of Sproughton and the Gipping Valley. Radiocarbon dates are in years bp

beneath the floodplain of the River Gipping at Sproughton (TM 133443) near Ipswich, Suffolk (Fig. 12.1). The study of the landforms and sediments is complemented by widely based palaeo-environmental interpretations derived from the analysis of associated fossils of macroscopic plant remains, coleoptera, and terrestrial and freshwater mollusca. The timescales attributed to the events are derived from a series of radiocarbon dates (Otlet and Slade, 1974) determined on unabraded terrestrial wood fragments, and from the related biostratigraphy.

The results from this study are the first known from a lowland catchment in the British Isles which is not directly influenced by changes of base level. However, similar evidence is known from catchments with a high relief (relief ratio >40 m km^{-1}; Strahler, 1957) (Kerney *et al.*, 1964; Evans, 1966; Peake, 1971; Rowlands and Shotton, 1971; Osborne, 1972), and from catchments where rivers have developed across estuarine or lacustrine sediments newly exposed by a relative fall of water level (Sissons *et al.*, 1965; Sissons, 1969; Gaunt *et al.*, 1971). The importance of the low relief situation is discussed, along with the relationship with similar studies from other parts of northern Europe (Kozarski and Rotnicki, 1977; Starkel, 1977).

Site Location and Geomorphic Province

At present the River Gipping is a 4th order stream (Strahler, 1957), with catchment area of 330 km^2 and a drainage density of 0.61 km km^{-2}. The catchment has a relief ratio of 3 m km^{-1}, and the 4th order segment, which is 25.5 km long, has a gradient of 1.0 m km^{-1}. Rock types in the area consist of chalky clay-till (Perrin *et al.*, 1973) which covers most of the interfluvial regions, and Pleistocene sands and gravels, Tertiary sands and clays, and Cretaceous chalk on the valley sides and valley bottom (Boswell, 1927; Rose and Allen, 1977). The site is located 2 km upstream from the present tidal limit of the River Orwell at Ipswich, and the surface elevation of the floodplain in the area is about 5 m O.D.

The sediments fill the upper part of the Gipping buried channel (Rose *et al.*, 1978) which originated as a sub-glacial tunnel-valley during the Anglian Glaciation (Woodland, 1970). At Sproughton, as along most of the Gipping Valley, this buried channel is cut in chalk and is infilled with a variety of unconsolidated sediments of Middle and Late Pleistocene age. The site is located well beyond the limit of Devensian glacierization and, in the time period concerned, is located beyond the influence of sea-level change (Emery, 1969; Devoy, 1977).

In addition to the evidence for river activity and palaeoenvironmental reconstructions, the site at Sproughton has also yielded archaeological evidence in the form of barbed points of late Zone III–early Zone IV age (Wymer *et al.*, 1975) and an Upper Palaeolithic long blade industry of Zone IV age (Wymer, 1976).

Stratigraphy

In common with many river valley sites where sediments have been channelled, the stratigraphy at Sproughton is far from simple. Fortunately, the commercial exploitation of sand and gravel has meant that the deposits have been well exposed and all the relationships described in this study have been observed rather than inferred. The general stratigraphic relationships are illustrated in Fig. 12.1, and the stratigraphic sequence is listed in Table 12.1. Details of the stratigraphy are illustrated in Figs. 12.2, 12.3, and 12.5.

Table 12.1 Late Devensian and Flandrian stratigraphy at Sproughton

Deposits and landforms	Geomorphic process	Inferred environment	Inferred age
Present floodplain Clay mud	Overbank sedimentation	Temperate climate with anthropogenic deforestation and ploughing	Present
Peat with lenses of sand and gravel Palaeosol on bars	Backswamp fen behind levées Soil formation	Temperate climate with extensive forest cover	9500 bp
Sand and gravel Small-scale cross sets with interdigitating chalk and flint head ground-ice Large-scale cross sets	Braided river sedimen- tation and contempor- aneous hillslope gelifluction Meandering river sedimentation	Arctic climate with seasonal development and possibly permafrost	11,000 bp
Channel of discontinuous gully	River incision	Arctic climate with extensive winter snow cover	11,300 bp
Laminated calcareous silt	Shallow, eutrophic lake development	Deteriorating climate	
Palaeosols on chalk mud and chalk head Chalk mud and nodular flints	Soil formation and slope stability Mudflow development	Cool temperate climate with grasses and shrub vegetation	12,200 bp
Chalk head	Hillslope gelifluction	Periglacial climate	

River Channel Changes

Valley-side Slope Development

Slope deposits form the base of the succession and provide a source of information about valley-side developments. The basal deposit consists of a chalk head composed of angular chalk clasts in a comminuted chalk matrix. The deposit is devoid of organic remains, and is considered to represent cold-climate gelifluction from the adjacent hillside during a later part of the Devensian glaciation.

The head is partially buried by a series of wedges of fine chalk mud containing fresh, unabraded nodular flints (Fig. 12.2). Each wedge of sediment is weathered at the top and retains a variably developed palaeosol characterized by a thin (<5 cm) eluvial horizon, *in situ* rootlets and a thin layer of felted vegetation. The surface of the deposits slopes towards the valley axis and the body of sediment is considered to represent the toes of a series of mudflows. This interpretation is supported by a rich fauna of terrestrial coleoptera and mollusca. Forty-one taxa of coleoptera were obtained from the chalk mud, but no insect fossils were recovered from the palaeosol horizons probably because they have been destroyed by fungus during the period of weathering. The coleoptera represent a rather nondescript assemblage of species that would today be found in damp

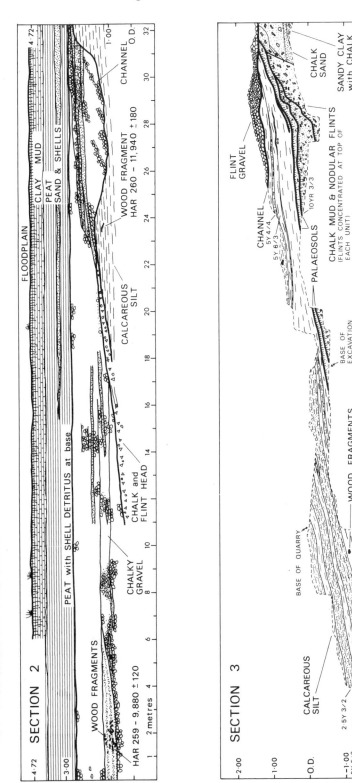

Fig. 12.2 Stratigraphy and sediments at Sections 2 and 3. These drawings show the relationship of the sands and gravels to the calcareous silt, chalk mud, and head. Radiocarbon dates are in years bp.

situations with *Carex* and *Salix* and on relatively open ground away from the valley bottom. Although this is the lowest fossiliferous deposit overlying the head, there is no evidence from the coleoptera to suggest that the mudflows were formed in an arctic climate. At their time of formation summer temperatures must have been only slightly cooler than those of the present day, and it is probable that their origin is related to a scant vegetation cover on the hillside slopes. On the basis of relating the coleoptera assemblage to radiometrically dated assemblages from other localities, it is most likely that they were formed shortly after the thermal maximum of the Windermere Intersta-dial about 12,200 years bp (Coope, 1977).

Valley-bottom Lake Development and Associated River Channel Activity

A very dark greyish brown (2.5Y3/2) and olive grey (5Y5/2) laminated calcareous silt is draped over the palaeosol and is extensive at both sides of the valley. It reaches a maximum observed thickness of 1.8 m and is composed predominantly of *Chara* oospores, except in the lowest part which is composed of small chalk clasts and felted organic detritus. The occurrence of *Chara* oospores, and the impressions of *Chara* stems and leaves, fragments of *Potamogeton* and *Hippuris*, aquatic insects, and a mollusc assemblage dominated by *Bithynia tentaculata* (Linn.), all indicate that this deposit accumulated in a shallow, moderate sized, eutrophic lake. The remains of *Juncus*, bulrush (*Schoenoplectus lacustris*), and beaked sedge (*Carex rostrara*) indicate that the margins of the lake were fringed with reedswamp. The fragments of *Salix* spp., dwarf birch (*Betula nana*), and dwarf toadflax (*Chaenorhinum minus*) from the lower part of the deposit, and the fruits of tree birch from the upper part of the deposit, reveal the nature of the adjacent terrestrial vegetation.

The recovery of the insect fossils from the lacustrine sediments was complicated by the enormous profusion of *Chara* oospores, which not only diluted the fauna but made extraction of the fossils very difficult. Thus, the faunal assemblages give a false appearance of being richest at the base and top. The profusion of Dytiscidae and Hydrophilidae reinforce the interpretation of a eutrophic and rather shallow pond rather than a large lake, and the phytophagous species of beetle suggest a rich marsh vegetation surrounding the pool. Some 131 named species of coleoptera were obtained from these sediments, which included, at the base, a number of relatively thermophilous species (*Panageus bipustulatus*, *Lebia crux-minor*, *Agrilus angustatus*, and *Malachius viridis*), but also included a number of north British species (*Patrobus assimilis*, *Otiorrhynchus nodosus*, and *Notaris aethiops*). On balance, the fauna at the base of the lacustrine sequence suggests average July temperatures of about 15 °C or even slightly higher. The upper part of the succession yielded no thermophilous species, but included a number of more northern species (*Agonum consimile*, *Deronectes griseostriatus*, *Gyrinus opacus*, *Pycnoglypta lurida*, and a large number of individuals of *Arpedium brachypterum*). A notable species from this horizon was the eastern palaeoarctic and North American species *Helophorous oblongus*, suggesting that towards the end of lacustrine sedimenta-tion the climate may have become rather more continental. On the whole, the insect faunas from the upper part of these lacustrine sediments indicate a considerable climatic deterioration with average July temperatures of about 12–13 °C.

Radiocarbon dates of 11,940±180 bp (HAR 260) and 11,740±190 bp (Birm. 750) were obtained, respectively, from a single willow branch and a fresh stick from near the base of the calcareous silts. These dates, together with the climatic reconstruction derived from the insect fauna and the occurrence of tree birch, suggest that lacustrine sedimentation at Sproughton took place in the later part of the Windermere Interstadial and including the period of time known traditionally as Pollen Zone II.

Although the lake deposits do not provide any direct evidence of river activity, certain inferences can be made about the character and behaviour of the River Gipping from their location in the valley bottom, their thickness, and their lithologic composition. The permeable nature of the bed material at this locality, and in the valley in general, means that the lake must have been supported by a high regional water-table rather than by a local dam such as could have been created by the valley-side mudflows. A backswamp position behind levées on a river floodplain is the most probable location for such a lake, and is not inconsistent with the palaeoenvironmental evidence. The relatively low inorganic content of the lacustrine sediments in all but the basal part of the calcareous silt indicates a dearth of particulate matter in the sediment load of the river. This, in turn, implies that there was little channel erosion at this time.

Taken together, these characteristics describe an extensively submerged floodplain crossed by a relatively stable, but gradually aggrading, river channel. At Sproughton, this environment was maintained for about 500 years.

River Channel Incision and Discontinuous Gully Development

The lake sediments and the deposits underlying them are channelled to a depth of at least 9 m, which is down to at least −7 m O.D. This channel forms a pattern that can be traced in the present day valley bottom, because it controls the extent of Flandrian alluvial sedimentation and is thus defined, in plan, by the distribution of Flandrian alluvium. A study of the channel pattern reveals a series of broad sections and narrow sections which recur at roughly 1.8 km (±0.73 km) intervals. The gravel pit at Sproughton is located in a broad basin. An old, and relatively unsuccessful, gravel pit further downstream at Sproughton was located in a narrow channel. Both in plan form and in such cross-sections as exist, this channel takes the form of a discontinuous gully system (Leopold *et al.*, 1964). Discontinuous gullies are considered to be ephemeral, low gradient features which develop in cohesive bed material as a response to increased fluvial efficiency. In the Gipping they would develop in response to increased peak discharges without a proportionate increase in sediment supply. They would be most efficient forms for transporting sediment through a low relief system. Their large size reflects the large discharges in the same way as there is a direct relationship between meander wave length and discharge (Leopold *et al.*, 1964).

Similar macroscale discontinuous gullies have been recognized in other drainage basins in eastern England, but the reason for their development, as opposed to large-scale meanders which have been well documented in midland England and elsewhere (Dury, 1953a, 1953b, 1964) is difficult to determine. It is possible that it reflects the original very low gradient of the river, or the confined nature of the buried channel which contains material more erodible than the valley sides.

It is possible to determine the period over which this channel erosion took place and the discontinuous gullies were developed. The lake silts continued to form until well after 11,700 bp and maybe as late as 11,300 bp (see pp. 169–170). According to the coleoptera assemblage derived from the lowest part of the sands and gravels, the basal sediments in the channel were deposited about 11,000 bp (see p. 170). Erosion therefore occurred over a period of less than 700 years, and possibly as little as 300 years, during an interval of time in which the climate was progressively deteriorating (Coope, 1977).

Sand and Gravel Sedimentation and Associated River Channel Development

The discontinuous gullies are infilled with sands and gravels. At Sproughton the basin

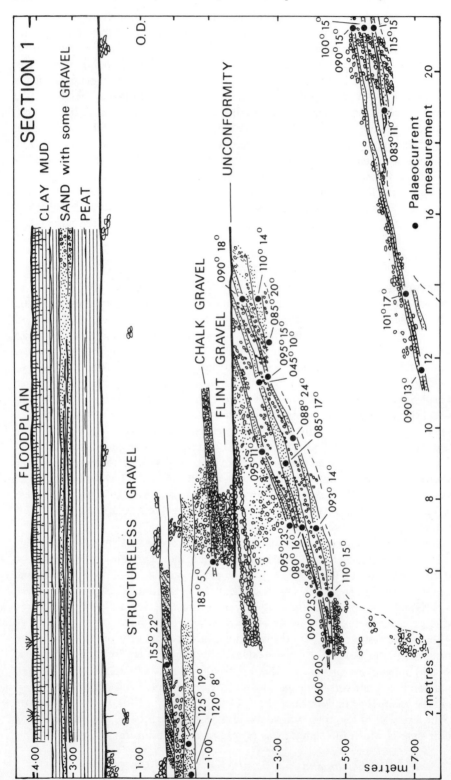

Fig. 12.3 Sand and gravel structures and stratigraphy at Section 1

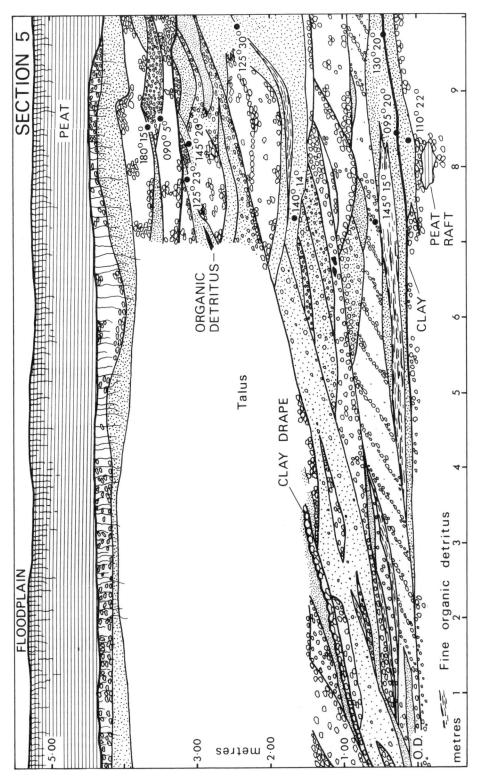

Fig. 12.4 Sand and gravel structures and stratigraphy at Section 5

section is infilled by a body of sediment up to 400 m wide and more than 11.9 m thick. However, these sands and gravels form two parts separated by an unconformity: a lower unit of large-scale cross-sets, that was deposited by a meandering river, and an upper unit of small-scale cross-sets, that was deposited by a braided river (Figs. 12.3 and 12.4).

Meandering channel sedimentation. Analysis of the lower, large-scale cross-sets indicates that they are composed of a series of fining-upwards units with an amplitude of up to 3 m. Particle size analysis indicates that the coarsest part of each set is characterized by well defined traction and saltation modes (Visher, 1969), while the finer part is dominated by the saltation mode alone (Fig. 12.5a). Occasional large clasts of peat (up to 0.6 m) are involved in some of these structures and the upper parts of many sets contain a high proportion of organic detritus including twigs, leaves, and fruit. The cross-sets show a wide range of dip directions (Fig. 12.5b) with a mode towards the east-south-east, and at particular localities there may be up to 180° variation separated

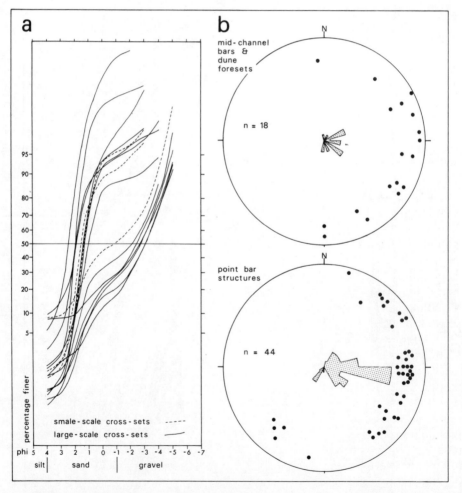

Fig. 12.5 Some sedimentary properties of the sands and gravels. (a) Particle size distribution of the sands and gravels. (b) Palaeocurrent measurements on the sands and gravels

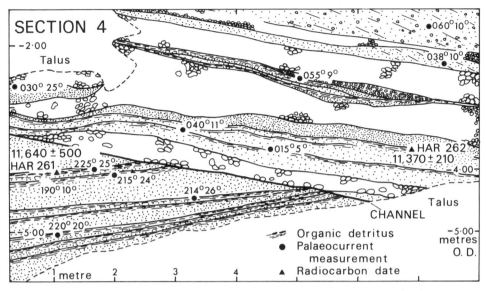

Fig. 12.6 Sand and gravel structures at Section 4. This shows the reversed point-bar structures separated by a meander channel. Radiocarbon dates are in years bp

by an erosional channel (Fig. 12.6). These properties suggest that sedimentation was accomplished as point bar bedforms in a meandering river with a water depth of up to 3 m. Palaeocurrent indicators suggest that the predominant direction of flow was towards the east-south-east, although the sinuous nature of the river is demonstrated by channels and cross-set infills with reversed directions.

Braided channel sedimentation. The small-scale cross-sets occur in the uppermost 0.8–3.9 m of the sand and gravel body. In places at the south side of the valley these units fill small, shallow channels (8.0 × 1.0 m) (Fig. 12.2). Individual sets have been measured with a maximum amplitude of 0.25 m and consist of low-angle (5°) gravel cross-sets, and steeper angle (10–25°) tabular sets in both sands and gravels. Particle size analysis (Fig. 12.5a) indicates both traction and saltation modes and the palaeocurrent indicators suggest a predominantly eastwards direction of flow (Fig. 12.5b). At some valley-side locations up to 13% of the clasts in the 16–32 mm size range are composed of chalk, whereas this material is absent from the rest of the deposit. The sets also include fragments of organic detritus. These properties suggest that this body of sand and gravel was deposited by a braided river in the form of low-angle mid-channel bars, with sub-aquatic dunes developed on the beds of the intervening channels. The amplitude of the dune foresets suggests that the river in the channel may have been up to 1.5 m deep, but of course would have been much shallower over the bars. The incorporation of non-durable chalk clasts reflects local erosion and limited transport, and appears to be related to limited erosion and channelling of the valley-side. The absence of reversed flow directions tends to confirm the braided mode of sedimentation (Smith, 1972; Bluck, 1974).

Some estimate of the time required for the deposition of the sands and gravels can be obtained from the radiocarbon dates and from the biostratigraphy of the enclosed peat lenses. Inevitably, both sources of information are subject to problems arising from the possible derivation of the organic material from the upsteam erosion of the underlying lacustrine sediments. However, the size of this error can be estimated from the type of material used to determine the radiocarbon dates and by comparison between the radiocarbon dates and the age inferred from the coleopteran assemblage. With regard to the radiocarbon ages, all of the materials used were fresh and unabraded and so had suffered only limited fluvial transport, and all of the material was derived from terrestrial plants so that there could be no source of error due to hard water contamination (Shotton, 1972). With regard to the insect fauna, secondary derivation is very unlikely as exposure during transport creates a situation in which the insect fragments are rapidly destroyed by weathering processes.

The positions of the materials used for radiocarbon dating are indicated in Figs. 12.1, 12.2, and 12.6. The insect faunas are dominantly arctic/alpine in character (including *Amara alpina, Helophorus glacialis, Olophrum boreale*, and *Hippodamia arctica*), and suggest that all of the exposed gravels were deposited during Younger Dryas time. Hence, there is a discrepancy between the two radiocarbon dates from the base of the gravels and the associated insect fauna, suggesting in fact, that the twigs have been washed from the adjacent lacustrine silt. It would appear, therefore, that the entire body of sand and gravel was deposited during the thousand years of the Younger Dryas Stadial and the first few centuries of the Flandrian Interglacial.

Flandrian River Channel and Floodplain Development

The sand and gravel deposits are invariably buried by peat and gyttja which form the floodplain of the present day River Gipping. The thickness of these deposits varies from about 0.8 m where the surface of the sands and gravels forms a bar to 2.4 m where it forms a channel. The deposits are mainly confined within the upper parts of the discontinuous gullies, and have a surface form that shows little relief except where modified by man. These deposits represent the growth of a body of topogenous peat and the accumulation of fine-grained organic and inorganic detritus. As such, they represent the effects of backswamp sedimentation in a frequently submerged floodplain in an environment with a high input of fine organic and inorganic detritus.

Occasional lenses of sand and gravel occur in the parts of this floodplain deposit which are below, and adjacent to, the present channel, and indicate spasmodic transport of bedload along the river channel and on to the adjacent floodplain. The present channel of the Gipping is confined between artificial levées, and in many places, such as the Chantry Cut at Sproughton, it has been canalized. However, the location of the present natural channel above the thickest part of the peat and gyttja, and above the part which contains the sand and gravel lenses, suggests that at Sproughton, at least, changes of channel position have been rare in the past 9500 years, and that the present channel still follows the main course of the braided river which deposited the final part of the main sand and gravel body.

Backswamp sedimentation and channel development of this type are typical of river activity in a well vegetated, low-relief environment with high infiltration, small discharge variation, and limited bedload transport (Knox, 1972). Such conditions were characteristic of lowland Britain during the early temperate zone of the Flandrian with the development of forest cover and deep soils. Because of the uneven base to these backswamp deposits they must inevitably be diachronous in their lower part, and this is demonstrated by the soil development beneath the peat or gyttja on the higher parts of the sand and gravel surface. It was on one of these bars that the artifacts of the Upper Palaeolithic long blade industry were discovered (Wymer, 1976), although their position beneath the soil indicates that the human activity preceded soil development. The pollen assemblages from the base of the peat suggest that the higher parts of the sands and gravels were submerged in Atlantic times (Wymer, 1976).

Therefore, in the Gipping Valley, Flandrian river development is characterized by a relatively stable channel, a gradual build-up of bed and sides with fine organic and inorganic detritus, and a progressive extension of the floodplain area. It would appear that by Atlantic times the area subject to periodic submergence by river flooding was similar to that at the present day.

Causes of River Channel Changes

The changes in the activity of the River Gipping and the associated development of its channel are paralleled by changes in the regional climate and vegetation development.

The period of valley-bottom submergence between about 12,200 and possibly 11,300 years bp is characterized by a temperate but cooling climate. The absence of particulate matter from the sediment transport system is characteristic of this period of time and there is much evidence for fine-grained calcareous sedimentation in enclosed basins elsewhere in the British Isles (Mitchell, 1965; Pennington and Bonny, 1970; Jones, 1977). These deposits appear to reflect the effects of rainwash or rillwater processes on a landscape that is relatively undisturbed by cryogenic activity, and relatively protected by a cover of grasses, herbs, and shrubs (Wilkinson and Bunting, 1975). The limited period of time available for soil development since the last stages of periglacial ground disturbance means that the surface deposits are base rich, and this accounts for the high carbonate content of the runoff and the associated base-loving vegetation. At Sproughton the stable channel reflects the cohesive nature of the bed material and the regional sedimentation reflects the excess supply of fine-grained sediment into the drainage system. There is no reason to believe that sedimentation was related to a rise of sea-level as the eustatic level at this time was about -75 to -70 m O.D. (Emery, 1969).

The erosion of the discontinuous gullies between 11,300 and 11,000 years bp is by far the most dramatic event in the development of the Gipping river channel during the past 13,000 years. Their formation took place during a further deterioration of climate, and was accomplished by a river with a very high discharge. Their formation is therefore attributed to erosion during peak discharges caused by the spring and early summer melt of winter snow and seasonally frozen ground, accompanied by restricted infiltration and high surface runoff (Kerney *et al.*, 1964; McCann and Cogley, 1972; McCann *et al.*, 1972). There is no reason to invoke either high annual discharges, which are not in accord with the faunal evidence for increased continentality, or variations in sea-level which was rising in the time period concerned (Emergy, 1969).

The change from erosion to sedimentation is associated with the sudden deterioration of climate, and the main body of sediment was deposited during the Younger Dryas Stadial for which there is evidence of permafrost in Britain (e.g. Kerney, 1963; Rose, 1975; Watson, 1977; Coope, 1977). At Sproughton the effects of this climatic deterioration on slope stability can be seen in the development of the upper chalk and flint head (Figs. 12.1 and 12.2). In addition, the decrease in the size of river bedforms from discontinuous gully, to point bar, to mid-channel bar and dune indicates a progressive decrease in discharge and steepening of channel gradient (Leopold *et al.*, 1964). Discharge and gradient are probably mutually interdependent and associated with increased continentality and a consequent reduced snow-melt runoff.

The change from erosion to sedimentation is therefore attributed to a reduction in the magnitude of the peak discharge, and to an increased supply of sediment geliflucted into the channel from the adjacent hillside slopes. The change in the balance between the magnitude of the peak discharge and the quantity of the sediment supplied to the channel can be explained by the fact that runoff would show an instantaneous response to climatic change, whereas slope instability, which is a function of soil moisture conditions, weathering processes, and vegetation, would show a delayed response to the time required to break up and loosen the surface materials. In effect, the discontinuous gullies are a response to load deficiency, and represent an adaptation of the channel form and gradient to the excess river energy. As such, they are a most efficient shape for transporting channel-derived sediment through the river system. In contrast, the sand and gravel sedimentation is a response to excess load, and the progressive changes of channel pattern, bedform, and gradient represent an adjustment to this condition.

During the spring and early summer thaw the area needed to maintain channel runoff (constant of channel maintenance; Leopold *et al.*, 1964) would diminish considerably. The result is that during these conditions it is most probable that each of the dry channels which today characterize the headwaters and valley-side regions of the Gipping catchment carried a stream and were subjected to erosion. There are 663 dry valleys in the catchment and, if they were in use, it of interest to note that the Gipping would achieve the status of a 5th order stream with a drainage density of 1.75 km km^{-2}.

The stable channel and the low rate of flood-plain sedimentation that characterize the development of the Gipping during the Flandrian reflect the depressed state of geomorphic activity in a fluvial environment that is dominated by an extensive vegetation cover and high infiltration rates. The result is that the channel is confined between cohesive banks of fine organic and inorganic detritus, and the position of the channel and the extent of the floodplain are largely determined by antecedent landforms of Late-glacial age.

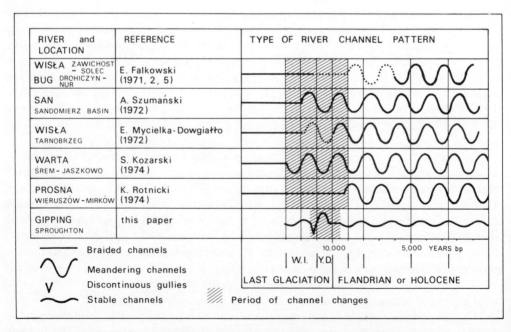

Fig. 12.7 Summary of river channel patterns and channel changes at Sproughton, and on lowland rivers on the Polish plain. Based on Kozarski and Rotnicki (1977)

Comparison with Other Sites in Britain and Northern Europe

The evidence from Sproughton in the lowland catchment of the River Gipping can be compared with other sites that have been investigated from the North Downs (Kerney *et al.*, 1964; Peake, 1971), the Chilterns (Evans, 1966), the Longmynd (Rowlands and Shotton, 1971; Osborne, 1972) and the Isle of Man (Mitchell, 1965), where evidence exists for effective snow-melt erosion during Young Dryas time. However, in each of these cases the catchment relief is much greater and erosion is restricted to the steep headward section, while deposition takes the form of fan accumulation on the less steep downstream section. In the Gipping valley the erosion/sedimentation pattern is not so simple, as successive periods of both erosion and deposition are recorded at a point in a low gradient section.

It is of interest to note that similar activity to that at Sproughton has been recorded in low-relief situations on the Polish Plain (Falkowski, 1971, 1972, 1975; Szumański, 1972; Mycielska-Dowgiałło, 1972; Kozarski, 1974; Rotnicki, 1974). These patterns of changes are recorded in Fig. 12.7 together with a summary of the changes at Sproughton. Discontinuous gullies have not yet been described from the Polish valleys, and these rivers, unlike the Gipping, have maintained channel mobility throughout the Flandrian. This is because of the greater catchment size, and consequently the greater river energy.

Acknowledgements

The authors thank Brush Aggregates for permission to visit Devil's Wood Quarries at Sproughton. They also thank Mr. P. Allen and Mrs. K. Adcock for help in surveying the exposures, and Professor J. R. L. Allen and Professor E. H. Brown for reading earlier versions of the manuscript.

References

Bluck, B. J. (1974). Structure and directional properties of some valley sandur deposits in southern Iceland. *Sedimentol.*, **21**, 533–554.

Boswell, P. G. H. (1927). The geology of the country around Ipswich. *Mem. Geol. Surv. UK.*

Coope, G. R. (1977). Fossil coleopteran assemblages as sensitive indicators of climatic changes during the Devensian (Last) cold stage. *Phil. Trans. R. Soc. Lond., B*, **280**, 313–337.

Coope, G. R., and Brophy, J. A. (1972). Late Glacial environmental changes indicated by a coleopteran succession from North Wales. *Boreas*, **1**, 97–142.

Coope, G. R., and Pennington, W. (1977). The Windermere Interstadial of the Late Devensian. *Phil. Trans. R. Soc. Lond., B*, **280**, 337–339.

Devoy, R. J. N. (1977). Flandrian sea-level changes in the Thames Estuary and the implications for land subsidence in England and Wales. *Nature, Lond.*, **270**, 712–715.

Dury, G. H. (1953a). The shrinkage of the Warwickshire Itchen. *Proc. Coventry Nat. Hist. Sci. Soc.*, **2**, 208.

Dury, G. H. (1953b). The shrinkage of Midland streams. *Proc. Birm. Nat. Hist. Phil. Soc.*, **18**, 81–95.

Dury, G. H. (1964). Principles of underfit streams. *US Geol. Surv. Prof. Pap.*, No. 452A, 1–67.

Emery, K. O. (1969). The continental shelves. *Sci. Am.*, **221**, 106.

Evans, J. G. (1966). Late-Glacial and Post-Glacial sub-aerial deposits at Pitstone, Buckinghamshire. *Proc. Geol. Assoc.*, **77**, 348–364.

Falkowski, E. (1971). Historia i prognoza rozwoju układu koryta wybranych odcinków rz ek nizinnych Polski (Summary: History and prognosis for the development of bed configurations of selected sections of Polish lowland river). *Biul. Geol.*, **12**, 5–121.

Falkowski, E. (1972). Regularities in the development of lowland rivers and changes in river bottoms in Holocene. *INQUA Excursion Guide. Changes in the palaeogeography of valley floors of the Vistula drainage basin during the Holocene*, 2nd part, 2–35.

Falkowski, E. (1975). Variability of channel processes of lowland rivers in Poland and changes of the valley floors during the Holocene. *Biul. Geol.*, **19**, 45–78.

Gaunt, G. D., Jarvis, R. A., and Matthews, B. (1971). The Late Weichselian sequence in the Vale of York. *Proc. Yorks. Geol. Soc.*, **38**, 281–284.

Jones, R. L. (1977). Late Devensian deposits from Kildale, north-east Yorkshire. *Proc. Yorks. Geol. Soc.*, **41**, 185–188.

Kerney, M. P. (1963). Lateglacial deposits on the Chalk of south-east England.. *Phil. Trans. R. Soc. Lond., B*, **246**, 203–254.

Kerney, M. P., Brown, E. H., and Chandler, T. J. (1964). The Late-Glacial and Post-Glacial history of the Chalk escarpment, near Brooks, Kent. *Phil. Trans. R. Soc. Lond., B*, **248**, 135–204.

Knox, J. C. (1972). Valley alluviation in southwestern Wisconsin. *Ann. Assoc. Am. Geog.*, **62**, 401–410.

Kozarski, S. (1974). Stanowisko Jaszkowo kolo Śremu. Migracja koryta Warty na poludnie od Poznania w późnym glacjale i holocenie—generacje meandrów (Summary: Site Jaszkowo near Śrem. Migrations of the Warta channel to the south of Poznań during Late-Glacial and Holocene—generations of meanders). *Krajowe Sympozjum, Wroclaw—Poznan, 1974*, 46–49.

Kozarski, S., and Rotnicki, K. (1977). Valley floors and changes of river channel patterns in the north Polish Plain during the Late-Wurm and Holocene. *Quaes. Geog.*, **4**, 51–93.

Leopold, L. B., Wolman, G. M., and Miller, J. P. (1964). *Fluvial Processes in Geomorphology*. Freeman, London.

McCann, S. B., and Cogley, J. G. (1972). Hydrological observations on a small arctic catchment, Devon Island. *Can. J. Earth Sci.*, **9**, 361–65.

McCann, S. B., Howarth, P. J., and Cogley, J. G. (1972). Fluvial processes in a periglacial environment: Queen Elizabeth Islands, N.W.T., Canada. *Trans. Inst. Br. Geog.*, **55**, 69–81.

Mitchell, F. G. (1965). The Quaternary deposits of Ballaugh and Kirkmichael districts, Isle of Man. *Q. J. Geol. Soc. Lond.*, **121**, 359–381.

Mycielska-Dowgiałło, E. (1972). Stages of Holocene evolution of the Vistula valley on the background of its older history in the light of investigations carried out near Tarnbrzeg. *INQUA Excursion Guide. Changes in the palaeogeography of valley floors on the Vistula drainage basin during the Holocene*, 2nd part, 69–82.

Osborne, P. J. (1972). Insect faunas of Late Devensian and Flandrian age from Church Stretton, Shropshire. *Phil. Trans. R. Soc. Lond., B*, **263**, 327–367.

Otlet, R. L., and Slade, B. S. (1974). Harwell Radiocarbon Measurements, I. *Radiocarbon*, **16**, 178–191.

Peake, D. S. (1971). The age of the Wandle Gravels in the vicinity of Croydon. With an Appendix by P. J. Osborne. *Proc. Croydon Nat. Hist. Sci. Soc.*, **14**, 145–175.

Pennington, W., and Bonny, A. P. (1970). Absolute pollen diagram from the British Lateglacial. *Nature, Lond.*, **226**, 871–873.

Perrin, R. M. S., Davies, H., and Fysh, M. D. (1973). Lithology of the Chalky Boulder Clay. *Nature Phys. Sci.*, **245**, 101–104.

Rose, J. (1975). Raised beach gravels and ice wedge casts at Old Kilpatrick, near Glasgow. *Scott. J. Geol.*, **11**, 15–21.

Rose, J., and Allen, P. (1977). Middle Pleistocene stratigraphy in south-east Suffolk. *J. Geol. Soc.*, **133**, 83–102.

Rose, J., Allen, P., and Wymer, J. J. (1978). Weekend field meeting in south-east Suffolk. *Proc. Geol. Assoc.*, **89**, 81–90.

Rotnicki, K. (1974). Stanowisko Mirków koło Wieruszowa nad Prosna. Stratigrafia osadów holoceńskich i glowne tendencje procesów fluwialnych w dolinie Prosny podczas holocenu (Summary: Site Mirków near Wieruszów on the Prosna. Stratigraphy of Holocene deposits and main tendencies of fluvial processes in the Prosna valley during the Holocene). *Krajowe Sympozjum, Wroclaw–Poznan, 1974*, 49–55.

Rowlands, P. H., and Shotton, F. W. (1971). Pleistocene deposits of Church Stretton (Shropshire) and its neighbourhood. *Q.J. Geol. Soc. Lond.*, **127**, 599–622.

Shotton, F. W. (1972). An example of hard water error in radiocarbon dating of vegetable matter. *Nature, Lond.*, **240**, 460–461.

Sissons, J. B. (1969). Drift stratigraphy and buried morphological features in the Grangemouth–Falkirk–Airth area, central Scotland. *Trans. Inst. Br. Geog.*, **48**, 19–50.

Sissons, J. B., Cullingford, R. A., and Smith, D. E. (1965). Some pre-carse valleys in the Forth and Tay basins. *Scott. Geog. Mag.*, **81**, 115–124.

Smith, N. (1972). Some sedimentological aspects of planar cross-stratification in a sandy braided river. *J. Sed. Petrol.*, **42**, 624–634.

Starkel, L. (1977). Late glacial and Holocene fluvial chronology in the Carpathian valleys. *Studia Geomorph. Carpatho-Balcanica*, **11**, 33–51.

Strahler, A. N. (1957). Quantitative analysis of watershed geomorphology. *Am. Geophys. Union Trans.*, **38**, 913–920.

Szumański, A. (1972). Changes in the development of the Lower San channel pattern in the Late Pleistocene and Holocene. *INQUA Excursion Guide. Changes in the palaeogeography of valley floors on the Vistula drainage basin during the Holocene*, 2nd part, 55–58.

Visher, G. S. (1969). Grain size distributions and depositional processes. *J. Sed. Petrol.*, **39**, 1074–1106.

Watson, E. (1977). The periglacial environment of Great Britain during the Devensian. *Phil. Trans. R. Soc. Lond., B*, **280**, 183–197.

Wilkinson, T. J., and Bunting, B. T. (1975). Overland transport of sediment by rill water in a periglacial environment in the Canadian High Arctic. *Geog. Ann.*, **57A**, 105–116.

Woodland, A. W. (1970). The buried tunnel-valleys of East Anglia. *Proc. Yorks. Geol. Soc.*, **37**, 521–578.

Wymer, J. J. (1976). A long blade industry from Sproughton, Suffolk. *East Anglian Archeol.*, **3**, 1–10.

Wymer, J. J., Jacobi, R. M., and Rose, J. (1975). Late Devensian and Early Flandrian barbed points from Sproughton, Suffolk. *Proc. Prehist. Soc.*, **41**, 235–241.

Timescales in Geomorphology
Edited by R. A. Cullingford, D. A. Davidson, and J. Lewin
© 1980 John Wiley & Sons Ltd

CHAPTER 13

Towards a reconstruction of time-scales and palaeoenvironments from cave sediment studies

Peter A. Bull

*Christ Church,
University of Oxford*

Introduction

The repetition of thin laminae within a sediment sequence reflects the pulsed input of that material during the original phase of deposition. It has long been the bane of sedimentologists to identify the time-for-sedimentation and any periodicities within the deposit in order that some degree of palaeoenvironmental significance can be attributed to the sediment assemblage as a whole. The establishment of the cause of pulsed, rhythmic sedimentation then becomes of prime importance since the identification of a sediment periodicity of trend is of use only when some timescale for deposition and the associated causal factor can be identified. Perhaps the most classic chronological reconstruction tool utilizing laminated sediments is that of varve counting where *annual* layers of coarse and fine couplets are deposited in proglacial lakes in response to spring thaw and winter freezing cycles (De Geer, 1912, 1921; Antevs, 1925, 1951; Anderson, 1964, 1967; Anderson and Kirkland, 1966). Indeed, teleconnections over large areas have been successfully attempted (De Geer, 1912; Schove, 1971), thus demonstrating the powerful absolute dating ability of varve counting methods.

Whilst the underlying tenet for varve studies is that the rhythmites are annual, many laminae units, although comprising coarse and fine alternations, do not necessarily represent annual deposition (Hansen, 1940; Schneider, 1945). Hence, counting laminae couplets does not necessarily yield absolute dates for sedimentation even if the layers can be demonstrated to be persistent over large areas in a similar way to varve distributions (Kirkland and Anderson, 1969).

A major problem encountered whilst counting laminae, whether they be varves or otherwise, is the degree of post-depositional modification that can occur, destroying the laminated character of a deposit. Many laminae studies are hindered by various degrees of weathering, subsequent erosion, biogenic disturbance, and lithological modifications. All of these post- or syndepositional processes combine to confuse the palaeo-record.

A further problem for dating laminated sequences (other than varves) concerns both the process involved in sedimentation and the factors that cause the pulsed nature of sediment deposition (Stow and Bowen, 1978). A detailed understanding of both of these factors is necessary in order that sedimentation rates, and hence the reflection of controlling palaeoenvironment, can be postulated.

With due regard for all of these restraints and requirements, a project was initiated that could utilize the spatially persistent, fine-grained laminae sequences found in caves in order that some indication of surface (and underground) palaeoenvironment could be identified. In the course of reconstructing surface palaeoclimatic sequences, times-for-sedimentation of individual laminae and sediment assemblages could be suggested. The principle outlined in this paper utilizes not only the remarkable persistence of fine-grained laminations encountered in the clastic cave sediments studied, but also the 'protective' nature of the cave environment. Many of the sediments investigated in this study were laid down in well developed passages that subsequently were abandoned by stream action. The lack of post-depositional erosion, weathering, or biogenic disturbance of any kind has left many clastic cave sediments unaltered since their initial deposition, perhaps up to 100,000 years ago, and hence affords them considerable relevance as a palaeoenvironmental reconstruction tool. Further, it is due to a number of unusual sedimentary mechanisms, identified during this study, that fine-grained laminations (Fig. 13.1) can be seen to be persistent in cave sediments across large areas of South Wales and south-west England. This technique, therefore, can be utilized to reconstruct palaeoenvironments across large areas of karst outcrop by establishing the factors that cause periodic sediment pulsing into subterranean lakes during laminae deposition.

Fig. 13.1 The laminated cap mud of Agen Allwedd. Note the basal
coarse material

The main part of this paper is centred upon work undertaken in Agen Allwedd (S0187158), a 24-km long, single-entrance cave, that has developed within the East Crop of the South Wales Coalfield, about 10 km west of Abergavenny (Fig. 13.2). The cave is developed within the shallow dipping Dinantian limestones that are locally underlain by Old Red Sandstone and overlain by Millstone Grit. The complete lithological assemblage represents cave development within a classic interstratal karst sequence (Thomas, 1974).

The Nature of the Laminated Sediments

Within Agen Allwedd a number of large-scale sedimentary sequences have been identified (Bull, 1978a) that indicate clastic deposition of an allochthonous quartz-rich sediment (Table 13.1). The earliest of these macrocycles suggests an original allochthonous, glacial source followed closely in time by further deposits of a periglacial environment. This mechanically derived deposit extends across much of Agen Allwedd and, indeed, across many other caves in South Wales. Following this major deposition cycle a hiatus in sedimentation occurred which was caused by stream abandonment. The subsequent desiccation phase dried and cracked many of the silt and clay deposits that capped this 'glacially derived' material and, through the protective nature of the cave

Table 13.1 Clastic sedimentation events in Agen Allwedd and surface palaeoenvironmental inferences

Approximate years bp	Event in cave	Palaeoenvironmental inference
ca. 5000 to present	Quiescent period and sediment winnowing. Downcutting of stream in adjustment to base level changes	Dry conditions. Climate continually ameliorating
7000–5000	Peat deposition in cave. Calcite speleothem development	Peat moor development. Generally wetter conditions
10,300–700	HIATUS	Climatic amelioration. Drier
ca. 10,300	Water drains from cave	Climatic amelioration
	Collapse of cave entrances. Scree development	Relatively cold
ca. 10,800	Cap mud laid down. Cave flood HIATUS	General climatic deterioration
ca. 17,000 (?)	Wedged glaciofluvial sediments	Corrie and gully glaciers and snow
	Angular sediment phase. Water flushes the rounded sediments through the cave HIATUS	Periglacial and Glacial (?) conditions
35,000–14,000	Rounded sediment phase	?
ca. 40,000	Doline 'controlled' cave boulder collapse	?
?	Various unknown sedimentary events	?
?	Cave passage completion	
?	Cave passage development	Proto-Usk drainage route (?)

environment, left the deposits unaltered until the next major sedimentation phase. A surface environmental change then occurred which caused the flooding of much of Agen Allwedd and, during this flooding, the influx of water resulted in the transportation and redistribution of the desiccated mud clasts as the 'basal conglomerate' of the subsequent deposit. Rhythmic pulsing of fine-grained sediment into a standing water body that existed throughout Agen Allwedd then caused the deposition of a laminated assemblage (Fig. 13.1), here termed the 'cap mud'. This sequence was essentially composed of quartz silt and clay-sized particles (Bull, 1978b) that were laid down by means of accretion parallel to the underlying cave passage topography (Reams, 1968; Bull, 1977a). In consequence, the sediments were not deposited in a horizontal manner but adhered to any cave passage irregularity, often up to, and exceeding, 90° from the horizontal. The resultant sedimentary sequences were also found to exhibit few, if any, dewatering effects, and have remained essentially unaltered upon the passage walls to the present

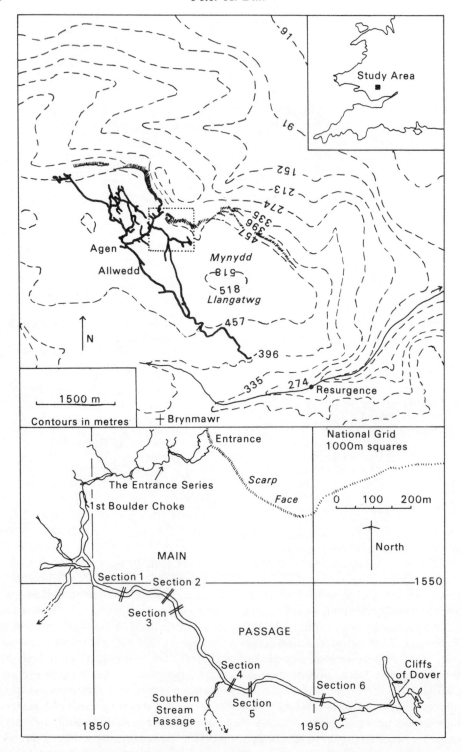

Fig. 13.2 Location map of Agen Allwedd. The dotted inset in the location diagram is
shown in the lower diagram

day (Bull, 1977b, 1978c). Thus, individual laminations, often no more than $10\,\mu$m thick, were deposited upon all surfaces within the flooded cave passages.

Within Agen Allwedd the cap mud was found to contain 196 major laminations that could be traced, layer for layer, throughout Main Passage (Fig. 13.2). This passage extends for about 1300 m with average cross-sectional dimensions of approximately 9 m square. Further, there is no evidence of any stream input along its length. The whole of the floor and part of the walls of the passage are coated with the cap mud deposit that consists of a laminated sequence of silts and clays. These laminations can be visually correlated along the entire length of Main Passage. Interlayer comparison of lamination thickness through the passage produced a correlation coefficient (Pearson's) of $+0.96$ (Bull, 1976). Further, individual grain sizes of laminations show remarkable persistence between sections taken along the passage (Fig. 13.3). The laminations also appeared to be laid down in a sequential manner (according to median grain size), and are probably not the result of random sedimentation.

The remarkable persistence of laminations, both in occurrence and in the median grain size of each lamination, provides this study with a unique uniformity of process. Since the laminated configuration of the sediments can be shown to be as persistent as proved varve correlations (Anderson and Kirkland, 1966), and since the grain size of individual sedimentary units is uniform, some major control of allochthonous origin can reasonably be postulated. The total lack of sedimentary flow structures, proximal and distal sedimentary assemblages, and erosional events throughout all of the cap mud blocks investigated in Agen Allwedd must suggest sedimentation by a mechanism other than simple uni-directional vadose (or phreatic) flow. Therefore, it is proposed that a multi-source sediment 'rain' occurred, similar in process to that described by Anderson (1967), and was transmitted from the surface via cracks and fissures. This sediment 'rain' would then represent the winnowed product of surface sediment runoff, accounting for both the discrete upper and lower limits of sediment size found in the cap muds of Agen Allwedd and surrounding caves (Fig. 13.3). The actual process of sediment transfer from surface to cave would then follow the translatory flow mechanism advocated by Hewlett and Hibbert (1967), with sediment inputs relating to surface climatic variations and affecting subsequent output into the subterranean standing water. Detailed evidence for this rather unusual sedimentation mechanism is beyond the scope of this paper and will be presented elsewhere. However, the inferences of these findings may be far reaching. Since lamination persistence and uniformity can be recorded in such an extensive area and can also be found in many of the South Wales and south-west England caves, localized anomalies in sedimentation can be discounted. The seemingly featureless internal nature of the laminations suggests neither discrete flow directions nor any hiatus in sedimentation other than to reflect the cyclic process that initiated the fine laminations. The widespread occurrence of this cap mud (both in Agen Allwedd and in many other caves of the region) suggests that the deposition of this, the last major sedimentation phase in the caves, was a response to a rapid climatic deterioration or, at least, to a large increase in rainfall. Investigations undertaken using electron microscopy (Bull, 1978b) indicated that these quartz-rich cap muds derived from a surface environment that was markedly colder than in the period that preceded this major sedimentation. As will be seen in a later section, logical inferences can be made to date this and other major sediment sequences in Agen Allwedd. In consequence, it is possible to throw light upon the time-for-sedimentation of the laminae that comprise the cap mud, helping towards a detailed palaeoclimatic reconstruction of both cave and surface, and identifying a time period for the duration of individual events.

Peter A. Bull

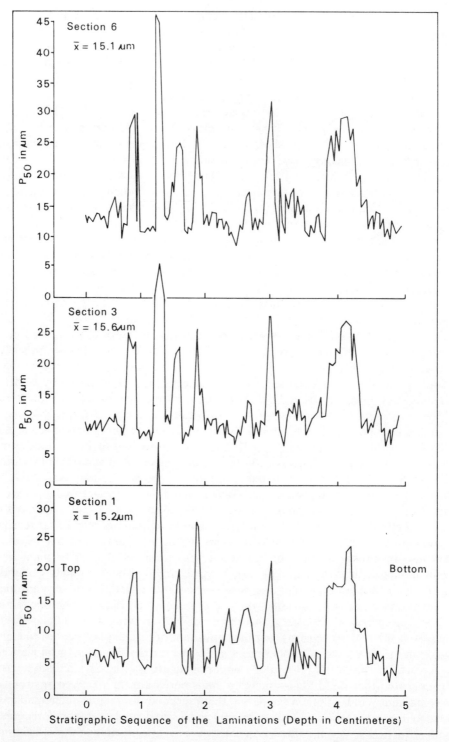

Fig. 13.3 Median grain size curves for Sections 1, 3 and 6 located in Fig. 2. Grain size analysis was undertaken by means of Quantimet 720 analysis (Bull, 1976)

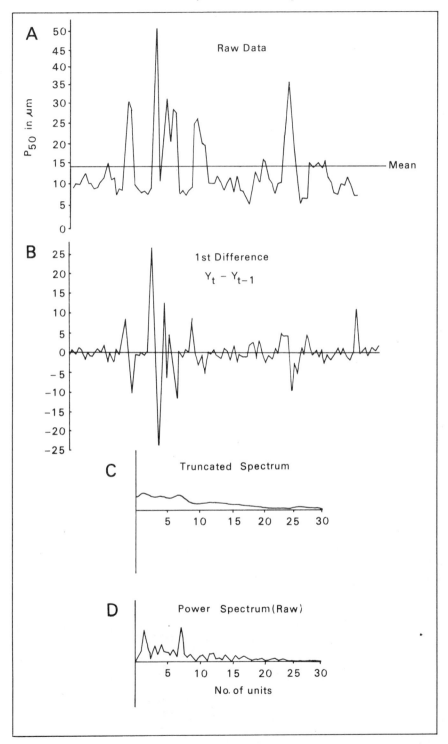

Fig. 13.4 Computed results of the first 100 units of the cap mud grain size curves

Results

The raw data plot of downsection median grain size variations (Fig. 13.4) consists of a signal that may represent pulsed sedimentation caused by surface climatic fluctuations. It was therefore important to separate the various superimposed cycles in order that the analysis of the fluctuations could be achieved and subsequent palaeoenvironmental significance be assessed. The general signal of grain-size fluctuations (Fig. 13.4a) consists essentially of three parts; a linear trend, a periodic component, and a random component. By computing the deviations from a fitted straight line of the original raw time series, that is, the first difference of the raw data plot ($Y_t - Y_{t-1}$ where Y_t is the observation in time, t), it could be shown that a linear trend was absent from the material (Fig. 13.4b) and no adjustment to the raw data was necessary. In a similar, but more surprising manner, the random component of the raw data plot could be seen to be generally absent as the computed similarity of both laminae grain size and lateral persistence was high. The raw data signal could then be shown to consist of a periodic component made up of a number of different harmonics. The smoothed power spectrum (Fig. 13.4c), averaged by a Parzen kernel at 30 cycles, shows that the peak at approximately 7 units in the raw power spectrum (Fig. 13.4d) is at least of significance. Other peaks can be shown to be of little statistical merit. Recognition of a 7-unit cyclic component within the first 100 measurements of the raw data plot of median grain size presents a series of problems regarding the geomorphic interpretations and the time-for-sedimentation of the 7 unit cycles. Original sampling procedures involved even-spaced sampling at the smallest possible interval. This micro-sampling adhered as much as possible to distinct laminations, especially as each laminae unit was of such even thickness (Fig. 13.1). However, it was inevitable that some samples were either composites of various laminae or consisted of serial samples within a thicker lamination unit. In either instance a degree of error was induced and must be acknowledged in these preliminary studies.

Whilst searching for a geomorphological process that may explain the 7-unit cycle, a number of points must be considered. The 7 units do not comprise 3 or 4 coarse–fine couplets; in other words the alternate light–dark layers visible in cross-section (Fig. 13.1) do not correspond to coarse–fine couplets. Rather, the 7-unit cycle contains a general gradation of coarse to fine grain size through the 7 units as a whole. It is difficult to ascribe a geomorphological cause to these cycles. The smallest repetitive cycle acceptable in this case would be a surface diurnal temperature change about freezing, although this would then imply weekly 7-unit cycles. However, Manley (1964, 1965) discusses such freeze–thaw cycles in Mid-Wales about the supposed time of the cap mud formation. More plausible, perhaps, is the recognition of the 7-unit cycle as a yearly deposit (a composite varve) as identified by Peach and Perrie (1975). The strikingly repetitive nature of the cycle would then provide 14 'varves' within the first 100 samples and approximately 20 varves within the whole cap mud.

The interpretation of the 7-unit cycle in terms of larger scale geomorphic processes is more difficult. Many natural cycles have been recognized to associate not only with small-scale precipitation and runoff phenomena, but also with global macroscopic and even solar influences, including 2–30-year cycles (Douglass, 1936; Anderson and Koopmans, 1963); 11 year, 22 year and 90 year activity (Anderson and Koopmans, 1963); and 100–300, 1000–3000, and 10,000–30,000-year sediment cycles (Anderson, 1964). Most of these orders of repetition would, however, fall outside the suggested timespan for sedimentation of the cap mud assemblage as argued below. In any instance, to ascribe a geomorphic causal factor to the recognised 7-unit cycle presented would be difficult and most probably erroneous.

Successful dating of the cave sediment units identified above is possible using logical inference and careful application of the count-from-top (CFT) method. Since the cap mud deposition in South Wales must represent the last major regional climatic change, by virtue of flooding so many large, well developed caves, it is plausible to place the timespan of deposition as approximating the Pollen Zone III climatic deterioration and subsequent amelioration. Coope *et al.* (1971) have shown that this climatic oscillation occurred between 10,800 and 10,300 years bp. It may be inferred, therefore, that if the cap-mud deposit does indeed represent this climatic oscillation, the time period for sedimentation of the deposit may be at the most 500 years.

To substantiate further the selected time period for sedimentation, it may be noted that a thin layer of peat (less than $10\,\mu$m thick) can be found overlying the cap mud (Bull, 1976). Peat has been shown (Thomas, 1956) to have developed upon the moors of Wales as a whole between 5000 and 7000 years bp. Indeed, the necessary hiatus in sedimentation of 3000 years between cap-mud formation and peat formation may also be documented in the record, as the peat was deposited over already desiccated cap-mud sediments (Bull, 1976). It can also be postulated that the 'glacial' and periglacial macro-cycles identified in Agen Allwedd, pre-dating the cap mud, represented the onset and/or the waning of the Devensian ice-sheet glaciation that was at its maximum some 17,000 years bp. The hiatus in sedimentation between these deposits and those of the Pollen Zone II/III climatic oscillation is also evidenced in the record by sediment desiccation and mud clast incursions into the basal cap-mud deposits (Fig. 13.1).

Comments and Conclusions

The combination of electron microscope techniques, detailed analysis of laminated sequences and the careful application of the CFT method all combine to provide an insight into the palaeoenvironmental conditions within and above Agen Allwedd. By utilizing not only the widespread persistence of the sediment assemblages, but also the remarkable similarity of small-scale features found within the cap muds of Agen Allwedd, it is possible to suggest a new and detailed method of timescale dating. A number of problems are yet to be overcome, not least the collection of micro-samples. However, perhaps more important is the establishment of an absolute timescale for sedimentation of the cap mud, and hence the deduction of time-for-sedimentation of various harmonics identified by time series analysis. Exciting advances are at present being made in the field of speleothem Ur/Th dating (Atkinson *et al.*, 1977), providing absolute ages of flowstones. It is in conjunction with such speleothem dating that the present study can reach its full potential by utilizing the continuous sedimentation and spatially invariant properties of the fine-grained sediments that are interbedded with the non-clastic materials. By 'filling in' the sedimentary record between absolute dates it is possible to reconstruct a detailed history of cave development across an area. It is then possible to date major climatic and environmental surface events, both on the micro-scale and across large areas hitherto barren of palaeoenvironmental indicators.

A number of points need refining, however, before accurate reconstructions can be made:

(1) The anomalous sedimentary mechanisms that give rise to persistent micro-laminations without any proximal and distal relationships need close investigation. Whilst the actual mechanisms of sedimentation are at present uncertain, evidence in limnological studies indicates that such cave sedimentation processes are possible,

though they are a considerable extension of previously published ideas (Ruttner, 1953).

(2) Present studies require absolute dating of overlying and underlying calcareous flowstone deposits in order that the floating timescales identified from laminae grain size variations can be calibrated. It is fortunate that these clastic/calcareous sequences can readily be found in the cave environment.

(3) A detailed investigation into the actual fine-grained sediment transportation through limestone cracks and fissures needs full investigation. Whilst this paper does not discuss the sedimentary mechanisms advocated for this translatory flow/parallel accretion of cave deposits, it does extend the published theory of both of these mechanisms in advocating surface climatic oscillations in direct and delicate balance with subterranean sedimentation. Furthermore, the association of grain-size fluctuations with such environmental variations as runoff and river discharge proposed, for example, by Kullenberg and Fromm (1944), remains an important part of the adovcated sedimentation processes and requires more laboratory and field examination.

Despite these problems, however, the usefulness of cave sediment studies for reconstructing palaeoclimatic change can clearly be seen. The protective nature of the cave environment has assured that the sediments have remained unaltered and undisturbed since initial deposition, and hence reflect both the depositional environment within the cave and also the provenance of the sediment. Investigation of such well preserved deposits will then permit the reconstruction of detailed histories and timescales in areas in which past environmental events are otherwise far from clear.

References

Anderson, R. Y. (1964). Varve calibration of stratification. In *Symposium on Cyclic Sedimentation* (Ed. D. F. Merriam). Geological Survey of Kansas Bulletin, No. 169, pp. 1–20.
Anderson, R. Y. (1967). Sedimentary laminations in time-series study. In *Computer Applications in the Earth Sciences* (Ed. D. F. Merriam). State Geological Survey Computer Contribution, No. 18, pp. 62–72.
Anderson, R. Y., and Kirkland, D. W. (1966). Intrabasin varve correlation. *Geol. Soc. Am. Bull.*, **77**, 241–256.
Anderson, R. Y., and Koopmans, L. H. (1963). Harmonic analysis of varve time series. *J. Geophys. Res.*, **68**, 877–893.
Antevs, E. (1925). Retreat of the last ice sheet in eastern Canada. *Geol. Surv. Can. Med.*, No. 146, 142pp.
Antevs, E. (1951). Glacial clays in Steep Rock lake, Ontario, Canada. *Geol. Soc. Am. Bull.*, **62**, 1223–1262.
Atkinson, T. C., Harmon, R. S., and Smart, P. L. (1977). Radiometric dating of Speleothems and Cavern Development in the Mendip Hills, *Proc. 7th Int. Speleol. Congr., Sheffield*, 5–10.
Bull, P. A. (1976). *Clastic Cave Sediment Studies*. Unpublished PhD Thesis, University of Wales, Swansea, 301pp.
Bull, P. A. (1977a). Laminations or varves? Processes and mechanisms of fine grained sediment deposition in caves, *Proc. 7th Int. Speleol. Congr., Sheffield*, 86–89.
Bull, P. A. (1977b). Surge marks in caves, *Proc. 7th Int. Speleol. Congr., Sheffield*, 89–92.
Bull, P. A. (1978a). A study of steam gravels from a cave: Agen Allwedd. *Z. Geomorph., N.F.*, **22**, 275–296.
Bull, P. A. (1978b). Observations on small sedimentary quartz particles analysed by scanning electron microscopy, In *Scanning Electron Microscopy* (Ed. O. Johari). S.E.M. Inc., Illinois, Vol. 1, pp. 821–828.
Bull, P. A. (1978c). The morphology and formation of surge marks. *Sedimentology*, **25**, 877–886.
Coope, G. R., Morgan, A., and Osborne, P. J. (1971). Coleoptera as indicators of climatic fluctuations. *Palaeogeog., Palaeoclimatol., Palaeoecol.*, **10**, 87–101.
De Geer, G. (1912). A geochronology of the last 12,000 years. *Proc. Int. Geol. Congr.*, **1**, 241–258.

De Geer, G. (1921). Correlation of late glacial annual clay-varves in North America with the Swedish time scale. *Geol. Fören. Förhandl.*, **43**, 70–73.

Douglass, A. E. (1936). *Climatic Cycles and Tree Ring Growth.* Carnegie Institute, Washington, D.C., 171 pp.

Godwin, H. (1959). Studies of the post glacial history of the British Isles. *Phil. Trans. R. Soc., B*, **242**, 127–149.

Hansen, S. (1940). Varvighed i danske og skaanske senglaciale Aflejringer. Med saerlig Hensyntagen Til Egernsund Issøsystemet. (English summary). *Dan Geol. Onders.*, ser. 2, No. 63, 478pp.

Hewlett, H. D., and Hibbert, A. R. (1967). Factors affecting the response of small watersheds to precipitation in humid areas. In *Forest Hydrology* (Eds. W. E. Sopper and H. W. Lull), Pergamon, Oxford, pp. 275–290.

Kirkland, D. W., and Anderson, R. Y. (1969). Composition and origin of the Rita Blanca varves. *Geol. Soc. Am. Mem.*, No. 113, 15–46.

Kullenberg, B., and Fromm, E. (1944). Nya försök att upphämta långa sedimentprofiles fran havsbotten. *Geol. Fören. Förhandl.*, **66**, 501–509.

Manley, G. (1964). The evolution of our climatic environment. In *The British Isles: A Systematic Geography* (Eds. J. W. Watson and J. B. Sissons). Nelson, London, pp. 152–176.

Manley, G. (1965) Possible climatic agencies in the development of Post-Glacial habitats. *Proc. R. Soc. Lond., B*, **161**, 363–375.

Peach, P. A., and Perrie, L. A. (1975). Grain-size distribution within glacial varves. *Geology*, **3**, 43–46.

Reams, M. W. (1968). *Cave Sediments and the Geomorphic History of the Ozarks.* Unpublished PhD Thesis, Washington University.

Ruttner, F. (1953). *Fundamentals of Limnology.* University of Toronto Press, Toronto, 242pp.

Schneider, J. M. (1945). Meterologisches zu Weltens Faulenseesediment und schwedisch-finnischen Warwen. *Verh. Schweiz. Naturforsch. Ges.*, 125–126.

Schove, D. J. (1971). Varve-teleconnection across the Baltic. *Geog. Annaler*, **53A**, 214–234.

Stow, D. A. V., and Bowen, A. J. (1978). Origin of lamination in deep sea, fine-grained sediments. *Nature, Lond.*, **274**, 324–328.

Thomas, T. M. (1956). Gully erosion in the Brecon Beacons area, South Wales. *Geography*, **41**, 99–107.

Thomas, T. M. (1974). The South Wales interstratal karst. *Trans. Br. Cave Res. Assoc.*, **1**, 131–152.

Timescales in Geomorphology
Edited by R. A. Cullingford, D. A. Davidson, and J. Lewin

CHAPTER 14

The dating of landslides in Longdendale, north Derbyshire, using pollen-analytical techniques

J. H. Tallis and R. H. Johnson

*Department of Botany and Department of Geography,
University of Manchester*

Introduction

When a landslide occurs, small surface depressions are formed in the slide debris, and these eventually become infilled with sediment. Peat infills from a number of such landslide depressions in Longdendale, a major east–west valley in the southern Pennines, have been sampled to try to determine from the pollen records the dates when landsliding ceased, and also to try to reconstruct the environment in which sliding occurred. Sampling of landslide depression deposits to obtain terminal dates for the cessation of slide movements has been undertaken before by several workers in Europe (Franks and Johnson, 1964; Morariu *et al.*, 1964; Gil *et al.*, 1974; Kujansuu, 1972), but in this paper we are also concerned with the episodic movements in compound landslide areas.

Fig. 14.1 shows the distribution of all major landslides in the upper Mersey catchment of Longdendale. A general geomorphological investigation of these landslides is given elsewhere (Johnson and Walthall, 1980), and only two—those at Didsbury Intake (6.i, 6.ii) and Bradwell Sitch (2.v)—will be described in detail here. Both are representative examples of the Longdendale landslides occurring at sites where the local relief is at its highest, and where the sandstone beds attain their maximum thickness. Reference will be made to other landslides in Longdendale where palynological work has been carried out, but special attention is given to these two slide areas, as both have several depressions in their slumps containing peats from which a stratigraphy could be determined for the area as a whole.

The Geology of Central Longdendale

The Longdendale valley is eroded in Carboniferous (Namurian) rocks, laid down as part of a 'slope association' comprising turbidite, delta slope and fluvial channel deposits. At the base of the succession, the Shale Grit formation contains thinly bedded sandstones up to 1 m in thickness, interbedded with shales; within these strata there are channel infills of sandstone, which are often of great thickness and form a buttress to the lower footslopes in the valley. These channel-infill sandstones crop out in the valley

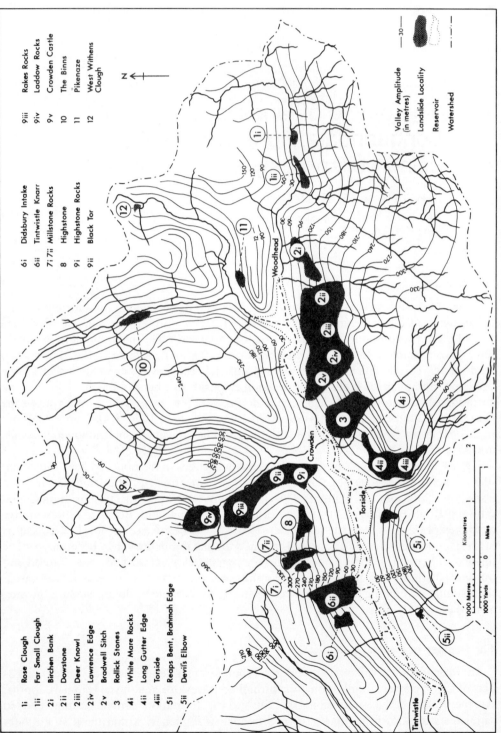

Fig. 14.1 The location of fossil landslides in Longdendale, North Derbyshire

floor in both landslide areas studied. Overlying the Shale Grit beds there is a thick succession of shales and mudstones, with occasional beds of siltstone and thin sandstone; these are the least resistant strata exposed in western Longdendale, and have had failure surfaces developed within them. On the upper slopes, the basal sandstone of the Kinderscout Grit, 90–110 m thick, forms a strong buttress 'cap rock' to the valley sides, and is a considerable burden to the less competent hillslope strata which lie beneath it.

In terms of structure, the rocks of Longdendale have been deformed in several ways. The Carboniferous rocks have been folded into a gentle west–east syncline, the axis of which pitches eastwards along the line of the valley. Dip of the strata, therefore, is inwards towards the valley axis, except where influenced by faulting or by local valley bulging and cambering. The rocks too have been disturbed by tensional jointing, and separated by bedding discontinuities.

Finally, during the Pleistocene period the hillslopes were ravaged several times by glacial and periglacial processes. Devensian tills and fluvio-glacial sediments veneer the floor of the valley, and the upper slopes are mantled by solifluctional and frost-disturbed debris. Such superficial materials are frequently up to 2 m thick, and have been overlain by, or incorporated into, the landslide debris.

The Study Areas

The Didsbury Intake Landslides

These two landslides occurred on the hillslope north of the Rhodeswood reservoir, in a region where the valleyside is capped by a massive, bedded, coarse-jointed sandstone. This bed is the basal sandstone of the Kinderscout Grit formation, and at Tintwistle Knarr quarry (Figs. 14.2 and 14.3, section CD) is 25 m thick. The landslide scar to the rear of the slumps is covered by rockfall and talus debris, and is itself over 70 m high, so that it is certain that the failure surface is at least 45 m beneath the Kinderscout Grit rock. Fig. 14.2 shows the general morphology of the slide areas, and from this it can be seen that the slumps have been affected by strong shear stresses as they became detached from the hill mass and moved downslope. Materials were transported at least 130 m downslope and down-dip, with a resultant vertical displacement of at least 70 m, and consequently the slump masses became fragmented into several slip blocks (B_1, B_2, etc.). In the toe areas, too, some ruckling of the slide debris (C) was produced by compressional forces as the slide movement ceased. It is certain, however, that the slides were not stable following slope failure, and parts of the landslides have subsequently been involved in mudslides and mudflow movements, some of which took place as recently as the last century. Bateman (1884) has recorded that the largest earthflow in the Tintwistle Knarr slide was re-activated during the reservoir construction work in 1852, and that movements in the flow extended from the reservoir edge up the slope some 545 m to a height of 245 m O.D. The thickness of the flow was observed to be 5.5 m, and this has been confirmed by boreholes drilled for the North-Western Road Construction Unit. This flow is typical in that its forward slope is lobate in form, and there are high lateral ridges along its margins. Its source area, however, was located high in the slump zone, where it has caused some dismemberment of the slump ridges. Several other mudslides have occurred in these landslides (Fig. 14.2). One caused the removal of part of a slump ridge in the Didsbury Intake slide (B_2), and a thick deposit of peat and other sediment has been deposited in the hollow which was created by the flow movement.

The slump masses vary in thickness. One borehole at Disbury Intake reached the base of the slide at 45 m (Fig. 14.3, A–B), and a similar thickness is exposed in a stream

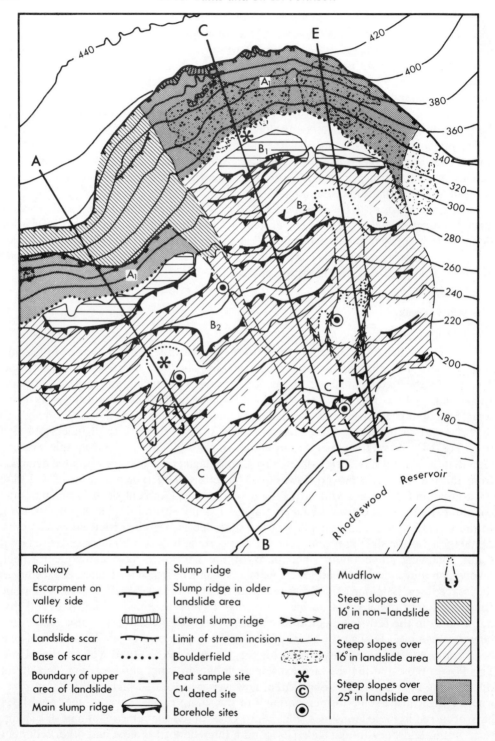

Fig. 14.2 Landslide morphology of Didsbury Intake and Tintwistle Knarr

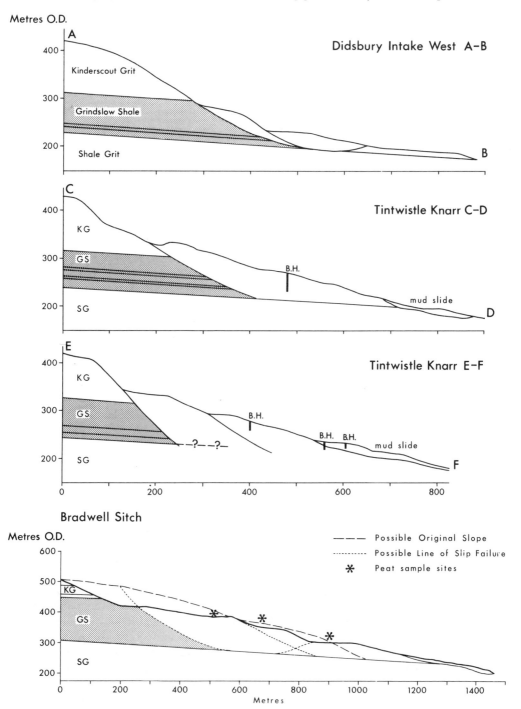

Fig. 14.3 Landslide profiles at Didsbury Intake, Tintwistle Knarr, and Bradwell Sitch (the local geology is represented schematically, using known available data)

section at the western edge of the Tintwistle Knarr slide. Other boreholes or stream sections (Fig. 14.3), however, have failed to reach the base of the slides, but a minimum thickness of 50 m is likely for the Tintwistle Knarr slump mass. The most likely location for a failure surface is again in the less competent rocks lying immediately over Shale Grit sandstones. The slides are probably best classified as rotational non-circular landslides, in which a competent sandstone layer prevented any large-scale rotation of the slump debris, though displacement probably did occur along bedding planes and in a down-dip direction.

The Bradwell Sitch Landslide

This landslide is part of a major landslide complex which extends along the valley for about 2·5 km. There are several different types of landslide in this complex, but at Bradwell Sitch (Fig. 14.4) the landslide is best described as a slump earthflow in which two distinct phases of mass movement can be detected. The first movement affected the lower slope, which became deformed as a result of deep-seated creep and bulge deformation of highly incompetent mudstone or shale strata. As a result, much of the debris was moved outwards and down-dip a considerable distance from the original valley slope. Consequently, the critical stress conditions were transferred further upslope and up-dip to the base of a new landslide slope, which in turn became reduced to a critical condition of instability. Slope failure then occurred for a second time, and took place probably along the same plane of weakness in the mudstone shales overlying the Shale Grit, but in this case with some slight rotation of the more coherent blocks from the upper slope strata. As these blocks were displaced they became increasingly fragmented, and the Lawrence Edge and Bradwell Sitch landslides were separated from each other. In the latter slide area, strong tensional forces have caused the blocks to become strongly displaced one from another, with the hillslope retreating progressively up-dip. This has resulted in a strong 'step and riser' pattern (Fig. 14.3), with peat and other sediments accumulating on the step surfaces. At the lower end of the slump, a mudslide has further disturbed the toe area and has transported debris to the valley floor close to the Woodhead Reservoir dam.

The Dating of Landsliding by Pollen Analysis

Methods

The landslide areas studied form a complex system resulting from episodic move-ments, so that a variety of datings for the basal peat infill deposits is to be expected. Dating by radiocarbon assay was not feasible, since the abundant wood remains in most of the Longdendale deposits made penetration with an auger extremely difficult and precluded the extraction of sufficient material for ^{14}C dating. The approach adopted involved the counting of pollen samples from cores spanning the complete depth of deposit at two sites (Bradwell Sitch A and Didsbury Intake A), and from basal samples or short basal cores at ten other sites in seven different landslide areas (Table 14.1 and Fig. 14.1). Samples were prepared for pollen analysis by the standard acetolysis technique, and for most samples at least 150 tree pollen grains (excluding *Corylus* but including *Salix*) were recorded. Both from the macro-remains preserved in the slide deposits and from the pollen counts, it was clear that there was a considerable local tree pollen component which varied from site to site; accordingly, all counts were compared on the basis of APC percentage values (arboreal pollen, *Salix*, and *Corylus*).

At each site the pollen samples were grouped into one or more pollen assemblage

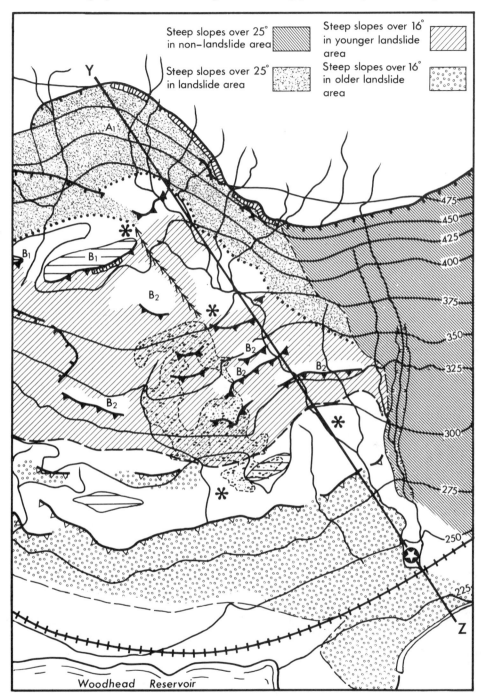

Fig. 14.4 Landslide morphology of Bradwell Sitch

zones, using the sequential correlation coefficient technique of Yarranton and Ritchie (1972); correlations were calculated for the APC components only. Grouping of contiguous samples into pollen assemblage zones was based on uniformly high *r* values

Table 14.1 Sites from which samples for pollen analysis were collected, with details of depths and frequency of sampling; the site abbreviations used in the text and in Figs. 14.5–14.8 are given in parentheses

Site	Altitude (m)	Sampling depth (cm)	Interval between samples (cm)	Comments
South side of Longdendale				
Bradwell Sitch A (BSA)	295	0–710	25	Complete series
Bradwell Sitch B (BSB)	295	600–670	5	Continuous core from base of deposit
Bradwell Sitch C (BSC)	295	500–625	125	Basal sample at 625 cm
Bradwell Sitch mudslide (BSM)	268	240–250	5	Three basal samples
Upper Bradwell Sitch (UBS)	400	275	—	Single basal sample
Long Gutter Edge (LG)	400	220–250	15	Basal series
North side of Longdendale				
Didsbury Intake A (DIA)	235	0–265	5, 10	Complete series
Didsbury Intake B (DIB)	225	90–120	5	Around embedded oak trunk
Tintwistle Knarr (TK)	330	200–230	15	Basal series
Crowden Great Brook				
Rakes Rocks A (RRA)	330	550–570	20	Near basal
Rakes Rocks B (RRB)	330	450–500	50	Near basal
Laddow Rocks (LR)	405	140–210	5,10	Basal series

between samples ($r > 0.8$), and assemblage zone boundaries were fixed at positions of minimum r values ($r < ca.\ 0.8$). Twenty-seven pollen assemblage zones were recognized, for each of which mean APC values were calculated. Nineteen of the pollen assemblage zones formed long (BSA-1 to BSA-5 and DIA-1 to DIA-8) or short (LR-1 to LR-4 and BSB-1 to BSB-2) time series.

Standard ordination techniques (Birks *et al.*, 1975) were used to display the similarities between the pollen assemblage zones graphically, so that the most similar samples were positioned spatially in close proximity. Different methods of analysis yielded different displays, and various displays were examined to find one which most nearly gave linear sequences along one axis for the two sets of pollen assemblage zones comprising complete pollen diagrams (BSA-1 to BSA-5 and DIA-1 to DIA-8). The spatial positions of the other pollen assemblage zones in this display relative to the two linear sequences were then interpreted as showing the likely temporal relationships between them. An approximate timescale along the axis aligned parallel to the pollen-assemblage-zone sequences was constructed by transposing radiocarbon dates for specific pollen features for other published pollen diagrams to this display.

The ordination techniques used were principal coordinates analysis and principal components analysis, using four different dissimilarity coefficients for the former and a covariance and a correlation matrix for the latter. The most appropriate display was given by axes 1 and 2 of a principal coordinates analysis using Gower's dissimilarity coefficient:

$$\sum_{}^{m} \frac{|x_{ik} - x_{jk}|}{R_k}$$

where x_{ik} is the percentage of pollen-type k in sample i, and R_k is the range of k. This coefficient places relatively greater emphasis on the rarer pollen-types, by virtue of its use of the term R_k, and hence might be expected to compensate for differing pollen productions by various plants.

Results of the Principal Coordinates Analysis

    The results are shown graphically in Fig. 14.5. It can be seen that the time sequences

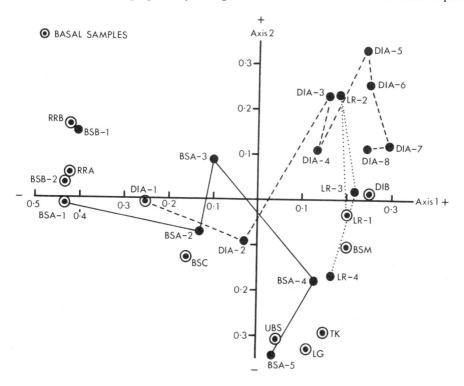

Fig. 14.5 Principal coordinates plot of 27 pollen assemblage zones (the various lines connect pollen assemblage zones constituting a time sequence)

displayed by pollen assemblage zones BSA-1 to BSA-5 and DIA-1 to DIA-8 are spread out in a general left–right direction along the first coordinate axis, and that the (presumably) much shorter time sequence of LR-1 to LR-4 occupies only a short horizontal distance along this axis. The sequences become progressively displaced from each other from left to right with respect to the second axis, and pollen assemblage zones with high positive scores on this second axis are characterized by high *Salix* pollen values; these undoubtedly represent local development of willow scrub at the site. Since pollen assemblage zones with low sample scores on axis 2 have high values of either *Quercus* or *Betula* pollen, and those with high negative scores have high *Corylus* values, differentiation of the pollen assemblage zones with respect to axis 2 appears to represent local dominance of a particular woodland type, depending upon local topographic conditions.

    The pollen assemblage zones from the basal slide deposits fall into four groups:

Group (1): BSA-1, RRA, RRB, BSB-2 (Bradwell Sitch and Rakes Rocks);
Group (2): DIA-1, BSC (Didsbury Intake A, Bradwell Sitch C);

Group (3): DIB, LR-1 (Didsbury Intake B, Laddow Rocks);
Group (4): LG, TK, UBS (Long Gutter Edge, Tintwistle Knarr, Upper Bradwell Sitch).

These four groups can be characterized in pollen terms which approximate closely to those of classical 'Godwin pollen zones' (Table 14.2).

Table 14.2 Pollen characteristics of the four groups of basal pollen assemblage zones, and their suggested equivalence with 'Godwin pollen zones'. For each group the range of mean values of selected taxa (% APC) is given

	Group 1	Group 2	Group 3	Group 4
Pinus	High 19–58	Moderate 17–24	Low 1–3	Low 3–11
Alnus	Low 0–1	Low/moderate 2–15	High 16–28	High 16–23
Ulmus	High 4–6	Moderate/high 2–4	Low *ca.* 1	Low *ca.* 1
Plantago	Absent	Absent	Present 0.3–0.7	Present 0.4–1.5
Calluna	Low *ca.* 1	Low *ca.* 1	Low 1–2	High 36–59
'Godwin zone'	VI	VI/VIIa	VIIb	VIIb/VIII

Dating of the Ordination Display

The Bradwell Sitch A pollen diagram. Organic deposits at this site extended down to 710 cm, and rested on rock rubble. Numerous included tree remains (probably all birch) made penetration by the auger difficult, so that samples for pollen analysis were mostly taken only at 25-cm intervals. Consequently the resolution of the pollen diagram (Fig. 14.6) is not very high, although the main features are clear.

The basal 1 m of deposit contains high pollen values of *Corylus* and *Pinus*, low values of *Quercus*, and only sporadic grains of *Alnus*. This pollen spectrum has similarities to that of pollen assemblage zone F1d (*Pinus–Corylus–Ulmus* p.a.z.) at Red Moss, Lancashire (Hibbert *et al.*, 1971), and appears to be earlier in date than any of the pollen spectra recorded from the basal deposits of upland blanket peats in the southern Pennines (Conway, 1954; Tallis, 1964). The rise in *Alnus* pollen in the Bradwell Sitch diagram at 575 cm and the first records of *Tilia* pollen at 525 cm conform to the Red Moss pattern, where they are dated at 7107 and 6880 bp respectively (Hibbert *et al.*, 1971). However, at Bradwell Sitch high *Pinus* values continue to above the level of the *Ulmus* decline (at a depth of 425 cm), and the pollen spectrum for 425–525 cm suggests pine–birch forest around the site rather than the deciduous forest of the lowlands. Appreciable *Tilia* values occur on either side of the *Ulmus* decline. Radiocarbon datings for the *Ulmus* decline in other southern Pennine pollen diagrams range from 5490 bp (Bartley, 1975) to 4990 bp (Hicks, 1971); the dating for Red Moss is 5010 bp (Hibbert *et al.*, 1971).

The upper part of the Bradwell Sitch pollen diagram is dominated by herbaceous pollen, with a sustained rise in *Calluna* pollen at 350–400 cm; the first records of *Plantago* occur at 325 cm. Most Pennine blanket peat diagrams show a major rise in Ericaceae pollen a short distance above the *Ulmus* decline, with datings of 4010 bp

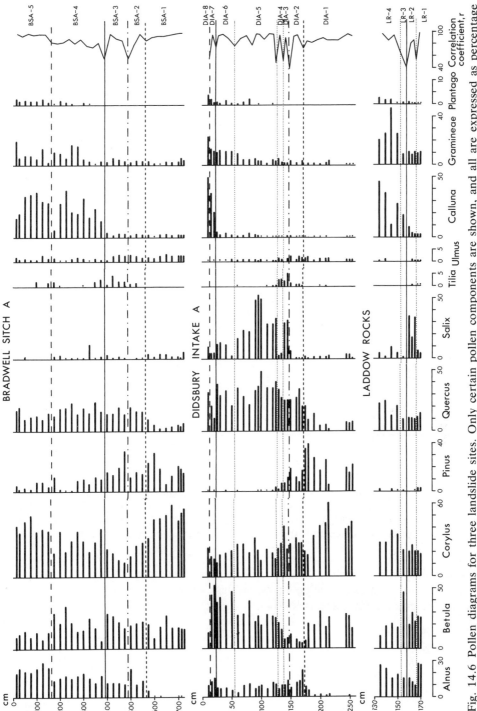

Fig. 14.6 Pollen diagrams for three landslide sites. Only certain pollen components are shown, and all are expressed as percentage arboreal pollen + *Salix* + *Corylus*; the likely relationships between the pollen assemblage zones in the three diagrams are indicated by the coding of the horizontal lines marking the zone boundaries

(Bartley, 1975), 3880 bp (Tinsley, 1975) and 3740 bp (Hicks, 1971); in the Lancashire lowlands at Red Moss, a similar feature is dated to 4370 bp (Hibbert *et al.*, 1971). The consistency of the *Calluna* rise suggests that it represents a major vegetational change in the area, and the absence of unequivocal evidence of forest clearance points towards expansion of blanket bog as being at least a contributory factor. The first indications of major forest clearance in the southern Pennine uplands (increased values of Gramineae and *Plantago* pollen) have been dated at 2200–2400 bp (Hicks, 1971; Tallis and Switsur, 1973; Bartley, 1975; Tinsley, 1975), and the changes in the Bradwell Sitch diagram at 250–275 cm are probably referable to this episode.

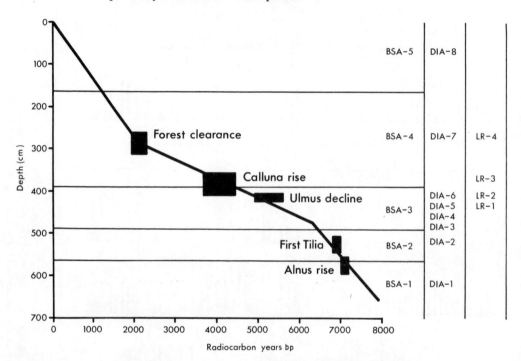

Fig. 14.7 Postulated datings for the Bradwell Sitch A deposits, and correlations of the pollen assemblage zones at this site with those at Didsbury Intake A and Laddow Rocks. The black rectangles indicate the depth-limits of certain features of the pollen diagram and the range of radiocarbon datings for these same features in other pollen diagrams

The possible datings for the Bradwell Sitch pollen diagram are summarized in Fig. 14.7. Approximate dates for the pollen assemblage zones, derived from Fig. 14.7 and the evidence presented above, are as follows:

BSA-1: before 7100 bp;
BSA-2: 6500–7100 bp;
BSA-3: 4400–6500 bp;
BSA-4: 1200–4400 bp;
BSA-5: <1200 bp;

(an error of at least ±200 years should be attached to each of these dates).

Reference has already been made above to the mudslide which forms the lower area of the landslide, and was derived from the toe area of the main slump mass (Figs. 14.3 and

14.4). A private roadway was constructed across this mudslide debris, and roadside sections have exposed a gleyed palaeosol 2.5 m beneath peat and mudflow debris. Fragments of birch wood (*Betula*) were found in abundance at this site, and a ^{14}C determination on two wood fragments gave a date of 1970±100 years bp (Birm. 481). This indicates that all movement in the landslide terminated about 2000 years ago, and that sliding had taken place intermittently for at least 6000 years on this slope. Pollen assemblage zone BSM refers to basal peats developed around the birch remains, and on the ordination display (Fig. 14.5) this pollen assemblage zone is positioned closest to BSA-4.

The Didsbury Intake A pollen diagram (Fig. 14.6). At the Didsbury Intake A site only 225 cm of deposit are present, but the pollen spectrum below a depth of 180 cm is very similar to that for Bradwell Sitch below 575 cm. The initial rise in *Alnus* pollen occurs at *ca.* 180 cm, and the *Ulmus* decline probably at 135 cm, though *Ulmus* values generally are lower than at Bradwell Sitch. *Salix* pollen reaches very high levels between depths of 60 and 145 cm, and the rise in *Calluna* pollen occurs only 20 cm below the present day surface. There is no reason to suppose that the *Alnus, Ulmus* and *Calluna* horizons are not synchronous between the two sites, so that very uneven rates of accumulation of sediment (as is suggested by the very low pollen frequencies in the upper parts of the deposit) must be postulated at Didsbury Intake. That being so, the correspondences given in Fig. 14.7 seem likely.

The Laddow Rocks pollen diagram (Fig. 14.6). *Plantago* pollen occurs right to the base of the Laddow Rocks diagram, and there is no evidence of the high *Tilia* and *Ulmus*

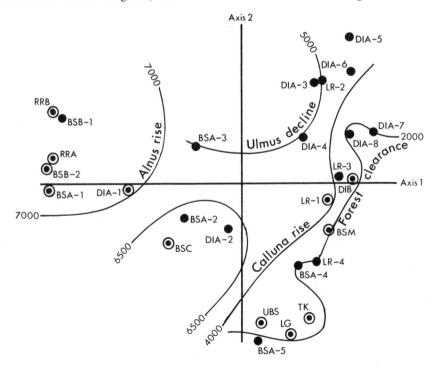

Fig. 14.8 Postulated dating isolines (years bp) superimposed on the principal coordinates analysis of 27 pollen assemblage zones

values characteristic of the first part of BSA-3 at Bradwell Sitch. However, the rise in *Calluna* pollen between 180 and 190 cm shows that LR-3 and LR-4 at Laddow Rocks correspond to BSA-4, so that both LR-1 and LR-2 must be the equivalent of late BSA-4. The high *Salix* values of LR-2 thus probably relate to the similar high values in DIA-5 at Didsbury Intake. The high Gramineae values at 160 cm in the Laddow Rocks diagram could correspond to similar high values in BSA-4 at a depth of 250–275 cm (2200–2400 bp).

The Dating of Peat Inception

The correlations between the three pollen diagrams discussed above, together with the tentative radiocarbon datings established in Fig. 14.7, can be used to insert approximate dating isolines on the principal coordinates plot. These are shown in Fig. 14.8. The dating of 5000 bp is approximate for the *Ulmus* decline, which is included within pollen assemblage zones BSA-3 and DIA-4. The first major forest clearance horizon, at *ca.* 2200–2400 bp, is included within BSA-4 and LR-4, and possibly within DIA-7; BSA-5 and DIA-8 are later in date, and LR-3 is earlier in date. Comparison of the mean pollen values suggests that the remaining pollen assemblage zones (LG, TK, DIB and UBS) are also earlier in date.

Datings for landslide inception are then as follows:

Before *ca.* 7000 bp:
   Bradwell Sitch A and B (altitude 295 m)
   Didsbury Intake A (235 m)
   Rakes Rocks (330 m)
6500–7000 bp:
   Bradwell Sitch C (295 m)
4000–5000 bp:
   Laddow Rocks (405 m)
4000–2200 bp:
   Long Gutter Edge (400 m)
   Tintwistle Knarr (330 m)
   Didsbury Intake B (225 m)
   Upper Bradwell Sitch (400 m)

The Basal Landslide Deposits

At the main Bradwell Sitch site (BSA), landsliding clearly resulted in the creation of local open-water conditions. The deposits between depths of 525 and 715 cm contain abundant colonies of *Pediastrum*, and are partly minerogenic. *Potamogeton* pollen was recorded in all samples between 475 and 625 cm (0.7–8.1% of total land pollen), and *Myriophyllum* sporadically from 600 to 715 cm. The more detailed analyses of the short core from Bradwell Sitch B (within the same slide area) also showed *Pediastrum*, *Potamogeton*, and *Myriophyllum* to be present, but more localized in occurrence. Macro-remains and herbaceous pollen types recorded from this core at a depth of 600–670 cm are indicative of swampy birch woodland.

However, there is no indication from overall herbaceous pollen levels that widespread destruction of the forest cover accompanied landsliding (in the BSB core, herbaceous pollen levels ranged from 7 to 30% total land pollen). Similar low herbaceous pollen levels were recorded from the other sites at lower altitudes, but at three out of the four higher altitude sites (Upper Bradwell Sitch, Tintwistle Knarr, and Long Gutter Edge) herbaceous pollen levels at the base were 37–41% total land pollen.

At Rakes Rocks the organic sediments are underlain by more than 1 m of stiff, white, non-polleniferous clay, also presumably deposited under open-water conditions. No evidence of aquatic deposits was found at the other sites, or of the more eutrophic taxa recorded from Bradwell Sitch B, and the original forest cover appears to have been quickly re-established.

At Didsbury Intake A and Tintwistle Knarr, one and two thin colluvial layers, respectively, were intercalated with the basal 50 cm of deposits.

At both Bradwell Sitch A and Didsbury Intake A, there is evidence in the subsequent deposits of hydrological changes within the landslide area. Leaves and stems of *Polytrichum* were recorded at depths of 175 and 400 cm at the former site, and at 50 cm at the latter. *Juncus* seeds occurred in the Didsbury Intake deposits at depths of 50–55 cm and 135 cm, in association with mineral particles, and *Salix* pollen values were at a maximum between these two levels. These features are indicative of periodic soligenous conditions at the sites.

Discussion

The Validity of the Evidence

The pollen evidence and derived datings presented in the preceding section relate only to biogenic deposits accumulated in landslide depressions; they do not necessarily relate to the actual time of landsliding, and it could be argued that peat formation in these depressions was, as elsewhere in the uplands, climatically determined. That being so, one might expect broad similarities between the pollen spectra of the basal biogenic deposits of the landslide areas and of the upland blanket bog areas. This is not the case, at least for the older deposits. There is no evidence that the basal landslide pollen spectra conform most closely to those of early Zone VIIa and early Zone VIII, when there is well documented evidence of increasing climatic wetness. Moreover, if climatic determination of peat accumulation in the slide depressions were involved, then some sort of altitudinal sequence of initiation might be expected, with older deposits at higher altitudes. This is also not the case. The pollen spectra from the basal biogenic deposits of the various slide areas show considerable differences, which appear to be a reflection of local vegetation differentiation in relation to topography. The evidence of local open-water conditions, of dominance of *Salix*, and of periodic soligenous episodes, all suggest the importance of local hydrology rather than of regional climate in determining peat accumulation in the slide depressions. Accordingly, there is no reason to suppose that accumulation did not follow fairly closely upon the cessation of slide movements.

The Validity of the Datings

There are at least three uncertainties connected with the datings derived from the pollen evidence: the coarse (wide spacing of samples) or fragmentary nature of the pollen diagrams, the transposition of radiocarbon datings from other pollen diagrams encompassing a broad geographical area, and the possibility of local vegetation characteristics overriding any regional patterns. Hence the datings can be regarded only as tentative. However, they do relate to major pollen changes visible in most or all pollen diagrams from the southern Pennine area—changes which are apparent also in the landslide diagrams. A more pertinent problem is the effect of altitude on pollen patterns. In the northern Pennines, pollen diagrams from *ca.* 450 m altitude in Teesdale show major differences from the lowland sequence (Turner *et al.*, 1973), with, for example, the rise in *Alnus* pollen occurring at a substantially later date in the uplands. The landslide diagrams from the southern Pennines suggest a persistence of pine forest on the hillslopes during Zone VIIa at a time when the lowlands were covered with deciduous forest; at higher altitudes hazel scrub may have been widespread. If some sort of migration of forest zones, both latitudinally and altitudinally, is envisaged during the early and mid-Flandrian, then pollen features such as the *Alnus* rise must necessarily be metachronous. However, even if *Alnus* and *Tilia* were prominent components only of the lowland forests during Zone VIIa, some sort of pollen representation, albeit at reduced frequencies, might be expected in upland deposits, and the datings of 7100 and 6500 bp are based upon this representation. The rise in Ericaceae pollen somewhere between 4370 and 3740 bp appears to be a recognizable feature of most pollen diagrams from the southern Pennine area, though its cause is not immediately obvious; the evidence either for climatic change or for forest clearance is not good. For dates more recent than *ca.* 4000 bp, the pollen diagrams are increasingly confused by local vegetation patterns, though the radiocarbon date of 1970 bp for the Bradwell Sitch slide does appear to set a terminal date for slide movements in this area.

The Causes of Landsliding

The immediate cause of landsliding appears in all cases to have been slope failure resulting from a weakening of the rocks at the base of the old hillslopes. One major factor was the presence of high pore water pressures in the slopes. Strong pressure differences would exist, since in the junction zone between the Shale Grit and Grindslow Shale formation there are several thin sandstones, all of which could have acted as aquifers, so providing suitable conditions for high artesian pore water pressures. Secondly, the Shale Grit rocks have been subjected to both cambering and bulging near the valley floor. Such deformations, probably a result of Pleistocene valley over-deepening, have caused the rocks to move outwards from the hillside, thereby increasing the stresses on the rocks cropping out higher up the slopes. Thirdly, the lower slopes on the hillslide were covered with till or 'head' deposits during the Devensian glacial period, at times when ice, snow-melt or permafrost caused an increase in the height of the local water table in the hillslopes. During and following deglaciation the lowering of the water table must have been very gradual, since the glacial deposits on the lower slopes are largely impermeable and would have prevented a rapid fall in groundwater levels. Under such conditions the hillslopes were reduced to levels that were critical for rock failure, and when this took place slide debris moved onto and over the Devensian deposits. When this occurred, as at Didsbury Intake, we have evidence that the slide movements occurred after and not during the glacial period.

The occurrence of landsliding can thus to some extent be seen as a natural process of landslope evolution in certain geological situations. There is the possibility, however, that environmental changes might also have been involved in actually triggering off slide movements. Thus climatic change, for example towards increased wetness, could perhaps be invoked as a trigger mechanism. However, the basal dates for the biogenic slide deposits do not support this hypothesis, since the earliest slide peats apparently started to accumulate under the relatively dry Boreal (Zone VI) climate, whilst the peat infills in the younger slides clearly are not related in their inception to times of climatic wetness: in other parts of Britain increased peat accumulation has been suggested particularly for the start of Zone VIIb (Pennington *et al.*, 1972) and Zone VIII.

It has also been suggested (Carrara and Merenda, 1976) that landsliding might be more liable to occur under conditions of reduced tree cover, and it is perhaps significant that none of the Longdendale slides has been dated unequivocally to the Atlantic period (*ca.* 5000–7000 bp), generally assumed to have been the period of maximum forest cover. Thus the basal deposits at Bradwell Sitch A, Didsbury Intake A and Rakes Rocks, pre-dating 7000 bp, mark a time when expansion of forest was still occurring and when the upper altitudinal limit of tree growth was well short of its maximum; the possibility of anthropogenic disturbance by fire at the upper forest margins at this time, however, cannot be discounted (Jacobi *et al.*, 1976). Most of the other slide deposits post-date 4000 bp in their inception, and originated during a period of steadily increasing prehistoric forest clearance (Hicks, 1971). The correlation may, however, be coincidental, and further evidence is required before any firm conclusions can be drawn.

Acknowledgements

The authors acknowledge the help given by Mr. E. J. Arrowsmith of the North-Western Road Construction Unit for allowing us access to valuable unpublished engineering and geological data. They also acknowledge the help given by Dr. J. G. Smart of the Institute of Geological Sciences. Lastly, they are greatly indebted to Dr. H. J. B. Birks, Cambridge University, for running the computer programs.

References

Bartley, D. D. (1975). Pollen analytical evidence for prehistoric forest clearance in the upland area west of Rishworth, W. Yorkshire. *New Phytol.*, **74**, 375–381.

Bateman, J. F. L. (1884). *A History and Description of the Manchester Waterworks.* Manchester.

Birks, H. J. B., Webb, T., and Berti, A. A. (1975). Numerical analysis of pollen samples from central Canada: a comparison of methods. *Rev. Palaeobot. Palynol.*, **20**, 133–169.

Carrara, A., and Merenda, L. (1976). Landslide inventory in northern Calabria, southern Italy. *Bull. Geol. Soc. Am.*, **87**, 1153–1162.

Conway, V. M. (1954). Stratigraphy and pollen analysis of southern Pennine blanket peats. *J. Ecol.*, **42**, 117–147.

Franks, J. W., and Johnson, R. H. (1964). Pollen analytical dating of a Derbyshire landslide. *New Phytol.*, **63**, 209–216.

Gil, E., Gilot, E. G., Kotarba, A., Starkel, L., and Szczepanek, K. (1974). An early Holocene landslide in the Niski Beskid and its significance for paleographical reconstructions. *Geom. Carpatho.*, **8**, 69–83.

Hibbert, F. A., Switsur, V. R., and West, R. G. (1971). Radiocarbon dating of Flandrian pollen zones at Red Moss, Lancashire. *Proc. Roy. Soc. B*, **177**, 161–176.

Hicks, S. P. (1971). Pollen-analytical evidence for the effect of prehistoric agriculture on the vegetation of north Derbyshire. *New Phytol*, **70**, 647–667.

Jacobi, R. M., Tallis, J. H., and Mellars, P. A. (1976). The southern Pennine Mesolithic and the ecological record. *J. Archaeol. Sci.*, **3**, 307–320.

Johnson, R. H., and Walthall, S. (1980). The Longdendale landslides. *Geol. J.*, **15**, in press.

Kujansuu, R. (1972). On landslides in Finnish Lapland. *Geol. Surv. Finland Bull.*, No. 256.

Morariu, T. (1964). Age of landslidings in the Transylvanian tableland. *Rev. Roum. Géol. Géophys. Géog., Stér. Géog.*, **8**, 149–157.

Pennington, W., Haworth, E. Y., Bonny, A. P., and Lishman, J. P. (1972). Lake sediments in northern Scotland. *Phil. Trans. R. Soc. B.*, **264**, 191–294.

Tallis, J. H. (1964). The pre-peat vegetation of the southern Pennines. *New Phytol.*, **63**, 363–373.

Tallis, J. H., and Switsur, V. R. (1973). Studies on southern Pennine peats. VI. A radiocarbon-dated pollen diagram from Featherbed Moss, Derbyshire. *J. Ecol.*, **61**, 743–751.

Tinsley, H. M. (1975). The former woodland of the Nidderdale Moors (Yorkshire) and the role of early man in its decline. *J. Ecol.*, **63**, 1–26.

Turner, J., Hewetson, V. P., Hibbert, F. A., Lowry, K. H., and Chambers, C. (1973). The history of the vegetation and flora of Widdybank Fell and the Cow Green reservoir basin, Upper Teesdale. *Phil. Trans. R. Soc. B*, **265**, 327–408.

Yarranton, G. A., and Ritchie, J. C. (1972). Sequential correlations as an aid in placing pollen zone boundaries. *Pollen Spores*, **14**, 213–223.

Timescales in Geomorphology
Edited by R. A. Cullingford, D. A. Davidson, and J. Lewin
©1980 John Wiley & Sons Ltd

CHAPTER 15

Radiocarbon and palaeoenvironmental evidence for changing rates of erosion at a Flandrian stage site in Scotland

K. J. Edwards

Department of Geography and Palaeoecology Laboratory,
The Queen's University of Belfast

and K. M. Rowntree

Department of Geography and History,
Sunderland Polytechnic

Introduction

Lake basins, as reservoirs of eroded material, contain a record of processes which have taken place within their respective lake catchments. If a sufficient number of cores are available from a lake, then its sedimentary morphology can be ascertained and this information may be used to estimate sediment *yields* within the catchment. This would involve a great deal of analytical work in core correlation and where it has been used (Davis, 1976) relatively few cores have been analysed for very few parameters, and rather gross assumptions have been made for inferential purposes. More usually, one or a small number of cores are used to obtain a more general idea of sediment *deposition*. This usually enables more palaeoenvironmental artifacts to be examined, representing a longer period of time, and without the crippling cost of an infinite number of radiometric determinations (Likens and Davis, 1975; Pennington *et al.*, 1976, 1977). In the present study the availability of 18 radiocarbon dates for a sediment profile taken from a small Scottish loch has provided the opportunity for studying the variation in deposition rates over the last 10,645 years. In addition, evidence from sediment characteristics, pollen counts, and archaeology is used to reconstruct the environment during this period. If changes in deposition rate can be assumed to reflect the relative changes in sediment erosion from the loch's catchment area, then the data enable the variation in erosion rates to be related to changing conditions in the drainage basin as reconstructed from the palaeoecological evidence. The inference of erosion rates from a single core is open to errors from a number of sources (see below). It was considered, however, that the information contained here was of sufficient relevance and interest to be presented at this stage.

Sediment deposition rates are related to the rates of erosion from the landsurface and channels, and to the delivery ratio, which varies with the efficiency of the flow network as a transport system for the eroded sediment. Changes in erosion rate over the 10,645-year period may be the result of one or more of a number of factors, including climate, vegetation, soils, and man. Climatic changes during the Flandrian stage could have had a direct effect on erosion rates through changes in the catchment hydrology. Climatic changes could also have affected erosion indirectly through the response of the vegetation cover and soil development. The direct and indirect effects of climate are difficult to distinguish, partly because they would have tended to be concurrent, partly because the evidence for climatic change is based on vegetation characteristics. A third factor causing changes in erosion rate is the change in vegetation cover associated with man's activities. Man may also affect the channel network through drainage schemes. Reconstruction of the environmental changes has allowed an assessment to be made of the relative importance of these different factors in the area of study. Most of the data examined in this paper were obtained as part of a study of environmental change by Edwards (1978).

The Study Area

The data were obtained from a sediment core taken from Braeroddach Loch (Ordnance Survey grid reference NJ 482003). This rock basin lake lies in a granite massif occupying the southern portion of the Howe of Cromar, a depression in the Grampian foothills north of the River Dee, Aberdeenshire. The area is rich in prehistoric remains (Ogston, 1931; Edwards, 1975). The location of the loch and its drainage basin is shown in Fig. 15.1.

Braeroddach Loch has a present-day area of 0.055 km^2 and drains an area of 1.9 km^2. The drainage basin rises from an altitude of 190 m OD to 300 m OD with average slopes estimated at around 7%. Locally slopes are considerably steeper. Soils have been mapped as belonging to the Counteswells Association. For an area to the north, Glentworth (1954) describes this Association as including coarse loamy sands to sandy loams, developed on shallow tills derived from granites and granitic schists. On the upper slopes the soils are podsolized with iron pan development. An extensive area of alluvium mapped around the loch represents a store of eroded sediment outside the present loch area.

The present-day land use consists of mixed arable and grazing with local stands of coniferous and deciduous woodland. The upland areas are predominantly rough grazing on land bearing communities of grassland, heather, bracken, and gorse. The better drained slopes are for the most part cultivated, whereas some of the gleyed soils and alluvium around the loch now consist of improved pasture or are under cultivation.

The drainage pattern has been modified in historical times by open ditching. Drains flow into the north and west of the loch. Whether or not these drains mark the position of former natural channels cannot be ascertained from the available evidence.

Methods

Core Collection

The sediments were obtained in 1973. The cores were sampled in open water from a rubber dinghy using a Russian borer (Jowsey, 1966). Anchor rope lengths, shore fixing points, and the need for dinghy stability dictated that the sediments were sampled in the

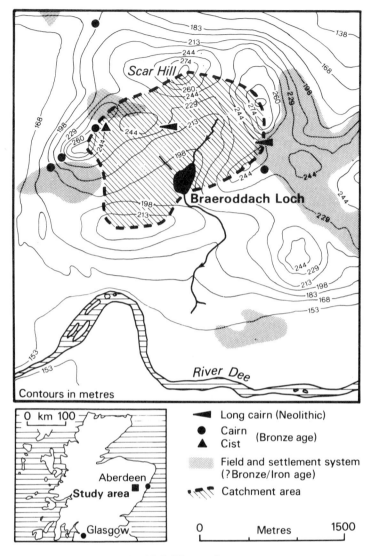

Fig. 15.1 The study area

northern section of the loch where water depth was about 1 m. Two parallel cores were taken in order to provide sufficient material for radiocarbon dating. Core correlation was facilitated by cross-matching pollen analysis.

Pollen Analysis

Pollen analytical data were obtained from the sediment profile in an attempt to infer vegetational and wider environmental changes within the pollen source area, which does not necessarily coincide with the loch catchment area. Samples of wet sediment 1 cm in thickness and at intervals of 2–16 cm were prepared for pollen and spore analysis by procedures described elsewhere (Edwards, 1978; Edwards and Gunson, 1978). A relative pollen diagram showing selected taxa as percentages of total land pollen is shown in Fig. 15.2. Fig. 15.3 depicts a relative summary diagram together with a total pollen

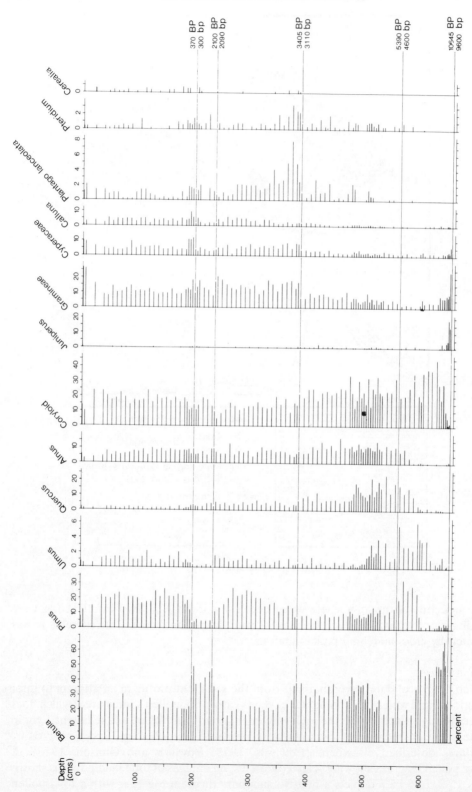

Fig. 15.2 Relative pollen diagram of selected taxa

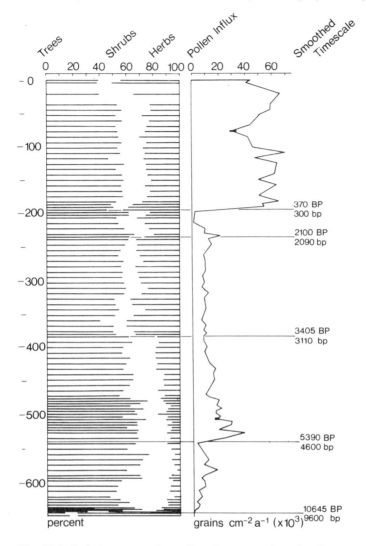

Fig. 15.3 Relative composite pollen diagram and total pollen
influx curve

influx curve. The latter shows the absolute numbers of land pollen expressed in units of number of pollen grains per square centimetre per calendar year.

Sediment Chemistry

Increases in the inputs of such metallic ions as sodium, potassium, and magnesium into lake sediments have been taken to indicate increased erosional activity within a lake catchment (Mackereth, 1966; Pennington *et al.*, 1972). For Braeroddach Loch, it was discovered that not only were these elements positively correlated with each other through the core, but also with such bases as Ca, Fe, and Mn. For this reason, only sodium will be considered in this paper (Fig. 15.4) where it is expressed in terms of influx or accumulation rate units of milligrams of sodium per square centimetre per calendar year (cf. Digerfeldt, 1975; Oldfield, 1978). Sodium determinations were made on an EEL 240 atomic-absorption spectrophotometer.

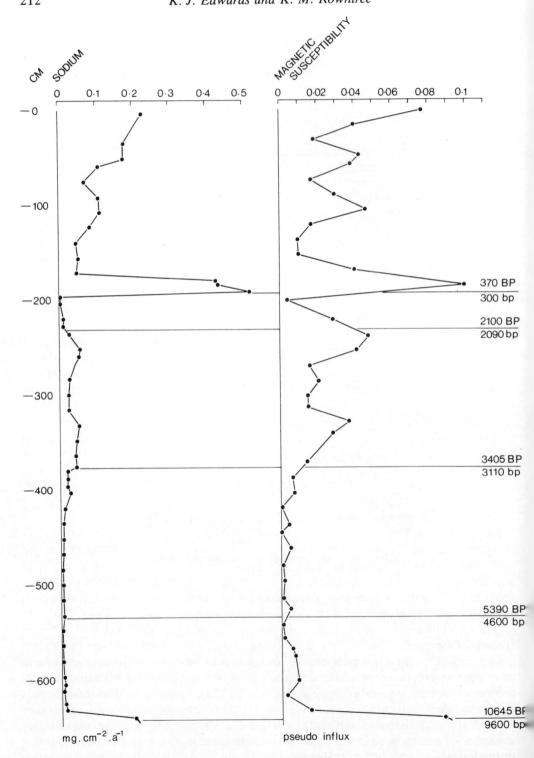

Fig. 15.4 Sodium and magnetic susceptibility accumulation curves

Organic carbon measurements (see Deposition Rates section) were obtained by the wet combustion method of Tinsley (1950).

Magnetic Susceptibility

The input of sediment into a lake often includes detritus rich in ferrimagnetic minerals. Variations in the values for magnetic susceptibility of the sedimentary materials is considered to provide a measure of variation in the erosion and deposition of ferrimagnetic minerals contributing to the apparent susceptibility of the lake sediment (Thompson *et al.*, 1975). Assuming that the ferrimagnetic minerals are allochthonous in origin and not authigenically produced at the mud-water interface or within the lake catchment (Edwards, 1978; Oldfield, 1978), then magnetic susceptibility measures and sediment chemistry provide a mutual check on inferences of erosion based on either method. In the present study, the initial magnetic susceptibility values for the Braeroddach Loch profile (in units of G Oe^{-1} cm^{-3} g^{-1}) have been subjected to accumulation rate correction to provide a measure of 'pseudo-influx' of susceptibility (Fig. 15.4). 'True' accumulation rates theoretically depend upon proving the consistency of various parameters of the ferrimagnetic mineral component in the sediment.

Radiocarbon Dating and the Depth—Time Curve

Eighteen radiocarbon dates were obtained from the 6.4 m-long Flandrian stage sections of the Braeroddach Loch core. The locations of samples depended on criteria of palynological and sedimentological variation. In view of the divergence between radiocarbon years and calendar years, and because palaeoenvironmental processes are under examination in this paper, it seemed appropriate that corrections be applied to the ^{14}C dates, even if they can only be approximate (cf. Maher, 1972; Donner, 1972; Aaby and Tauber, 1975; Hicks, 1975). For the period since 6500 radiocarbon years before present, various dendrochronological calibration curves have been constructed. The curve produced from dated American sources by Clark (1975) is statistically the most satisfactory and its similarity in slope for the period 3600–4550 bp (4100–5250 BP) with the Irish bog oak dendrochronological correction curve produced by the Palaeoecology Laboratory of The Queen's University of Belfast (Pearson *et al.*, 1977) has encouraged the correction of the dates accordingly, together with computed precisions.

For the period prior to 6500 bp, there is a paucity of dated tree-ring material for correction purposes. This problem has been overcome by employing the results of ^{14}C varve dating from Lake of the Clouds, Minnesota (Stuiver, 1970, 1971; Craig, 1972). The satisfactory overlap between dendrochronologically-derived correction curves and the varve data certainly encourages the use of such ^{14}C corrections as an approximation, and they have been used in this study largely after the method of Maher (1972).

The radiocarbon determinations and their corrected dates are listed in Table 15.1 (based on the conventional 5568 year half-life). Original ^{14}C dates and their calibrated ages represent approximations (hence the use of a stated *one* standard deviation precision on published radiocarbon dates). Failure to recognize this by basing subsequent deposion rates on straight-line projections between dates can suggest sharp and unlikely changes leading to possible spurious inferences. It was therefore considered appropriate to take the spot points of corrected ^{14}C dates as representing a scatter around the true distribution, and to recognize the uncertainty by fitting least-squares regression lines through series of dates which, upon inspection and with regard to the highest correlation coefficients, approximate to a straight line (cf. Maher, 1972; see also Davis and Deevey, 1964; Birks, 1972). This procedure produces the calendar-year dates employed in this study.

Table 15.1 Radiocarbon dates from Braeroddach Loch

Sample No.	Depth below sediment surface (cm)	Radiocarbon years bp	Corrected years BP
UB-2086	60–70	5010±90	(reverse date)
UB-2063	124–134	5215±115	(reverse date)
UB-2064	190–200	300±245	370±250
UB-2087	209–219	1985±70	1930^{+170}_{-130}
UB-2065	228–238	1990±475	1940^{+670}_{-450}
UB-2066	256–266	4480±90	(reverse date)
UB-2067	316–326	4110±80	(reverse date)
UB-2088	345–355	3675±50	(reverse date)
UB-2068	374–384	3065±120	3350^{+150}_{-180}
UB-2069	428–438	3680±125	4085^{+200}_{-170}
UB-2070	466–476	3960±135	4485^{+235}_{-210}
UB-2071	502–512	4285±130	4960^{+200}_{-180}
UB-2072	528–538	4460±85	5210^{+140}_{-165}
UB-2073	548–558	5295±155	6105^{+230}_{-185}
UB-2074	572–582	6325±155	7185^{+170}_{-140}
UB-2075	588–598	7570±185	8275
UB-2076	608–618	8550±170	9485
UB-2085	636–641	8945±225	9975

The depth–time curve for Braeroddach Loch (Fig. 15.5) is problematic for the last 3500 calendar years, where reversed dates occur. The probable reasons for this phenomenon are discussed later. A number of depth–time curves could conceivably fit the data and various strategies are discussed elsewhere (Edwards, 1978). For the present purpose it has been assumed that there was continuous constant deposition of sediment between about 3400 and 1930 BP, and similarly for the period since 370 BP. The policy involved here is not unique (cf. Pennington, 1975; O'Sullivan, 1976) and the inevitable compromise obviously affects the inferences drawn. Caution must therefore be exercised, but more positively, the difficult dating sequences have obvious implications for environmental impact, as will be seen later.

Deposition Rates

Deposition rates can be used as an index of erosion if the relationship between erosion and the rate of deposition at one point in the loch remains constant with time. This assumes that the depositional environment at that point remains the same. Davis (1976) found that for Frains Lake in southern Michigan, deposition rates were relatively uniform over the lake before forest clearance but that following disturbance and an increase in the sediment influx, the pattern of sedimentation became more variable. At Braeroddach Loch, the area of alluvium adjacent to the site may indicate a former extent of the water body which has been in-filled since an unknown point in time. Insofar as the difficult physical conditions permitted, a few borings were made in the alluvial material. These

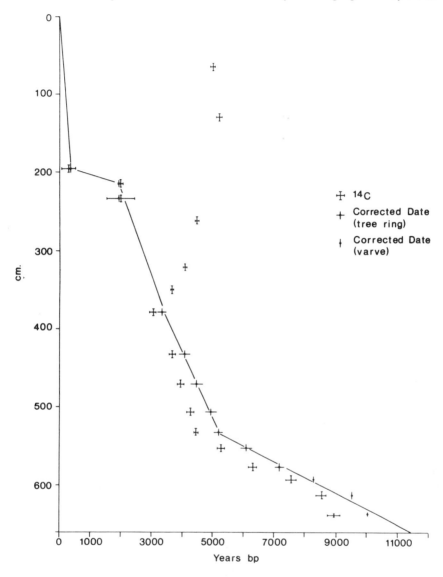

Fig. 15.5 Braeroddach Loch depth–time curve

suggested depths of less than 0.6 m which would appear to represent a relatively small proportion of the sediment store. Further work would be required to test this assumption fully.

Deposition rates (Fig. 15.6) were calculated from the weight of sediment deposited per unit cross-sectional area of core between dated sections. The weight of sediment was estimated from the sediment depth corrected for bulk density and organic content.

The accuracy of the estimated deposition rates depends especially on the accuracy of age determination. In certain cases the standard deviation of the radiocarbon date is large relative to the time interval between samples. A second source of error is the probable incorporation of older carbon as indicated by the reversed dates. The two corrected dates of 370 and 1940 BP fall between periods of reversed dates, but

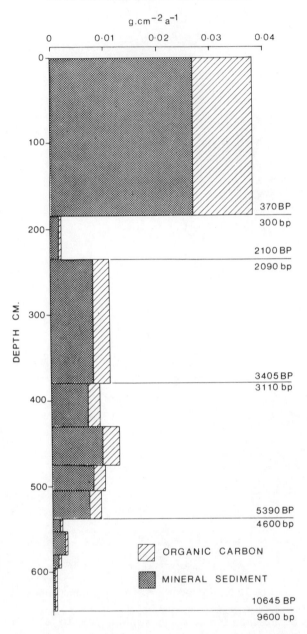

Fig. 15.6 Sediment deposition rate diagram

themselves give the assumed age sequence. Their adoption as valid dates between periods of reversed dates is only one of a number of options, but seems the most plausible approach on the basis of the palaeoenvironmental evidence.

Particle Size
    Variation in the particle size characteristics of a sediment may be attributed to a number of factors. Firstly, particle size distribution depends on the source of the material

so that the sediment may directly reflect the nature of the soils in the drainage basin. Secondly, particle size distribution depends on the erosive capacity of the flow transporting the sediment. Particle size may thus increase with flow capacity. Thirdly, the particle size characteristics of the sediment may reflect differences in the depositional environments. Coarse particles will tend to settle out near to their point of entry into the loch whereas clays tend to settle out in the centre (cf. Davis, 1976).

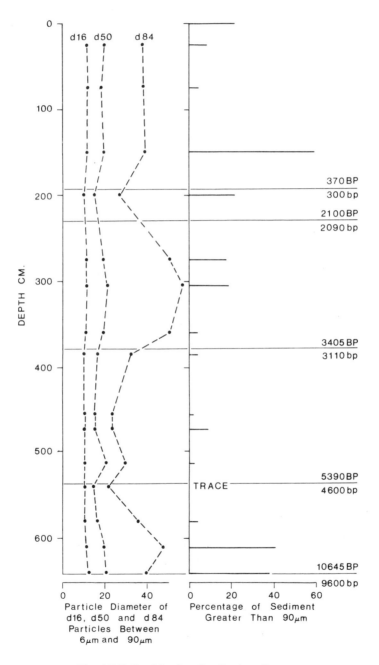

Fig. 15.7 Particle size distribution diagram

The particle size distribution of the sediment was found for sixteen of the 1-cm samples, taken at depths chosen to reflect the observed changes in deposition rates. After removal of organic material by oxidation with hydrogen peroxide, the mineral soil was dispersed using sodium hexametaphosphate. Particles coarser than $90\,\mu$m were separated by wet sieving and the fraction between 6 and $90\,\mu$m analysed using a Coulter Counter Model TA. The results are expressed in Fig. 15.7 as the percentage by weight of particles coarser than $90\,\mu$m and the d16, d50 and d84 particle sizes for the fine fraction. Thus the analysis was applied to a restricted size range, but gave a useful indication of variation in the particle size distribution.

Results: Sedimentation Rates and Environmental Change

Evidence from the sediment characteristics, pollen analysis and deposition rates suggests that the Flandrian stage in the Braeroddach area was characterized by five distinct episodes as outlined below.

(i) *ca. 10,645–5390 BP (ca. 9600–4600 bp)*. During the immediate post-glacial period pollen analysis indicates that the vegetation succession passed from birch–juniper communities into a prolonged period of birch and hazel wood and shrubland dominance. After 8120 BP pine expanded, followed by an expansion of alder and oak after 7330 BP.

Sediment deposition rates indicate low sediment yields throughout this period, although there was an increase in sedimentation coincident with the expansion of oak and alder. The particle size of the sediment was initially fairly coarse but became finer with the passage of time. Magnetic susceptibility and sodium values were initially high, doubtless reflecting the removal of less humified and mineral-rich substrates following deglaciation, but decreased over the period of pine–alder–oak dominance. The decreased sodium values suggest the onset of leaching conditions.

In attempting to explain these changes in sediment properties and vegetation, climatic change may be invoked. From the immediate post-glacial period until about 7330 BP (the Pre-boreal and Boreal climatic periods), conditions were thought to have been fairly dry (Godwin, 1975). Storms may well have been intense but infrequent, with high erosive capacities capable of transporting coarse sediments. After 7330 BP the supposed high rainfall of the Atlantic period, indicated in the pollen diagrams by the expansion of alder woodland, may have featured higher overall erosion rates, but finer sediments, due to frequent low-magnitude events causing a slow but continuous input of sediment into the loch. Increased leaching would also be compatible with a wetter climate. The very end of the period is marked by some evidence for small-scale anthropogenic activity, as indicated in particular by an absolute decline in tree pollen. There is no apparent change in the sediment deposition rate at this time.

(ii) *ca. 5390–3405 BP (ca. 4600–3110 bp)*. During this period the pollen diagrams suggest recurrent phases of anthropogenic activity referable to pastoral agriculture. Evidence of settlement is also provided by the presence of two neolithic long cairns within 0.8 km of the loch.

The absolute pollen counts showed that from 5250 BP the pollen influx rates increased greatly. This is not in keeping with the relative pollen evidence of woodland clearance. The production of pollen may have risen due to the increased vigour of new vegetation following the clearance of senile woodland communities, but a more likely explanation of the increased influx is that pollen-bearing soils were eroded within the catchment (Davis,

1976; Pennington *et al.*, 1976). Thus it can be seen that pollen influx rates cannot be used directly as an indicator of vegetation cover without allowance being made for the possible incorporation of secondary, though perhaps contemporary, pollen.

The start of this period is marked by a threefold increase in the sediment deposition rate from 0.0020 to 0.0072 g cm^{-2} a^{-1}. The particle size distribution over the sediment differs little from the preceding period, though a slight increase in the percentage of the coarse fraction was indicated. Together with the marked increase in sediment deposition rate, the overall rate of chemical influx and magnetic susceptibility pseudo-influx also increased. The metal ion values declined slightly during the first part of the period. The subsequent increase in the chemical influx rate was due in part to an increased concentration of metal ions in the eroded sediment and in part to an increased sedimentation rate.

The results suggest that the early forest clearances by man had a significant effect on erosion rates. The lower ion values at the start of the period may be indicative of erosion of soils which had been impoverished by prolonged leaching during the previous 2000 years. Only after a considerable period of erosion did nutrient-rich subsoils become the source of sediment, as inferred by the increased sodium values towards the end of this period.

(iii) *ca. 3405–2100 BP (ca. 3110–2090 bp).* This period covers the middle and late Bronze Age and the Iron Age cultural periods indicated in the area by the presence of large cairns, a cist and the extensive development of stone-built field and settlement systems. The first cereal pollen grains appear at the start of this period, whilst other pollen types also indicate rapid clearance of woodland for cultivation as well as continued grazing.

It would be expected that the introduction of cultivation practices would cause a further increase in erosion rates. The sediment deposition rate increased by 12.5%, but the influx rates for metal ions and magnetic susceptibility together with the particle size data suggest more extreme activity and impact within the drainage basin. The increased particle size of the sediment suggests that either the capacity of the erosive forces increased, or that silt-sized particles were somewhat depleted.

Accelerated erosion is also indicated by the reversal of ^{14}C dates up the profile, a phenomenon found elsewhere (e.g. O'Sullivan *et al.*, 1973; Battarbee and Digerfeldt, 1976; Pennington *et al.*, 1976). The progressively older nature of the dates towards the top of the profile suggests that there was erosion of progressively older soils. There is also an increase in the carbon content of the sediment, which suggests erosion of either organic soils or of the organic-rich surface horizons.

The absence of a significant increase in deposition rates during this period is surprising, and is out of keeping with other erosion indicators. The high input of metallic ions and magnetic susceptibility values may indicate the erosion of unleached subsoils, though this is not in line with the inference above relating to surface erosion of organic horizons. Moreoever, an increase in the relative pollen values for *Pinus* and *Calluna* may suggest acidification of soils. Erosion of nutrient-rich subsoils and leaching of soils under *Calluna* communities could be occurring concurrently in different parts of the drainage basin.

There has been a suggestion of a general middle Bronze Age climatic deterioration (Burgess, 1974), but indicators of a cooler, wetter climate, such as an increase in wetland pollen taxa, does not fully support this, either from the pollen diagram at Braeroddach Loch itself or from that of Loch Davan 4 km to the west (Edwards, 1978). For both sites the differentiation between climatically or man-induced edaphic and vegetation changes during the anthropogenic period is impossible to determine unequivocally.

(iv) *ca. 2100–370 BP (ca. 2090–300 bp)*. During this period, which covers the local Iron Age up to historical times, estimated deposition rates were low. Because of the small amount of sediment available few samples were available for analysis, but all other erosion indicators also show a considerable reduction in representation. Although there are signs of continued grazing and cultivation in the pollen record, the vegetation appears to have become dominated by birch and hazel. This may represent a regeneration community within a largely abandoned landscape. It could be that such vegetation cover significantly hindered erosion.

The estimate for the deposition rate could be in error for two reasons. Firstly, there may have been a change in the depositional environment or even a truncation of the profile. Secondly, the dating may be in error due to the large standard deviation for the upper date as well as to the potential reversal of dates in this part of the sediment profile. The lower date, *ca.* 1930 BP, may predate the time of deposition and thus underestimate the deposition rate. If so, this means that the rate for the previous period would have been overestimated, thus exacerbating the problem of relatively low rates in that period. It therefore seems reasonable to accept at least a general reduction in erosion rates from around 1930 BP, but the change may be more gradual than that inferred from the radiocarbon dates.

(v) *ca. 370 BP (ca. 300 bp) to the present*. The last period represents that of modern agricultural practices, though one cannot be exact about the start of the period because of the large standard deviation on the radiocarbon date (300 ± 250 bp). The pollen and documentary records indicate that both oats and barley were commonly cultivated during the historical period. The Old Statistical Account of Scotland (1797) tells of the poor nature of the soils as well as the intensity of agriculture in the area. An eighteenth century lime kiln which lies close to Braeroddach Loch provides an indication of the methods necessary to obtain a satisfactory living from the soils of the area. Further changes associated with agriculture include the digging of drainage channels. Major drains leading into the loch are indicated on the 6-inch O.S. map surveyed in 1868.

Estimates of deposition rates indicate greatly accelerated erosion associated with historical times. About one quarter of the sediment deposited during the last 10,645 calendar years would appear to have been deposited within the last few hundred years. At the beginning of this period the deposition of a 5-cm sand layer suggests a sudden change of conditions in the drainage basin leading to greatly accelerated erosion. The excavation of drainage ditches may have had a significant, if short-lived, effect on sediment influx to the lake and may account for the sand layer as well as at least part of the overall increase in deposition rates. However, the pollen influx rates, geochemical and magnetic susceptibility data, the inclusion of the two reversed dates in the upper profile, and the high organic contents of the sediment all give supporting evidence for an increase in erosion from the land surface, which can be attributed to agricultural activities in the drainage basin.

Conclusions

General Remarks and Comparisons with Research Elsewhere

In examining the data presented above the evidence for changing rates of erosion permits a distinction to be made between the pre-anthropogenic section of the sediment profile and that portion relating to the period of man's influence. Before *ca.*5390 BP, the generally constant low sedimentation rates are referable to possible climatic developments acting upon a landscape going through major vegetation changes. These environmental interactions took on a marked deviation with the impact of Neolithic activity in the area. Predominant leaching and minimal sediment deposition gave way to accelerated erosion as pastoral and later arable land-uses called for the removal of, or led to changes in, vegetation communities. The rate of soil removal and sediment deposition under prehistoric management was eventually to be surpassed by the agricultural practices of the last few centuries, characterised by the extreme erosion of catchment soils and their deposition in Braeroddach Loch.

In their studies at Blelham Tarn in the English Lake District, Pennington *et al.* (1976, 1977) mention an increase in sediment deposition around 5000 bp, which is assigned to climatic change and higher runoff rates rather than to man (cf. Pennington, 1975). There was no obvious evidence for increased runoff rates at Braeroddach Loch at this time, although there did appear to be some anthropogenic interference with the vegetation (Edwards, 1978). The main disturbances to the Blelham Tarn catchment occurred from 950 bp onwards with sediment accumulation increases, which also occur again from about 1500 AD. These changes are attributed to cultural impact, the second coinciding with increases in potassium levels and the appearance of pollen from cultivated crops. Further evidence of the importance of man is provided by the work of Davis (1976). It was found at Frains Lake, South Michigan, that the first clearance of forest cover around 1830 AD brought the first significant changes in sediment yields to the lake.

Accuracy of Erosion Rates

The data presented in this study have come from only one part of the loch, and produced measures of relative erosion rates. Absolute sediment yields would require a survey of the total mass of sediment in the loch, estimated from a number of cores taken over the loch area (cf. Davis, 1976) and the adjacent alluvium. Such a programme of work would require good core correlation between a master core which has been comprehensively analysed for a number of parameters, and supplementary cores used to estimate total sediment accumulation and its variation within the Loch. Although core matching can be achieved by palynological, diatom, chemical, stratigraphic, or radiometric comparisons, the rapid and inexpensive correlations made possible by the use of magnetic susceptibility measures (Thompson *et al.*, 1975; Oldfield, 1978) may establish it as a widely used technique in palaeoenvironmental studies.

There is obviously a need to study present-day lake catchment processes. This should not only be concerned with the commonly investigated facets of hydrology and sediment sources and characteristics. If palaeoenvironmental reconstruction is to take place, then such studies must also consider the artifacts of pollen, chemistry, and magnetism and evaluate their part in deciphering the ecosystem budget (Peck, 1973; Pennington, 1974; Likens and Davis, 1975; Oldfield *et al.*, in press).

Timescale Resolution

The resolution of the sediment profile timescale depends on the accuracy of the radiocarbon dating. Sediment low in organic carbon may necessitate age determinations with wide standard deviations, while 'saturation dating' of a profile is expensive. Radiocarbon dating is applicable to fairly long timespans, but taking into account stated dating precision, it should probably be restricted to a minimum of 1000 years of sedimentation if erosion rates are to be gauged with any degree of confidence.

As the radiocarbon dating of new lake sediment cores has increased, then instances of dating reversals similar to those found at Braeroddach Loch have also come to light. Where lake sediments are suitable, then palaeomagnetic dating of profiles can overcome such problems and provide a useful check on the ^{14}C determinations (O'Sullivan et al., 1973; Battarbee and Digerfeldt, 1976).

For the recent past, especially where lake catchment land use may be historically documented, then the use of radionuclides such as ^{210}Pb and ^{137}Cs has proved very useful for obtaining fine resolution on sedimentation rates (Pennington et al., 1976; Oldfield, 1978; Battarbee, 1978). The use of such isotopes in investigating recent processes of erosion and deposition is certain to increase (cf. Wise, this volume, Chapter 9). As such, they provide a relatively inexpensive complement to the much greater time periods and sedimentary processes capable of examination by the radiocarbon method.

Acknowledgements

K.J.E. thanks Mr. Gordon Pearson and the staff of the Palaeoecology Laboratory of The Queen's University of Belfast for the radiocarbon dates.

References

Aaby, B., and Tauber, H. (1975). Rates of peat formation in relation to degree of humification and local environment, as shown by studies of a raised bog in Denmark. Boreas, 4, 1–17.

Battarbee, R. W. (1978). Observations on the recent history of Lough Neagh and its drainage basin. Phil. Trans. R. Soc., B, 281, 303–345.

Battarbee, R. W., and Digerfeldt, G. (1976). Palaeoecological studies of the recent development of Lake Vaxjosjon. I. Introduction and chronology. Arch. Hydrobiol., 77, 330–346.

Birks, H. H. (1972). Studies in the vegetational history of Scotland. III. A radiocarbon-dated pollen diagram from Loch Maree, Ross and Cromarty. New Phytol., 71, 731–754.

Burgess, C. (1974). The Bronze Age. In British Prehistory, A New Outline (Ed. C. Renfrew). Duckworth, London, pp. 165–232.

Clark, R. M. (1975). A calibration curve for radiocarbon dates. Antiquity, 49, 251–266.

Craig, A. J. (1972). Pollen influx to laminated sediments: a pollen diagram from northeastern Minnesota. Ecology, 53, 46–57.

Davis, M. B. (1976). Erosion rates and land-use history in southern Michigan. Environ. Conserv., 3, 139–148.

Davis, M. B., and Deevey, E. S., Jr. (1964). Pollen accumulation rates: estimates from late-glacial sediment of Rogers Lake. Science, 145, 1293–1295.

Digerfeldt, G. (1975). The Post-Glacial development of Ranviken bay in Lake Immeln. III. Palaeolimnology. Geol. Foren. Stockh. Forh., 97, 13–28.

Donner, J. J. (1972). Pollen frequencies in the Flandrian sediments of Lake Vakojarvi, South Finland. Comment. Biol., 53, 1–19.

Edwards, K. J. (1975). Aspects of the prehistoric archaeology of the Howe of Cromar. In Quaternary Studies in North East Scotland (Ed. A. M. D. Gemmell). Dept. of Geography, Univ. of Aberdeen, Aberdeen, pp. 82–87.

Edwards, K. J. 1978. Palaeoenvironmental and Archaeological Investigations in the Howe of Cromar, Grampian Region, Scotland. Unpublished PhD Thesis, Univ. of Aberdeen.

Edwards, K. J., and Gunson, A. R. (1978). A procedure for the determination of exotic pollen concentrations with a Coulter Counter. Pollen Spores, 20, 303–309.

Glentworth, R. (1954). The soils of the country round Banff, Huntly and Turriff (Lower Banffshire and north-west Aberdeenshire) (Sheets 86 and 96). Mem. Soil Surv. Scot. HMSO, Edinburgh.

Godwin, H. (1975). History of the British Flora. Cambridge University Press, Cambridge.

Hicks, S. (1975). Pollen analysis and archaeology in Kuusamo, North-east Finland, an area of marginal human interference. Trans. Inst. Br. Geog., New Ser., 1, 362–384.

Holeman, J. N. (1975). Procedures used in the Soil Conservation Service to estimate sediment yield. In *Present and Perspective Technology for Predicting Sediment Yields and Sources.* U.S. Dept. Agric., Washington, Publ. ARF-S-40, pp. 5–9.

Jowsey, P. C. (1966). An improved peat sampler. *New Phytol.,* **65,** 245–248.

Likens, G. E., and Davis, M. B. (1975). Post-glacial history of Mirror Lake and its watershed in New Hampshire, U.S.A.: an initial report. *Verh. Int. Verein. Limnol.,* **19,** 982–993.

Mackereth, F. J. H. (1966). Some chemical observations on post-glacial lake sediments. *Phil. Trans. R. Soc., B,* **250,** 165–213.

Maher, L. J., Jr. (1972). Absolute pollen diagram of Redrock Lake, Boulder County, Colorado. *Quat. Res.,* **2,** 531–553.

Ogston, A. (1931). *The Prehistoric Antiquities of the Howe of Cromar.* Third Spalding Club, Aberdeen.

Oldfield, F. (1978). Lakes and their drainage basins as units of sediment-based ecological study. *Prog. Phys. Geog.,* **1,** 460–504.

Oldfield, F., Dearing, J., Thompson, R., and Garrett-Jones, S. E. (in press). Some magnetic properties of lake sediments and their possible links with erosion rates. *Proc. 2nd Int. Symp. Palaeolimnol. Polish Archives for Hydrobiol.*

Old Statistical Account of Scotland (1797). Vol. 19.

O'Sullivan, P. E. (1976). Pollen analysis and radiocarbon dating of a core from Loch Pityoulish, Eastern Highlands of Scotland. *J. Biogeog.,* **3,** 293–302.

O'Sullivan, P. E., Oldfield, F., and Battarbee, R. W. (1973). Preliminary studies of Lough Neagh sediments. I. Stratigraphy, chronology and pollen analysis. In *Quaternary Plant Ecology* (Ed. H. J. B. Birks and R. G. West). Blackwells, Oxford, pp. 267–278.

Pearson, G. W., Pilcher, J. R., Baillie, M. G. L., and Hillam, J. (1977). Absolute radiocarbon dating using a low altitude European tree-ring calibration. *Nature, Lond.,* **270,** 25–28.

Peck, R. M. (1973). Pollen budget studies in a small Yorkshire catchment. In *Quaternary Plant Ecology* (Ed. H. J. B. Birks and R. G. West). Blackwells, Oxford, pp. 43–60.

Pennington, W. (1974). Seston and sediment formation in five Lake District Lakes. *J. Ecol.,* **62,** 215–251.

Pennington, W. (1975). The effect of Neolithic man on the environment in north-west England: the use of absolute pollen diagrams. In *The Effect of Man on the Landscape: the Highland Zone* (Ed. J. G. Evans, S. Limbrey, and H. Cleere.). Res. Rep. No. 11, Council for British Archaeology, London, pp. 74–86.

Pennington, W., Haworth, E. Y., Bonny, A. P., and Lishman, J. P. (1972). Lake sediments in Northern Scotland. *Phil. Trans. R. Soc., B,* **264,** 191–294.

Pennington, W., Cambray, R. S., Eakins, J. D., and Harkness, D. D. (1976). Radionuclide dating of the recent sediments of Blelham Tarn. *Freshwat. Biol.,* **6,** 317–331.

Pennington, W., Cranwell, P. A., Haworth, E. Y., Bonny, A. P., and Lishman, J. P. (1977). Interpreting the environmental record in the sediments of Blelham Tarn. *Forty-fifth Annual Report,* Freshwater Biological Assoc., pp. 37–47.

Stuiver, M. (1970). Tree-ring, varve and carbon-14 chronologies. *Nature, Lond.,* **228,** 454–455.

Stuiver, M. (1971). Evidence for the variation of atmospheric C^{14} content in the late Quaternary. In *The Late Cenozoic Glacial Ages* (Ed. K. K. Turekian). Yale University Press, New Haven, pp. 57–70.

Thompson, R., Battarbee, R. W., O'Sullivan, P. E., and Oldfield, F. (1975). Magnetic susceptibility of lake sediments. *Limnol. Oceanog.,* **20,** 687–698.

Tinsley, J. (1950). The determination of organic carbon in soils by dichromate mixtures. *Trans. 4th Int. Congr. Soil Sci.,* **1,** 161.

Timescales in Geomorphology
Edited by R. A. Cullingford, D. A. Davidson, and J. Lewin
© 1980 John Wiley & Sons Ltd

CHAPTER 16

Dating the Main Postglacial Shoreline in the Montrose area, Scotland

D. E. Smith, J. Morrison, and R. L. Jones

Department of Geography,
Lanchester Polytechnic, Coventry

and R. A. Cullingford

Department of Geography,
University of Exeter

Introduction

Studies of raised shorelines in Scotland since 1962 have revealed a more complex pattern of Late Devensian and Flandrian features than had previously been recognized. In each area studied, a large number of differentially uplifted shorelines have been identified, often within a relatively small height range, and since isostasy was a major element in their formation, each raised shoreline is likely to be slightly diachronous, the parts nearer to the centre of uplift having been lifted clear of the sea earlier than the peripheral parts. In such a situation, increasing attention has been paid to dating these raised shorelines, not only as an aid to correlation between different areas, but also to test the degree of diachroneity of major shorelines, and to provide data for the construction of curves of sea level change and land uplift.

This paper is concerned with the age of one shoreline in an area near Montrose. Studies of its altitude and morphology, and of the stratigraphy of associated deposits, together with pollen analysis and carbon-14 assay, show that it can be correlated with the Main Postglacial Shoreline of Sissons *et al.* (1966), recognized in the Forth and Tay areas to the south. Information has also been obtained concerning the nature of the transgression which led to the formation of the Main Postglacial Shoreline in eastern Scotland.

The Area

The Montrose Basin is an area of tidal mudflats at the mouth of the river South Esk, surrounded by discontinuous areas of raised mudflats, generally known as carselands and very similar to the carselands of the Forth and Tay valleys. Overlooking the carselands are marine and fluvioglacial terraces formed in association with the decay of Late Devensian ice (Cullingford and Smith, 1980). The area studied in detail lies at the

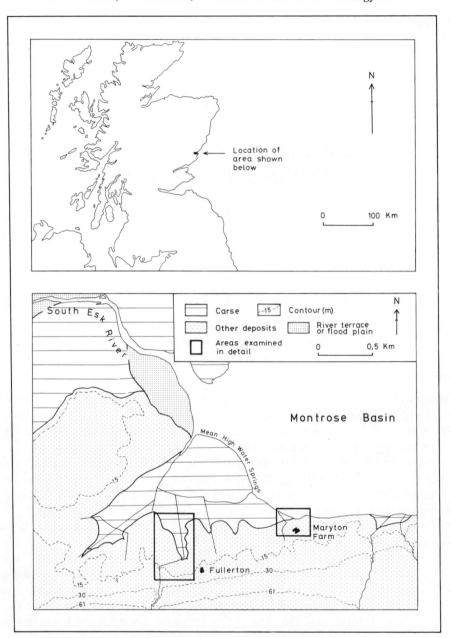

Fig. 16.1 Location of the area studied

south-western margin of the Basin (Fig. 16.1). Here, the Late Devensian features have been intensively dissected by gullies, now partially filled by carse deposits to form collectively an elongate embayment running westwards from the edge of the Basin. The area has not previously been studied in detail, but work by Howden (1868) on the glacial and marine deposits of the Montrose area generally provides valuable information. From terrace deposits above the carse Howden obtained remains of an arctic marine fauna, but from the carse deposits he recorded the widespread occurrence of a more temperate marine fauna. Howden found that the deposits from which he had obtained the arctic fauna descend beneath the carse on the north side of the Basin, where a buried peat can be identified between the two deposits. In addition, he observed the carse surface to be covered by peat in some localities.

The relationships between carse deposits and peat, and the temperate fauna of the carse deposits, are very similar to those in the Forth carselands noted by Jamieson (1865), and it would appear that in both areas the carse deposits accumulated at a broadly similar time. Sissons and Brooks (1971) have shown that the Forth carselands accumulated during the main Flandrian marine transgression in that area. The culmination of the transgression was marked by the formation of the Main Postglacial Shoreline (Sissons *et al.*, 1966), which lies at the back of the extensive raised estuarine flats of the highest carse surface. Following the culmination of the transgression, relative sea level fell to its present level. This fall was punctuated by the formation of three lower shorelines in the Forth area, equivalent to three lower surfaces in the carselands there.

The Present Study

This study began with morphological mapping of the area at a scale of 1:10560. Following this, the altitude of the inner break of slope of all terraces, including the carselands, was determined at 50-m intervals by instrumental levelling from Ordnance Survey bench marks (altitudes given in the text below are therefore in metres OD unless otherwise stated). Next, a detailed programme of boring was carried out in selected localities in the carse and related deposits, using a Hiller type peat sampler. The top of each borehole was instrumentally levelled from Ordnance Survey bench marks. Finally, pollen analysis was carried out at three sites where the stratigraphy was thought to be of particular significance. Samples of peat from two of these sites were submitted to Birmingham University and to the Scottish Universities' Research and Reactor Centre for carbon-14 assay.

Morphology

The deposits surrounding the carse embayment consist largely of sands and gravels at higher altitudes, becoming finer at lower levels. Fragmentary outwash terraces lying at 27–29 m occur on the south side, declining markedly eastwards. Below the outwash, terraces occur at 21–22, 18–19, 15–17, and 11–12 m as small fragments on the spurs between gullies leading into the embayment. The laminated silty clays of the lowest of these terraces can be seen descending beneath the carse deposits at Maryton, confirming the relative age of the deposits.

The carse surface in the embayment is a distinctly uniform feature, changes in level as great as 0.5 m in 100 m of distance being very rare. The surface ends abruptly against the surrounding materials in a marked break of slope, though augering and borehole information indicate that the carse deposits continue for a short distance beneath colluvium (see sections below). Measurement of the carse surface at the break of slope at 63 points shows a rise in altitude westward from 6.4 m at the edge of the Basin in the east to 8.0 m at the head of the embayment in the west. However, for the most part the carse surface lies between 6 and 7 m.

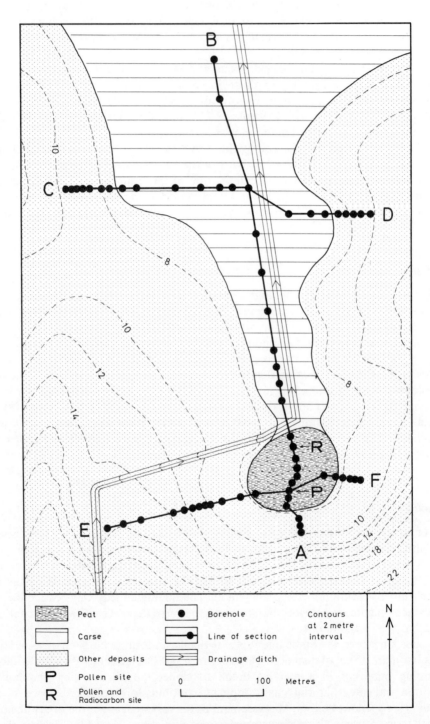

Fig. 16.2 The Fullerton gully

Stratigraphy

Borings through the carse at the centre of the embayment showed up to 9 m of a grey silty clay containing shells, overlying a tough pinkish silty clay with stones. Closely spaced borings at the margins of the carse area, however, revealed a more complex stratigraphy. Two areas were examined in detail, at Fullerton (Fig. 16.2) and Maryton (Fig. 16.4).

At Fullerton, 62 boreholes were put down in the mouth of a gully leading into the embayment. Fig. 16.2 shows the borehole locations, and Fig. 16.3 shows the stratigraphy, summarized in Table 16.1. In this locality, the carse deposits and associated

Table 16.1 Summary of the stratigraphy at the Fullerton and Maryton sites

Fullerton	
At the peat moss	At the mouth of the gully
7. Peat	
6. Grey silty clay	6. Grey silty clay (carse)
5. Peat	5. Grey, micaceous, silty fine sand
4. Grey, micaceous, silty fine sand	4. Grey silty clay
3. Peat	3. Peat
2. Sand and fine gravel	2. Sand and fine gravel
1. Laminated pink silty clay	1. Laminated pink silty clay

Maryton
At the bluff
5. Grey silty clay (carse)
4. Peat
3. Grey, micaceous, silty fine sand
2. Peat
1. Laminated pink silty clay

materials rest on a laminated pink silty clay, which has a discontinuous covering of fine gravel and sand, usually also pink. These deposits together form an irregular surface which is largely covered by a layer of peat. This peat increases in thickness up-gully, eventually reaching the surface to form a small peat moss. Above the peat at the mouth of the gully occurs a grey silty clay. This gradually decreases in thickness up-gully, eventually disappearing. Above this occurs a conspicuous layer of grey, micaceous, silty fine sand, which extends up the gully, forming a wedge in the peat. Above this distinctive sand layer at the mouth of the gully lies a further layer of grey silty clay which forms the carse surface. This too forms a wedge in the peat moss. In all three sections shown in Fig. 16.3 colluvium occurs on the margins of the carse and peat areas, and the detrital fan of a small stream west of the peat moss covers up to 4 m of peat. Although it is possible to identify clearly the junctions between lowest peat, grey micaceous silty fine sand, middle peat, carse, and upper peat, there are frequently indications of transitional zones, particularly in the case of the carse/peat boundaries, where abundant *Phragmites* remains can be identified in the carse.

At Maryton, an exposure in a low bluff overlooking the Basin (Fig. 16.4) shows a sequence of deposits with similarities to that at Fullerton. The Maryton sequence is summarized in Table 16.1. It is similar to the Fullerton section near the head of the gully, but outside the peat moss there, and it seems possible that the Maryton sequence belongs to a fragment of the deposits of a gully area similar to that at Fullerton, which has since been truncated by erosion of the bluff at the edge of the Basin.

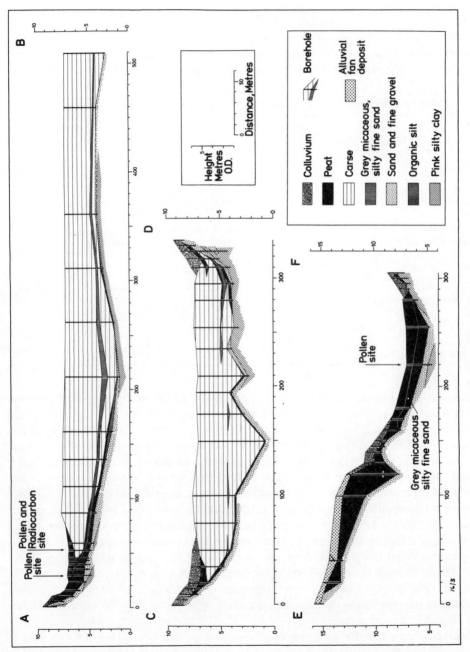

Fig. 16.3 Sections in the deposits at Fullerton

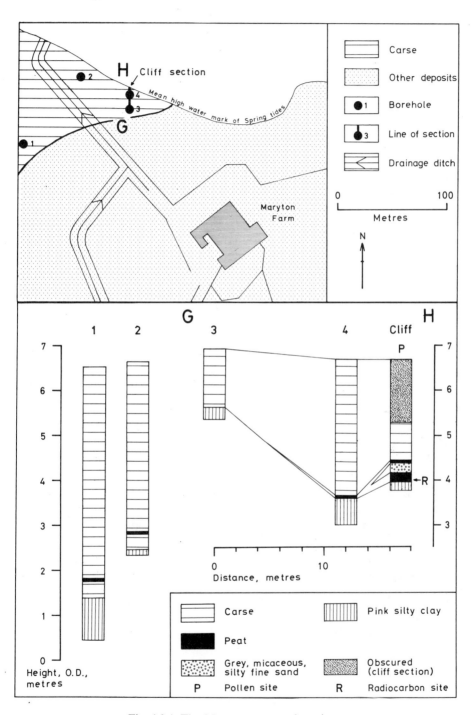

Fig. 16.4 The Maryton area and sections

The detail of the stratigraphy at Fullerton and Maryton suggests fluctuating depositional activity against the background of continued peat accumulation, and gradual junctions between the layers above the basal laminated clay suggest no evidence of a hiatus in the depositional record. In an attempt to date the sequence of events, pollen analysis was carried out at selected sites, and samples of peat from the stratigraphy were submitted for carbon-14 assay.

Pollen Analysis

Two sites at Fullerton and one at Maryton were sampled for pollen. Both Fullerton sites lie in the peat moss. Site A (pollen site P, Figs. 16.2 and 16.3) is located at the up-gully limit of minerogenic deposits in the peat. Here, a thin wedge of grey micaceous silty fine sand occurs within peat which overlies gravels and a basal laminated pink clay. A Hiller peat sampler was used to sample the deposits. Site B (pollen and radiocarbon site R, Figs. 16.2 and 16.3) is located north of site A at a point where both the carse and the grey micaceous silty fine sand form wedges in the peat, here lying directly on silty clay. A 'Russian'-type peat sampler was used at this site, and the basal clay was not sampled. At both Fullerton sites the sampling interval for pollen analysis was 10 cm. At Maryton, samples were collected for pollen analysis from the cleared bluff exposure (Fig. 16.4) at intervals of 2.5 cm. All three sites were levelled instrumentally from Ordnance Survey bench marks to permit comparison of the various horizons, whose altitudes are listed in Table 16.2.

Table 16.2 Horizons at the Fullerton and Maryton pollen sites

Site	Stratum	Depth of top below surface (m)	Altitude of top (m OD)
Fullerton Site A (P, Figs. 16.2 and 16.3)			
	5. Peat	0	6.94
	4. Grey, micaceous, silty fine sand	0.45	6.49
	3. Peat	0.54	6.40
	2. Sand and fine gravel	1.46	5.48
	1. Laminated pink silty clay (base not reached)	2.03	4.91
Fullerton Site B (R, Figs. 16.2 and 16.3)			
	6. Peat	0	6.80
	5. Grey silty clay	0.46	6.34
	4. Peat	1.23	5.57
	3. Grey, micaceous, silty fine sand	1.30	5.50
	2. Peat	1.48	5.32
	1. Sand and fine gravel (base not reached)	1.98	4.82
Maryton			
	5. Grey silty clay (surface obscured)	0	5.28
	4. Peat	0.85	4.43
	3. Grey, micaceous, silty fine sand	0.95	4.33
	2. Peat	1.13	4.15
	1. Laminated pink silty clay (base not seen)	1.28	4.00

All samples were prepared for analysis using the appropriate laboratory techniques outlined by Faegri (1975). Local pollen assemblage zones (West, 1970) were adopted for each site, but regional correlations between sites and with the British pollen zonation scheme of Godwin (1940) are also made below.

Fullerton Site A

The pollen diagram for site A (Fig. 16.5) is divided into three pollen assemblage zones. Zone FA-1 coincides stratigraphically with the basal laminated pink clay. Here, pollen is scarce and in a poor state of preservation, with eroded and pitted exines. An open habitat is indicated, with Cyperaceae, Gramineae, *Juniperus*, Tubuliflorae and Saxifragaceae pollen present in small amounts. No detailed ecological inferences can be made from such barren spectra.

Zone FA-2 is broadly coincident with the gravel, basal peat, and grey micaceous silty sand. Pollen is much more abundant and in a better state of preservation. This, together with the vegetation indicated, suggests a hiatus between the basal clay and the deposits immediately above it. The zone is characterized by a rise in *Corylus*-type pollen (probably of *Corylus* rather than *Myrica* in this situation) to reach a maximum of 45% of the total at the base of the peat. Values for *Betula, Pinus sylvestris, Salix*, and *Juniperus* are low but persistent, whilst *Ulmus, Quercus*, and *Alnus glutinosa* appear during the zone, in gradually increasing amounts. An initial *Betula-Pinus sylvestris* dominated woodland, gradually joined by *Corylus* and later *Ulmus, Alnus glutinosa*, and *Quercus*, is indicated.

The peat here changes upwards from being predominantly composed of sedges at the base to contain much wood, suggesting drying conditions. This is supported by the herbaceous pollen content. At the base, Cyperaceae, *Filipendula*, and spores of *Selaginella selaginoides* and Lycopodiaceae indicate damp conditions, but then decline upwards. However, local areas of open water and swamp are indicated in the upper part of the zone by taxa such as *Potamogeton, Equisetum* and Umbelliferae.

Zone FA-3 conforms approximately with the surface peat. *Alnus glutinosa* values rise strongly here to constitute 20% of the total pollen, while those of *Corylus* type decline. The presence of local damp habitats is suggested by slight rises in *Sphagnum*, Rosaceae undiff., Umbelliferae, and Cyperaceae, and the presence of *Cochlearia* pollen.

Fullerton Site B

Three pollen assemblage zones are delimited on the pollen diagram for this site also (Fig. 16.6). Zone FB-1 equates stratigraphically with the basal peat, grey micaceous silty sand, middle peat, and lowest part of the grey silty clay (carse). It is marked by high values of *Corylus*-type pollen, consistent amounts of that of *Betula* and *Pinus sylvestris*, and increasing frequencies of *Ulmus, Quercus*, and *Alnus glutinosa*. High values of Cyperaceae pollen suggest local damp conditions, but significant amounts of *Filipendula* and Nymphaceae point to freshwater habitats, rather than brackish water conditions or saltmarsh.

Zone FB-2 coincides stratigraphically with the bulk of the grey silty clay of the carse. A decline in *Pinus sylvestris* and slight increase in *Alnus glutinosa* pollen are notable here, whilst *Corylus* type maintains high values and *Quercus* increases. Persistent values of Chenopodiaceae and Cyperaceae suggest damp environments locally, possibly including saltmarsh.

Zone FB-3 coincides approximately with the surface peat. Here, a marked rise in *Alnus glutinosa* pollen takes place, while that of *Corylus* type declines. A local transition from a brackish or salt water environment with marsh to one of freshwater with swamp is inferred by increases in Nymphaceae and Cyperaceae pollen, together with Filicales spores.

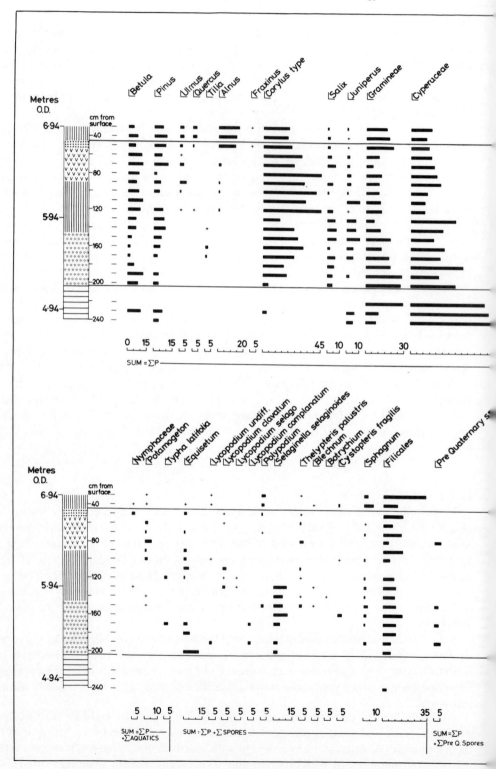

Fig. 16.5 Fullerton site A pollen diagram

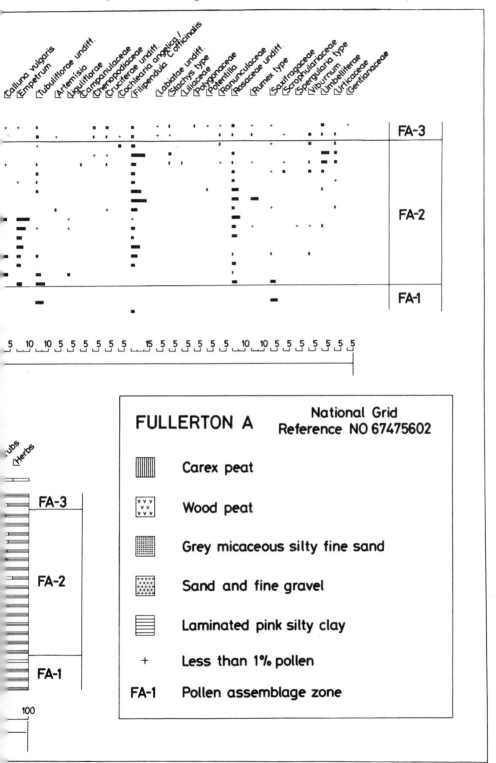

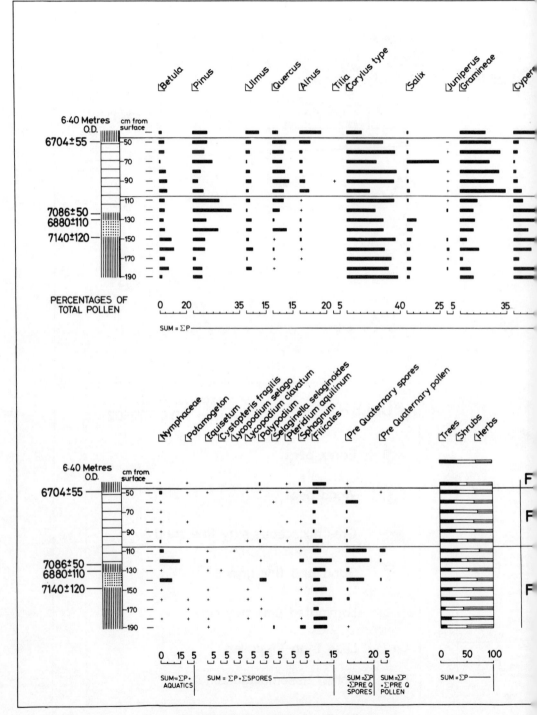

Fig. 16.6 Fullerton site B pollen diagram

FULLERTON B — National Grid Reference NO 67485605

	Carex peat
	Grey silty clay (Carse)
	Grey micaceous silty fine sand
+	Less than 1% pollen
FB-1	Pollen assemblage zone
7140±120	Radiocarbon date (years bp)

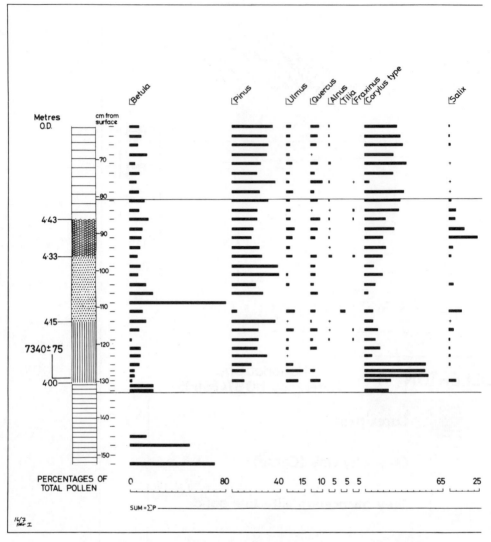

Fig. 16.7 Maryton pollen diagram (continued on pp. 240 and 241)

Maryton

At Maryton, the pollen was frequently in a poor state of preservation and variable in its occurrence. Three pollen assemblage zones are distinguished on the diagram (Fig. 16.7). Zone M-1 corresponds to most of the laminated pink silty clay at the base of the bluff section. Pollen is particularly poorly preserved and scarce here, leading to statistical artefacts exemplified by the samples with high *Betula* values. Despite the low frequencies and restricted taxal range, however, the pollen present indicates the existence of an open habitat locally.

Zone M-2 corresponds to the uppermost layers of the pink silty clay, basal peat, grey micaceous silty sand, the sub-carse peat, and the lowest part of the grey silty clay of the carse. Pollen is much more frequent here than in the layer below, and this, together with the strong contrast in the pollen assemblages, points to a hiatus in time between this zone and Zone M-1. Zone M-2 is notable for persistent values of *Betula* and *Pinus sylvestris*

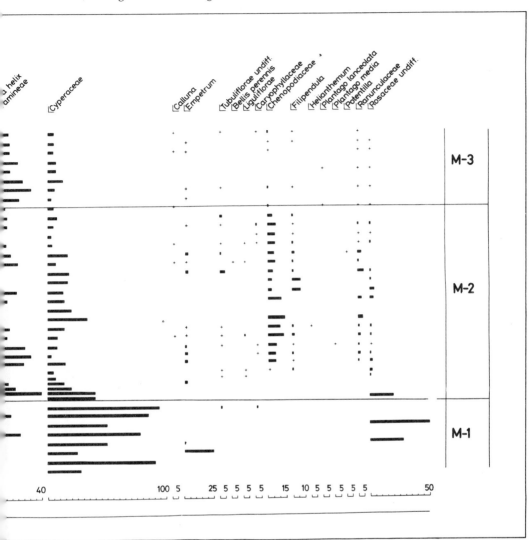

together with variable amounts of *Corylus*-type pollen. *Ulmus* and *Quercus* pollen are present in small amounts, while *Salix* is variable in occurrence. High values for Gramineae and Cyperaceae pollen, also persistent amounts of Chenopodiaceae, Nymphaceae and *Filipendula*, suggest a damp environment nearby.

Zone M-3 corresponds to most of the grey silty clay of the carse at the top of the section. *Pinus sylvestris* and *Corylus*-type pollen values are high, and that of *Betula*, *Ulmus*, and *Quercus* persistent. Substantial amounts of Nymphaceae and Cyperaceae pollen probably reflect local damp conditions.

Correlation

The pollen content of the laminated pink silty clays at both Fullerton site A and Maryton is similar in both type and preservation, and is probably indicative of a Late

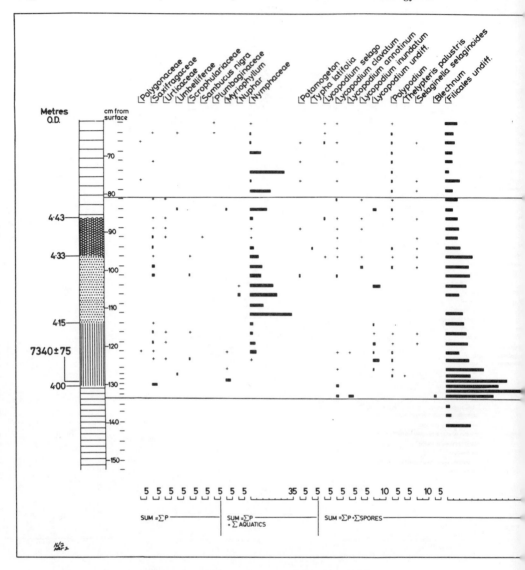

Fig. 16.7 Maryton pollen diagram (continued)

Devensian environment in which a mosaic of open habitat plant communities existed, though it is impossible to characterize them on the evidence available. A hiatus between this and the overlying deposits at both locations is suggested by the distinct and non-sequential change between the respective pollen assemblages.

The basal pollen assemblage zone at Fullerton site B (FB-1) appears to correspond to FA-2 and M-2, in that both the tree and herbaceous pollen contents are broadly similar. The second zone at Fullerton site B (FB-2) is correlated with FA-3 and M-3, particularly in view of the tree pollen content. These zones (FB-1, FA-2, M-2 and FB-2, FA-3, M-3) are suggested as indicative of a predominantly boreal environment, belonging to zones IV, V and VI of Godwin (1960) and chronozone Fl I of the Flandrian (West, 1970). Pollen zone FB-3 has no equivalent at either Fullerton site A or Maryton. It is considered indicative of the Atlantic environment of zone VIIa and chronozone Fl II.

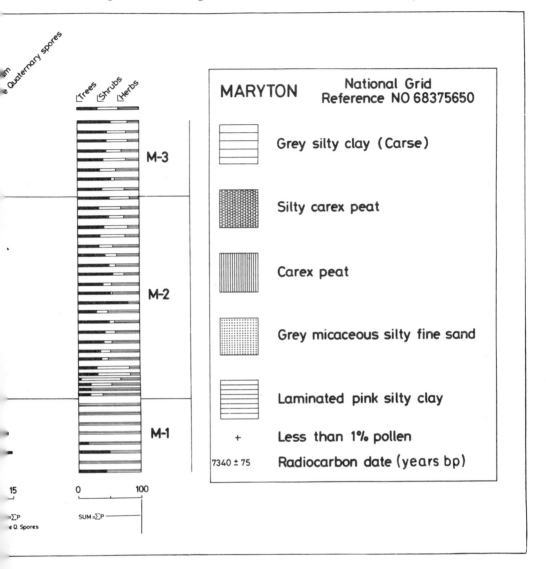

Carbon-14 Assay

At Fullerton, samples of peat for radiocarbon dating were collected from 2 cm-wide bands above and below the grey micaceous silty sand layer and above and below the carse layer at pollen site B (R, Figs. 16.2 and 16.3). Collection was by multiple shot sampling, using the 'Russian'-type peat sampler. Each sample weighed *ca*. 5 g dry weight, obtained from three insertions of the instrument in the closest possible proximity. Results were as follows (see also Fig. 16.6):

SRR-1148: 6704±55 bp (peat above grey silty clay [carse])
SRR-1149: 7086±50 bp (peat below grey silty clay [carse])
Birm-867: 6880±110 bp (peat above grey, micaceous, silty fine sand)
Birm-823: 7140±120 bp (peat below grey, micaceous, silty fine sand)

At the Maryton exposure, one sample of peat collected from a 2 cm-wide band directly above the laminated silty clay at the base of the bluff section (see also Figs. 16.4 and 16.7) gave the following result:

(IGS-186) SRR-869: 7340±75 bp

The apparent reversal in the dates for the peat that separates the carse deposits and the silty sand at Fullerton (SRR-1149 and Birm-867) might possibly result from the peat layer being so thin (7 cm) that contamination between the two samples has occurred, either in the coring process or as a result of their *in situ* stratigraphic proximity. Another possibility is that the peat was reworked to a degree at the onset of carse deposition. However, the two dates are not statistically different at the 95% significance level, and therefore the most reasonable approach to the problem of the reversed dates is probably to calculate from them a mean age for the peat layer. This mean age is 6983±60 bp.

Comparing these results with the pollen evidence, it appears that the boreal (Fl I) conditions indicated in zone FB-1 persisted hereabouts rather longer than in more southerly British locations (Godwin, 1960; Hibbert *et al.*, 1971; Hibbert and Switsur, 1976), in view of the radiocarbon dates. A similar conclusion holds for the boreal environment of M-2, where the radiocarbon date of 7340±75 bp was obtained. The Boreal/Atlantic (Fl I/Fl II) transition occurs at about 6700 radiocarbon years bp at Fullerton site B, again later than the transition in more southerly locations. These dates are, however, similar to those obtained from other sites in eastern Scotland. For example, in the Forth area, Sissons and Brooks (1971) obtained a date of 6490±125 bp from a 10 cm-thick sample at the Boreal/Atlantic transition in the western Forth valley. Thus the dating evidence from both pollen analysis and carbon-14 assay appears to be in broad agreement.

The Formation of the Deposits

At both Maryton and Fullerton, the morphological, stratigraphical, and palynological evidence suggests that the laminated pink silty clay at the base of each sequence is probably Late Devensian in age. The contrast in the pollen record between the clay and the deposits above suggests a hiatus in time, during which occurred the dissection of the clay deposit by gullies. Thus the clay surface in the sections is probably erosional.

The earliest growth of peat on the surface of the clay in the general area is probably not recorded at either Fullerton or Maryton. Possibly initial peat growth began in lower and more poorly drained localities, extending along the clay surface. At Maryton, the lower peat in the section was forming in a boreal environment by 7340±75 radiocarbon years bp. About or soon after 7140±120 bp at Fullerton, while boreal conditions still persisted, peat growth was arrested by the deposition of a grey micaceous silty fine sand, and a similar situation occurs at Maryton. The pollen evidence does not confirm a marine environment for the deposition of this sand layer, but since the stratigraphy at Fullerton indicates that it is both underlain and overlain by estuarine carse deposits, it seems likely. Subsequently, however, deposition ceased and renewed peat growth at both localities occurred. Still in a boreal environment (Fl I), and possibly at a date not earlier than 6983±60 bp at Fullerton, peat growth was once more arrested at both sites, this time by the deposition of the grey silty clay of the carse. The pollen evidence suggests possible saltmarsh conditions, consistent with an estuarine origin for the deposit. Subsequently, at Fullerton, the carse deposits ceased to accumulate and renewed peat growth began around 6704 ± 55 bp, as a saltmarsh environment gave way to more freshwater and swamp conditions, early in the Atlantic (Fl II).

The stratigraphy at Fullerton shows that this site is located at the landward limit of carse deposition. The pollen and carbon-14 dating here suggest that the transgression in which the carse deposits were laid down culminated between late Boreal (Fl I) and early Atlantic (Fl II) times, or between 6983 ± 60 and 6704 ± 55 radiocarbon years bp in this locality.

Comparison with Other Areas

The main carse surface in this area can be correlated with the Main Postglacial Shoreline in the Forth and Tay areas for three reasons. Firstly, it is the highest Flandrian marine surface. Secondly, it lies at a similar height to the highest carse surface in the Montrose area generally (the results of a wider study of the Montrose Basin carselands will be published later). Thirdly, there is no evidence of overlapping marine surfaces in the carse stratigraphy such as might result from the Main Postglacial Shoreline descending beneath later shorelines beyond the Forth and Tay areas. Both the pollen and stratigraphic evidence concur in indicating a continuous depositional sequence commencing in the formation of the basal peat. The dates obtained for the culmination of the transgression in which the carse deposits accumulated in this area agree very broadly with dates from the western Forth valley, where Sissons and Brooks (1971) concluded that the carse deposits accumulated between 7480 ± 125 and 6490 ± 125 bp. Their site was not at the landward limit of carse deposition, however, and their carbon-14 samples each consisted of a 10 cm-wide peat band, so that detailed comparisons are not possible. It may be significant, however, that they placed the Boreal/Atlantic transition at the junction between carse and overlying peat, as at Fullerton site B in the present study.

In East Fife, Chisholm (1971) examined a site where carse deposits were underlain and overlain by peat. Carbon-14 assay of the peat at the respective peat/carse junctions gave dates of 7605 ± 130 bp and 5830 ± 110 bp. The present authors believe from their own studies that the carse surface in this area too belongs to the Main Postglacial Shoreline, but again the great thickness (15 cm) of the samples taken does not allow detailed comparison, though there is broad agreement. The other dates for peat found in association with carse deposits in eastern Scotland, summarized by Sissons (1967, 1974, 1976), are not strictly comparable in detail.

Although Chisholm's work did not involve pollen analysis of the deposits, it would seem reasonable to conclude from the present study and other available evidence that the main Flandrian marine transgression in eastern Scotland culminated between the late Boreal and early Atlantic, and that abandonment of the Main Postglacial Shoreline also occurred at about this time. Unfortunately, there are at present insufficient data to allow measurement of the diachroneity of the shoreline, though work along similar lines to that described above, in progress at several sites in eastern Scotland, may rectify this shortcoming.

It does appear from the present study, however, that even the later stages of the transgression involved at least two episodes. An earlier phase, in which a grey silty clay and a grey micaceous silty fine sand were deposited, was succeeded by a slight regression before the second phase, when the grey silty clay which forms the carse surface accumulated. The stratigraphy of the carse deposits in East Fife (Chisholm, 1971) shows a similar sequence, and this may prove to be a widespread feature in eastern Scotland.

Conclusion

Measurement of the age of a time-transgressive shoreline necessarily involves the study of the shoreline at a range of locations from the area of maximum uplift to the periphery. However, comparable sites need to be studied at each location. Although the Main Postglacial Shoreline is marked by well defined morphological and stratigraphic features in eastern Scotland, measurements of its age have sometimes been made from sites determined more by the ready availability of datable material than by the appropriateness of the sites. Only those sites studied by Sissons and Brooks (1971) and Chisholm (1971) are strictly comparable to those in the present study, and there are significant differences in the detail in which these sites have been studied. It is suggested that the type of location described in this paper, where estuarine deposits wedge out in peat mosses located at the former shoreline flanking the carselands, are the most appropriate for study. Such locations probably mark the extreme limit of deposition, and are most likely to record the culmination of the transgression from which the Main Postglacial Shoreline was formed. When similar studies to the present one have been completed at several other sites, measurement of the diachroneity of the Main Postglacial Shoreline may be possible. This in turn may provide information on the nature of the isostatic–eustatic relationships which caused its formation and abandonment.

There are other, wider, advantages to be gained from more accurate dating of the Main Postglacial Shoreline. It is the best developed and least fragmented raised shoreline in large parts of Scotland, and in the areas bordering the firths in eastern and south-western Scotland its associated raised estuarine flats and deposits cover extensive tracts of land. It is therefore a very convenient reference marker for studies of Flandrian landform evolution in the low-lying areas, and its deposits form an important stratigraphic marker. Reference has been made in this paper to the presence of colluvial material that has moved downslope after the formation of this shoreline, and to an alluvial fan that postdates both the shoreline and the surface peat. Furthermore, the investigations described above were carried out in a large gully or valley that has been partially infilled by carse and other sediments. Any future attempts to study rates of mass movement during the Flandrian, or the chronology of dissection, valley development, or alluvial fan formation, could benefit greatly from a more accurate knowledge of the age of the Main Postglacial Shoreline, whether or not its age varies measurably from centre of uplift to periphery.

Acknowledgements

The authors are grateful to NERC and the Scottish Universities' Research and Reactor Centre, and to Birmingham University, for radiocarbon dates; and particularly to Dr. D. Harkness and Mr. R. Williams. They also thank Lanchester Polytechnic and the University of Exeter for grants towards fieldwork costs.

References

Chisholm, J. I. (1971). The stratigraphy of the Post-Glacial marine transgression in N.E. Fife. *Bull. Geol. Surv. Gr. Br.*, **37**, 91–107.
Cullingford, R. A., and Smith, D. E. (1980). Late Devensian shorelines in Angus and Kincardineshire. *Boreas*, **9**, in press.
Faegri, K. (1975). *Textbook of Pollen Analysis*. Munksgaard, Copenhagen.

Godwin, H. (1940). Pollen analysis and forest history of England and Wales. *New Phytol.*, **39**, 370–400.

Godwin, H. (1960). Radiocarbon dating and Quaternary history in Britain. *Proc. Roy. Soc. Lond.*, *B*, **153**, 287–320.

Hibbert, F. A., Switsur, V. R., and West, R. G. (1971). Radiocarbon dating of Flandrian pollen zones at Red Moss, Lancashire. *Proc. Roy. Soc. Lond.*, *B*, **177**, 161–176.

Hibbert, F. A., and Switsur, V. R. (1976). Radiocarbon dating of Flandrian pollen zones in Wales and northern England. *New Phytol.*, **77**, 793–807.

Howden, J. C. (1868). On the superficial deposits of the estuary of the South Esk. *Trans. Edinb. Geol. Soc.*, **1**, 138–150.

Jamieson, T. F. (1865). On the history of the last geological changes in Scotland. *Quart. J. Geol. Soc.*, **21**, 161–203.

Sissons, J. B. (1967). *The Evolution of Scotland's Scenery.* Oliver and Boyd, Edinburgh.

Sissons, J. B. (1974). The Quarternary in Scotland: a review. *Scott. J. Geol.*, **10**, 311–337.

Sissons, J. B. (1976). *Scotland.* Methuen, London.

Sissons, J. B., and Brooks, C. L. (1971). Dating of early postglacial land and sea level changes in the Western Forth Valley. *Nature Phys. Sci.*, **234**, 124–127.

Sissons, J. B., Smith, D. E., and Cullingford, R. A. (1966). Late-glacial and post-glacial shorelines in southeast Scotland. *Trans. Inst. Br. Geog.*, **39**, 9–18.

West, R. G. (1970). Pollen zones in the Pleistocene of Great Britain and their correlation. *New Phytol.*, **69**, 1179–1183.

Timescales in Geomorphology
Edited by R. A. Cullingford, D. A. Davidson, and J. Lewin
© 1980 John Wiley & Sons Ltd

CHAPTER 17

Pollen analyses, radiocarbon dates and the deglaciation of Rannoch Moor, Scotland, following the Loch Lomond Advance

M. J. C. Walker

Department of Geography,
St. David's University College, Lampeter

and J. J. Lowe

Geography Section,
City of London Polytechnic

Introduction

Rannoch Moor lies in an extensive rock basin of approximately 400 km² in the heart of the south-west Grampian Highlands, Scotland (Fig. 17.1). The floor of the basin is at an altitude of between 300 and 400 m OD and is underlain largely by granite, while the surrounding mountains, which attain heights of up to 1000 m OD, are composed of metamorphic and volcanic rocks. A number of troughs lead outward from the basin, forming spectacular breaches through the encircling mountains, and these, together with the distribution of erratics and patterns of glacial striae, indicate that the Rannoch basin was a major centre of ice accumulation and dispersal during Pleistocene glacial periods (Sissons, 1967a). Indeed, the evidence suggests that during successive glacial maxima, the major Scottish ice dome was centred over Rannoch Moor (Sissons, 1976).

It has long been recognized that, following the decay of the main Devensian ice sheet about 13,000 radiocarbon years ago (Sissons and Walker, 1974), glaciers subsequently built up on a much more restricted scale in many areas of the Scottish Highlands. Radiocarbon dates on shells incorporated in moraines of the Forth and Lomond glaciers (Fig. 17.2) indicate that this recrudescence of glacier ice (termed the Loch Lomond Advance*) occurred during Jessen-Godwin pollen zone III (Sissons, 1967b). At that time ice is believed to have occupied the whole of the Rannoch basin, reaching thicknesses of 400 m in places. It is difficult to determine the extent of Rannoch ice to the west of the Moor, although limits have been established at the seaward ends of Loch

---

* The term Loch Lomond Advance (Sissons, 1977) is preferred to the more widely used Loch Lomond Readvance as there is evidence to suggest that ice disappeared completely from Scotland during the Lateglacial Interstadial period (pollen zone II).

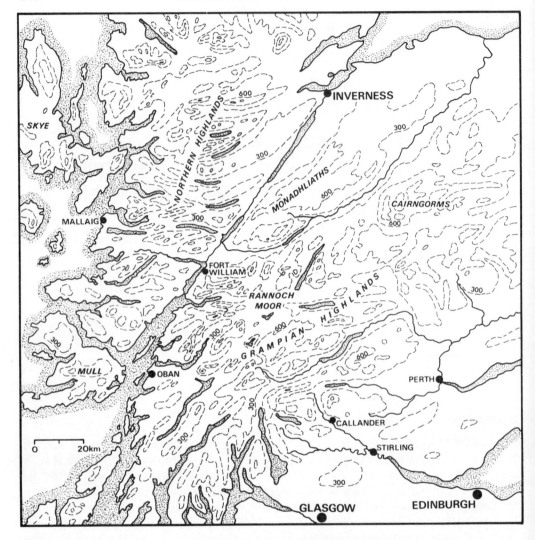

Fig. 17.1 Map to show the location of Rannoch Moor

Creran and Loch Etive (Gray, 1975). To the south and east, however, there is good evidence to show that glacier ice was continuous from the dispersal centre to limits at Loch Lomond, Menteith, and Callander; the heads of Loch Earn and Loch Tay; and to the eastern end of Loch Rannoch (Fig. 17.2). Outlet glaciers also flowed northwards to occupy parts of the Loch Ericht and Loch Treig valleys and Strath Ossian (Sissons, 1976; Sissons *et al.*, 1973; Thompson, 1972).

It would seem likely that, because of the altitude and thick ice cover, the Rannoch basin would have been one of the last localities to be deglaciated following the Loch Lomond Advance. The Rannoch Moor area is therefore a critical region for Lateglacial and early Postglacial environmental history, for if the age of the earliest post-glacial deposits on the Moor can be determined, then it should be possible to assign a date to the final disappearance of glaciers from the Scottish Highlands.

This paper describes pollen-stratigraphic investigations and presents radiocarbon dates on sediments of early Postglacial age from a number of sites on Rannoch Moor. The

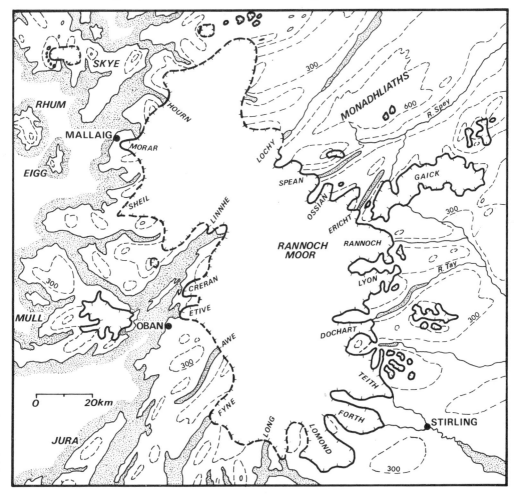

Fig. 17.2 The extent of the Loch Lomond Advance in the west-central Grampian Highlands (modified after Sissons 1976)

pollen evidence provides a detailed record of vegetation succession and colonization of the Rannoch area immediately following the decay of the Loch Lomond Advance glaciers, while the radio-carbon dates suggest that the Grampian Highlands may have become ice-free earlier than has hitherto been suspected.

Field and Laboratory Methods

Large areas of the Rannoch basin are characterized by extensive deposits of hummocky moraine that are the products of stagnating Loch Lomond Advance ice. The earliest Postglacial deposits would have accumulated in small basins between the morainic hummocks, but these former lake basins are now difficult to find as they are buried beneath varying thicknesses of mid- and late-Postglacial blanket peat. Thus, in order to locate sites that contain limnic sediments of early Postglacial age, it was necessary to traverse the hummocky moraine systematically, taking soundings in, and extracting basal samples from, all likely depressions. This procedure is laborious and extremely time consuming, and hence it was impossible to cover the entire area of the Moor. Four widely separated areas where well developed hummocky moraine occurred were therefore selected for detailed investigation, these being near Corrour Station, Rannoch Station, the Kingshouse Hotel, and Tyndrum, and a total of eight enclosed and infilled basins suitable for subsequent study were discovered (Fig. 17.3).

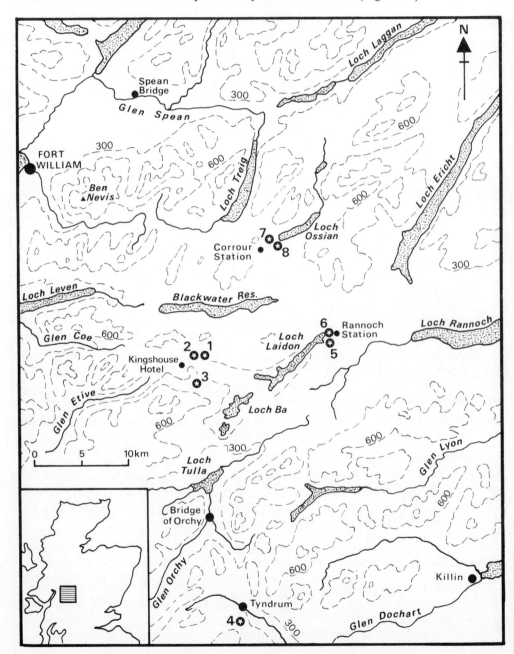

Fig. 17.3 The distribution of sampling sites on Rannoch Moor 1 Kingshouse 1; 2 Kingshouse 2; 3 Kingshouse 3; 4 Tyndrum; 5 Rannoch Station 1; 6 Rannoch Station 2; 7 Corrour 1; 8 Corrour 2

At each site, the subsurface contours were first established by sounding the basin infill along a 5 × 5 m grid (5 × 10 m at some of the larger sites), using a level mounted at the side of the site to provide a common datum for individual test bores. In this way, the deepest point in the basin, where the oldest sediment would be expected to have accumulated, could be located accurately. Successive cores of 5 cm diameter were then removed from that point with a piston corer, and subsequently analysed for pollen content.

Material for radiocarbon dating was obtained at five of the sites from four cores put down as near as possible to the deepest point in each basin. It has frequently been customary in work of this nature to use sediment from a single core for radiocarbon dating as, it has been argued, only in this way can a representative and uncontaminated sample be obtained. Unfortunately, where this method has been employed, it has been necessary to extract up to 10 cm of sediment from a core to provide enough material for dating. Clearly, such a thickness of sediment can have taken hundreds of years to accumulate, and thus the eventual age determination will be of little value for the critical dating of narrow horizons (Gray and Lowe, 1977). Hence, for the purposes of the present study, thin lenses of sediment are essential if dates are to be meaningful. Slices of sediment of between 1 and 2 cm thickness were therefore removed from the four cores and then bulked to provide a sufficiently large sample for dating. This procedure is considered to be satisfactory because of the well defined stratigraphy of the lowest sediments of each of the basins (samples being taken in relation to clearly defined litho-stratigraphic boundaries), and because at each site the four cores were closely spaced, being only 20–30 cm apart. Details of the radiocarbon determinations obtained are shown in Table 17.1

Samples for pollen analysis were prepared using Erdtman's acetolysis (Faegri and Iversen, 1964) following deflocculation in 5% potassium hydroxide solution. For samples containing a high proportion of minerogenic material, acetolysis was preceded by the hydrofluoric acid treatment described by Pennington *et al.* (1972). The residues were mounted in safranin-stained glycerine jelly, and counted on Vickers M15C microscopes at ×400 magnification, with critical identifications at ×1000. The total sum (excluding obligate aquatic pollen and spores) was normally of 300 land pollen, but this was increased where a particular taxon dominated the spectrum.

Pollen Analytical Data

The pollen records from the eight sites present a detailed picture of the changing vegetation pattern of the Rannoch Moor area from the time of the disappearance of the Loch Lomond Advance glaciers to the forest clearance phase of the mid/late-Postglacial period. In most of the profiles, the earliest spectra indicate a period of *Empetrum* heath and open grassland conditions immediately following deglaciation. These communities were subsequently invaded by large numbers of shrubs of *Juniperus communis* and by trees of *Betula*. Following a period of open birch woodland, hazel, and later pine arrived in the area, and for much of the mid-Postglacial, forests of birch and pine appear to have blanketed this region of the Grampian Highlands. With the onset of wetter conditions, alder began to arrive in the area, but subsequent increases in rates of leaching and in growth of ombrogenous blanket peat led to the decline of the pine and birch woodland and to the development of the blanket bog and heather moor landscape of the present day. This sequence of vegetation changes can be recognized in all of the profiles from the study area, and a representative pollen diagram is shown in Fig. 17.4. The vegetational

RANNOCH   STATION   1   1976

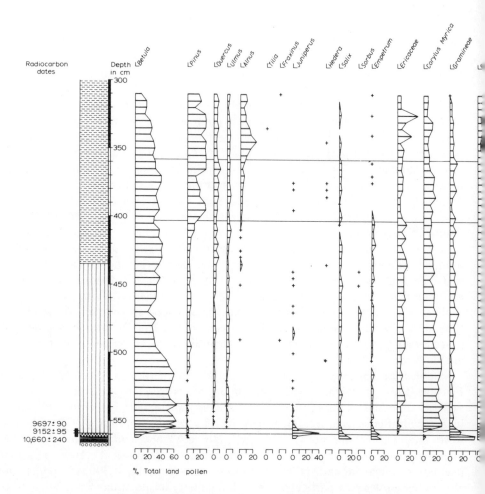

Fig. 17.4 Postglacial pollen diagram from Rannoch Station 1

history of the Rannoch Moor area has been discussed more fully elsewhere (Walker and Lowe, 1977).

Of more immediate concern to the present paper are the pollen records from the basal horizons in the profiles. It might be expected that the earliest pollen records would be characterized by high percentages of herbaceous pollen, reflecting the colonization of newly exposed substrates by pioneer plant communities immediately following deglaciation. However, in almost all of the diagrams, the earliest spectra are dominated by *Empetrum* and *Juniperus*. The absence of a basal herbaceous zone may be due in part to the impoverished nature of the pioneer pollen rain, and indeed in most of the sites up to 10 cm of virtually non-polleniferous minerogenic sediment underlie the earliest horizon that yielded sufficient pollen for counting. An alternative explanation involves the late melt-out of ice blocks within the kettle-holes. Studies in North America have shown that it is possible for ice to remain buried within a kettle-hole for hundreds of years after the disappearance of glaciers from the surrounding area (Porter and Carson, 1971). It is possible therefore that, during the initial period of colonization of Rannoch Moor by

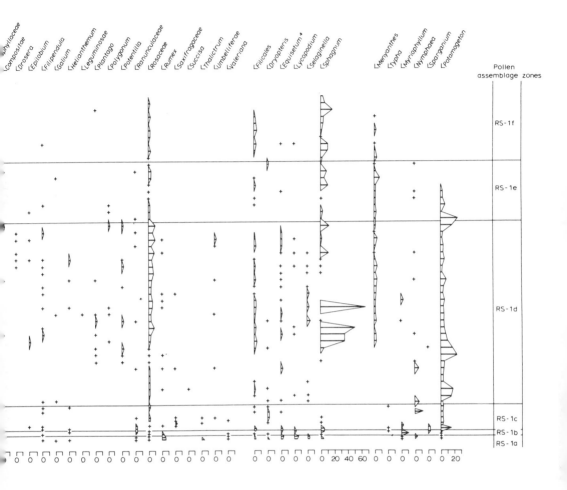

herbaceous vegetation, sedimentation in the basins was prevented by the late melt-out of stagnant ice in the kettle-holes. By the time these residual ice blocks had melted and sediment accumulation had commenced, *Empetrum* heath and juniper scrub had become firmly established locally.

The trend towards soil stability and the development of a closed vegetation cover is reflected in all the profiles by an abrupt litho-stratigraphic change from minerogenic to organic sediment, and by the appearance of large numbers of juniper and birch in the pollen spectra. The sequence at the Kingshouse 2 site is more complicated. In that profile, the basal minerogenic sediments are succeeded by a thin lens of gyttja, then by a layer of moss fragments which grade upwards into a second minerogenic horizon rich in moss remains. The entire sequence is overlain by organic lake muds (Fig. 17.5). This litho-stratigraphy at the site reflects a period very soon after deglaciation when parts of Rannoch Moor experienced marginal climatic conditions during which more severe winter temperatures may have led to a reduction in the vegetation cover and to a marked increase in the washing of skeletal mineral soils (Lowe and Walker, 1976). The high *Empetrum* and *Juniperus* pollen percentages associated with the macrofossil evidence of

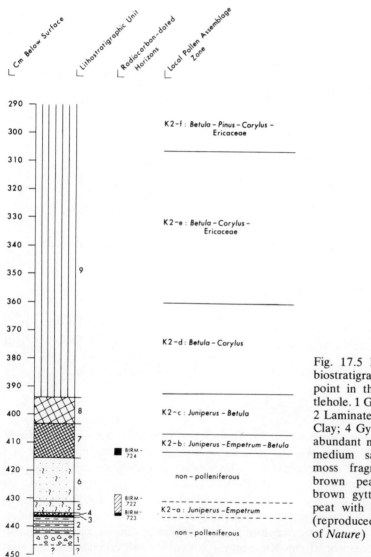

Fig. 17.5 Lithostratigraphy and biostratigraphy at the deepest point in the Kingshouse 2 kettlehole. 1 Gravel and coarse sand; 2 Laminated silt and fine sand; 3 Clay; 4 Gyttja; 5 Fine sand with abundant moss remains; 6 Fine-medium sand with occasional moss fragments; 7 Greenish-brown peaty gyttja; 8 Light brown gyttja; 9 Black telmatic peat with occasional fine roots (reproduced by kind permission of *Nature*)

Rhacomitrium lanuginosum suggest a vegetation cover very similar to the *Rhacomitreto-Empetretum* (*Rhacomitrium-Empetrum* heath) and *Juniperetum nanae* (dwarf juniper scrub) associations which are common in parts of the western and northern Scottish Highlands today (McVean and Ratcliffe, 1962). The former association occurs on block scree or bedrock with undeveloped soils, or on gently sloping ridges and summits below true *Rhacomitrium* heaths. *Juniperetum nanae* is a transitional association between subalpine scrub and low alpine dwarf shrub heath. The pollen and macrofossil evidence from the Kingshouse 2 profile therefore suggests that *Empetrum* and juniper heath became established fairly soon after the disappearance of ice from the vicinity of the site while the soils were still relatively immature, with the heath communities being interspersed with ground covered predominantly by a moss carpet or by grasses (Walker and Lowe, 1977).

Chronology

The palynological data outlined above are important not only from the point of view of vegetational reconstruction, but also because they provide a framework for the dating of events. The *Empetrum* and *Juniperus* pollen assemblage zones which are found at the base of most of the profiles can be correlated with the earliest Postglacial pollen assemblage zones at sites in other areas of the Scottish Highlands (e.g. Pennington *et al.*, 1972; Walker, 1975b; Lowe 1977). Furthermore, the evidence suggests that within enclosed basins on Rannoch Moor, sediment began to accumulate very soon after the disappearance of the last glaciers, although in some kettle-holes deposition may have been delayed by the late melt-out of residual ice blocks. Any dates therefore that are obtained from basal organic material within these basins must relate very closely to the disappearance of glacier ice from the Rannoch Moor area.

With the exception of the results from Tyndrum and Corrour 2, the basal radiocarbon dates are earlier than expected (Table 17.1). In assessing the reliability of the dates, a number of factors must be borne in mind. Firstly, most of the dates have fairly large standard errors (in excess of ±150 years). This is due in part to the small amounts of material submitted for dating purposes, but is more likely to be a function of the very low percentages of organic carbon in the lowermost sediments of the basin infills (e.g. the total carbon content of the dried gyttja of sample SRR-1074 was only 4.07%). Thus, the precision of the radiocarbon determinations is not as good as might have been expected.

Table 17.1 Radiocarbon dates from Rannoch Moor

Site	Sample number	Depth (m)	$\delta^{13}C_{PDB}(\%)$	Date (bp)
Kingshouse 2	Birm-724	4.13–4.15	−23.30	9910±200
	Birm-722	4.30–4.35	−22.45	10,290±180
	Birm-723	4.35–4.36	−22.37	10,520±330
Rannoch Station 1	SRR-1072	5.56–5.575	−33.4	9697± 90
	SRR-1073	5.575–5.59	−33.0	9152± 95
	SRR-1074	5.59–5.61	−31.6	10,660±240
Tyndrum	Birm-857	5.14–5.16	−26.3	8120±140
			−26.3	8180±110
	Birm-856	5.28–5.30	−22.9	8340±160
Rannoch Station 2	Birm-859	4.43–4.45	−22.4	10,160±200
	Birm-858	4.45–4.47	−22.0	10,390±200
Corrour 2	Birm-854	4.39–4.41	−24.4	9800±160
	Birm-855	4.56–4.58	−17.5	9440±310

Secondly, it is possible that some of the dated horizons may have been contaminated by younger material. One way in which this could occur is through sediment mixing on the former lake floors, although the close similarities between the basal pollen records from the eight sites suggest that this is unlikely to have been a serious problem. Alternatively, the basal sediments could have been affected by percolating groundwaters carrying younger carbon down through the profiles once the lakes had become infilled (cf. Birks, 1973; Walker, 1975a). Both of the dates from Tyndrum appear to be younger by up to 2000 years than comparable horizons at the other sites determined on the basis of pollen content, and may have been affected in this way. Finally, contamination by younger carbon may have occurred during the field or laboratory work. The middle date in the series from Rannoch Station 1 and the basal date from Corrour 2 are clearly aberrant and can most probably be explained by the incorporation of younger material into the dated sediment sample. The Corrour 2 date (Birm-855) is particularly surprising in view of the age determination of 9800 ± 160 (Birm-854) from 17 cm further up the profile. Pollen analytical evidence suggests that the latter date is reliable (Walker and Lowe, 1979), and thus an age in excess of 10,000 years bp would have been expected from Birm-855. It is therefore hoped to obtain an additional basal date from Corrour 2 in the near future.

A potentially more serious problem can arise from the contamination of the dated sediment by older carbonaceous material, especially through the phenomenon known as 'hard-water error', which may be particularly acute when gyttja is the dating medium. There is no obvious source of carbonate material in this part of the Grampian Highlands, but the possibility cannot be excluded that small amounts of older carbon could have become incorporated into the sediment of the basins from glacial rock flour derived initially from the complex metamorphic rocks that surround the Rannoch basin. As shown in Table 17.1, the $\delta^{13}C_{PDB}$ values on the dated material do not depart significantly from the 'normal' range observed for wood, peat, gyttja, and charcoal from European localities, i.e. $\delta^{13}C_{PDB} = -25 \pm 5\%$ (Oeschger *et al.*, 1970), which would seem to indicate that if hard-water error has been a factor, its overall effect is likely to have been small. However, it is recognized that gyttja is a complex sediment with an organic fraction composed of terrestrial and aquatic plant material, and which may also be made up in part from the remains of phytoplankton and zooplankton that lived in the waters of the former lake. The $\delta^{13}C_{PDB}$ values for each of these carbon sources are different, and thus to a large extent the $\delta^{13}C_{PDB}$ value for any sample of gyttja will be determined by the relative proportions of terrestrial, aquatic, and planktonic material contained within that body of sediment. If this is so, then it may be dangerous to attach too much importance to the $\delta^{13}C_{PDB}$ values obtained from the dated material from Rannoch Moor. A more detailed discussion of these problems can be found in Walker and Lowe (1979).

The most significant dates to emerge from the investigation were those obtained from Kingshouse 2, for at that site gyttja and moss fragments were used for dating purposes. The moss remains were of *Rhacomitrium lanuginosum*, which is a terrestrial species (Tallis, 1958), and thus hard-water error would seem to be very unlikely here. The dates from that site were carefully checked (Lowe and Walker, 1976) and show good internal agreement. As far as is possible to determine, they appear to be reliable within the limitations of the radiocarbon method.

It is important to emphasize that the basal dates obtained, if correct, are minimal for deglaciation, for at each site several centimetres of minerogenic lacustrine sediment underlie the lowermost dated horizon. The Kingshouse 2 dates were the first to be published from a kettle-hole site within the Loch Lomond Advance limits and these, together with the determinations from Rannoch Station, provide a minimal date for the disappearance of glacier ice from the vicinity of these basins. Collectively the dates suggest that Rannoch Moor became ice-free before 10,000 bp and perhaps even before 10,200 bp.

Only one other radiocarbon date has so far been obtained on basal organic deposits from within the Loch Lomond Advance limits in the Scottish Highlands. At Mollands, near Callander in the Teith Valley, over 7 m of sediment have accumulated in a deep basin on the upvalley side of prominent terminal moraine which is believed to mark the maximal extent of Loch Lomond Advance ice in the south-east Grampians (Thompson, 1972). The lowest organic horizon at that site yielded a date of 10,670 ± 80 bp (Lowe and Walker, 1977). If that date is correct, it implies that glacier ice had disappeared from the Callander area by *ca.* 10,500 bp. Taken together, the radiocarbon dates suggest total deglaciation of Scotland some time before 10,000 bp.

Conclusions

The basal pollen spectra at the Rannoch Moor sites, in association with the radiocarbon dates, indicate a very rapid plant colonization of this area of the Grampian Highlands following the wastage of Loch Lomond Advance glaciers. The evidence suggests that, in spite of the relative remoteness of Rannoch Moor and the distance from Lateglacial refugia, *Empetrum* heath and juniper scrub had become well established in the area some time before 10,000 bp. The complex biostratigraphic sequence at the Kingshouse 2 site implies that the early part of this period may have been one of fluctuating climatic conditions with more severe intervals of very short duration within the overall trend to climatic improvement. Tree birches appear to have arrived in the Rannoch basin in large numbers shortly after 10,000 bp and were followed by the uninterrupted spread of woodland across the previously barren hill slopes.

With the exception of the date from the Teith Valley, the radiocarbon dates obtained from Rannoch Moor are the only ones so far available from basal organic sediments in kettle-hole basins within the Loch Lomond Advance limits. In view of the fairly large standard errors on some of the dates, and because of the possibility that some of the age determinations have been affected by hard-water error, it is difficult to be precise about the timing of deglaciation. Nevertheless, the evidence does suggest that glaciers disappeared from Rannoch Moor and, by implication, from much of the Scottish Highlands well before 10,000 bp, and perhaps even before 10,200 bp, a date for deglaciation which is significantly earlier than had hitherto been suspected. Further work is being undertaken on Rannoch Moor in an attempt to obtain more precise dates on the time of ice wastage.

Geomorphological Implications

Several papers in this volume have described the operation of geomorphological processes over relatively short timespans, but few attempts have been made to relate the findings of these research projects to geomorphological activity over longer time periods. The problem appears to be largely one of establishing a regionally applicable chronology, for while it is possible to use direct field observations, remote sensing, historical records, etc., to assess landform changes over a period of a few hundred years, the evaluation of such changes over a longer timescale, e.g. the Holocene, presents a much more formidable obstacle. A major difficulty over most of the British Isles lies in the absence of dated reference levels to which the operation of geomorphological processes can be related. However, this problem can be at least partially overcome in the Scottish Highlands. Landforms and deposits of Loch Lomond Advance age are found throughout the Grampian Highlands and, if the timing of deglaciation can be established, this would provide a much needed reference datum for the study of landform modification in those parts of Scotland affected by the last glaciers.

There are numerous examples in the Scottish Highlands of present-day streams cutting into landforms and deposits which are believed to be of Loch Lomond Advance age. These include the River Teith near Callander, which breaches eskers and a marked terminal moraine, the River Dochart, which winds its way through spreads of pronounced hummocky moraine in Strath Fillan and Glen Dochart en route to Loch Tay, and the many rivers which radiate from Rannoch Moor along glacial troughs blanketed by ice stagnation landforms. The dating of ice wastage from these localities would provide the basis of a medium-range timescale for the modification of landforms by fluvial activity. Moreover, it should then be possible to effect meaningful comparisons between, for example, rates of stream erosion in the Holocene and stream channel changes over the shorter timespan of a few hundred years.

Similarly, in many areas of Loch Lomond Advance hummocky moraine, there are exposures which display clear weathering and soil profiles. Weathering rates, Postglacial slope adjustment and rates of pedogenesis could all be assessed if the age of formation of the substrate could be established. It is clear that numerous other studies in physical geography would benefit from a known absolute age of the surface upon which processes have been operative. Thus, in addition to furnishing information on glacial and vegetational history, the results of this study have implications for rates of stream erosion, slope processes, and pedogenesis in the Scottish Highlands following the disappearance of the last glaciers.

Acknowledgements

This research was financed by the Natural Environment Research Council, the Pantyfedwen Fund of St. David's University College, Lampeter, and the City of London Polytechnic. We thank the Natural Environment Research Council and the City of London Polytechnic for the initial radiocarbon dates, and the University of Birmingham for additional radiocarbon measurements. We are grateful to Mr. D. Almond for assistance in the field, and to the Forestry Commission for allowing us access to the sites at Corrour. Helpful discussions with Mr. D. G. Sutherland and Mr. R. E. G. Williams are also gratefully acknowledged.

References

Birks, H. J. B. (1973). *The Past and Present Vegetation of the Isle of Skye—a Palaeoecological Study*. Cambridge University Press, Cambridge.
Faegri, K., and Iversen, J. (1964). *Textbook of Pollen Analysis*. Munksgaard, Copenhagen.
Gray, J. M. (1975). The Loch Lomond Readvance and contemporaneous sea-levels in Loch Etive and neighbouring areas of western Scotland. *Proc. Geol. Assoc.*, **86**, 227–238.
Gray, J. M., and Lowe, J. J. (1977). The Scottish Lateglacial environment: a synthesis. In *Studies in the Scottish Lateglacial Environment* (Eds. J. M. Gray and J. J. Lowe). Pergamon Press, Oxford, pp. 163–181.
Lowe, J. J. (1977). *Pollen Analysis and Radiocarbon Dating of Lateglacial and Early Flandrian Deposits in Southern Perthshire*. Unpublished PhD Thesis, University of Edinburgh.

Lowe, J. J., and Walker, M. J. C. (1976). Radiocarbon dates and deglaciation of Rannoch Moor, Scotland. *Nature, Lond.*, **246**, 632–633.

Lowe, J. J., and Walker, M. J. C. (1977). The reconstruction of the Lateglacial environment in the southern and eastern Grampian Highlands. In *Studies in the Scottish Lateglacial Environment* (Eds. J. M. Gray and J. J. Lowe). Pergamon Press, Oxford, pp. 101–118.

McVean, D. N., and Ratcliffe, D. A. (1962). *Plant Communities of the Scottish Highlands.* HMSO, London.

Oeschger, H., Riesen, T., and Lerman, J. C. (1970). Bern Radiocarbon dates, VII. *Radiocarbon*, **12**, 358–384.

Pennington, W., Haworth, E. Y., Bonny, A. P., and Lishman, J. P. (1972). Lake sediments in northern Scotland. *Phil. Trans. R. Soc., B*, **264**, 191–194.

Porter, S. C., and Carson, R. J. (1971). Problems of interpreting radiocarbon dates from dead ice terrain, with an example from the Puget Lowland of Washington. *Quat. Res.*, **1**, 410–414.

Sissons, J. B. (1967a). *The Evolution of Scotland's Scenery.* Oliver and Boyd, Edinburgh.

Sissons, J. B. (1967b). Glacial stages and radiocarbon dates in Scotland. *Scott. J. Geol.*, **3**, 375–381.

Sissons, J. B. (1976). *Scotland.* Methuen, London.

Sissons, J. B. (1977). The Loch Lomond Readvance in the Northern Mainland of Scotland. In *Studies in the Scottish Lateglacial Environment* (Eds. J. M. Gray and J. J. Lowe). Pergamon Press, Oxford, pp. 45–59.

Sissons, J. B., and Walker, M. J. C. (1974). Lateglacial site in the central Grampian Highlands. *Nature, Lond.*, **249**, 822–824.

Sissons, J. B., Lowe, J. J., Thompson, K. S. R., and Walker, M. J. C. (1973). Loch Lomond Readvance in the Grampian Highlands of Scotland. *Nature Phys. Sci.*, **244**, 75–77.

Tallis, J. H. (1958). Studies in the biology of *Rhacomitrium lanuginosum* Brid. I. Distribution and ecology. *J. Ecol.*, **46**, 271–288.

Thompson, K. S. R. (1972). *The Last Glaciers in Western Perthshire.* Unpublished PhD Thesis, University of Edinburgh.

Walker, M. J. C. (1975a). Two Lateglacial pollen diagrams from the eastern Grampian Highlands of Scotland. *Pollen Spores*, **17**, 67–92.

Walker, M. J. C. (1975b). Late Glacial and Early Postglacial environmental history of the central Grampian Highlands, Scotland. *J. Biogeog.*, **2**, 265–284.

Walker, M. J. C., and Lowe, J. J. (1977). Postglacial environmental history of Rannoch Moor. I. Three pollen diagrams from the Kingshouse area. *J. Biogeog.*, **4**, 333–351.

Walker, M. J. C., and Lowe, J. J. (1979). Postglacial environmental history of Rannoch Moor. II. Pollen diagrams and radiocarbon dates from the Rannoch Station and Corrour areas. *J. Biogeog.*, **6**, in press.

SECTION III

Long Timescales
(*ca.* 10^4 to 10^5 Years and above)

Timescales in Geomorphology
Edited by R. A. Cullingford, D. A. Davidson, and J. Lewin
© 1980 John Wiley & Sons Ltd

CHAPTER 18

Dating Quaternary deposits more than 10,000 years old

J. T. Andrews and G. H. Miller

Institute of Arctic and Alpine Research and Department of Geological Sciences, University of Colorado

Introduction

The importance of chronology is frequently overlooked and/or understressed in geomorphological texts and in many geomorphological studies. The present is the key to the past—so they say; but, in fact, there are substantial reasons why such a statement, at the best, is misleading and, at the worst, is simply incorrect. The dominance of studies on modern processes in the field of geomorphological research needs to be balanced by the longer perspective that falls traditionally within the area of Quaternary geology and geomorphology. Of great interest is the rate at which various geomorphological processes work. The rate of work is usually measured by the removal of material and can be expressed as millimetres per 1000 years or kg cm^{-2} ka^{-1}. The complementary process of sedimentation measures the rate at which material accumulates. Changes in the rates of erosion and sedimentation provide indexes for evaluating shifts in basic systems, frequently, but not always, forced by factors associated with climatic change. The dating of events that have led to significant changes in the rates of erosion and sedimentation, and in their patterns, is clearly of fundamental concern in geomorphology. It is also worth pointing out that many landscapes of the world are not the product of the present (interglacial) climate and processes. Indeed, if studies of land and deep-sea stratigraphic records are correct, then we are living in a rather unusual period when viewed over the last 10^6 years—a period that may represent, climatically, a mere 10% of this interval. Thus, present geomorphological processes must be examined in the light of the longer geological record. In addition, there is, of course, evidence that man can greatly influence the equilibria of natural systems.

Methods that are used to date events within the Holocene have been dealt with in earlier sections of this book. Here we are concerned with the presentation and evaluation of methods that can be used to date deposits >10,000 years old. By and large, we limit our appraisal to methods that can be used for the Quaternary System. We take the Pliocene/Pleistocene boundary at its type section in Calabria, Italy, and thus support the notion that the Quaternary System starts about 1.8 million years ago.

It is clear to our rather biased view that dating and the development of a time–stratigraphic framework is traditionally much more in vogue in North America than it is in Britain or Europe. This is especially so for deposits and their associated events that date from the Pleistocene. Indeed, it is fair to level a criticism at North American research in the sense that studies typically stress chronology over an understanding of the events (either climatic or sedimentological). However, the counter argument—and the one that we adopt—is that an adequate chronological framework is an absolute necessity for the studies of changes in the nature and patterns of geomorphic processes.

In the remainder of this chapter we set ourselves the following aims.

1. To discuss the basic types of dating methods that are available for deposits >10,000 years old.
2. To discuss specifically a few of these methods, especially stressing new methods that may be powerful, or commenting on problems with older accepted methods.
3. To comment on any methods that are still essentially at the drawingboard stage (an example would be the revolutionary method of ^{14}C dating by actually counting the carbon-14 atoms).

Classification of Dating Methods

Coleman and Pierce (1977) suggest that Quaternary dating methods fall into three broad classes, namely (1) numerical (i.e., physical and chemical) methods, (2) relative age methods, and (3) correlative methods (Fig. 18.1). The physical dating methods in the time range with which we are concerned are based on the decay or growth of radioactive isotopes. These systems function independently of climatic or environmental changes and are thus the most rigorous and unambiguous of dating methods. For these methods the isotopic ratio (I) is strictly a function of time (T) and initial isotopic composition (P) provided that the enclosing material has remained as a closed system since deposition. This does not mean, however, that there are no problems associated with the accuracy and precision of dates derived from radiocarbon, uranium series, potassium–argon or fission track methods.

A second major class of dating methods are those based on chemical reactions. Like most chemical reactions, the rates at which these reactions proceed are primarily a function of temperature. Examples of such methods include apparently disparate systems, such as amino acid dating and obsidian hydration, as well as a group of techniques which are traditionally associated with relative dating methods of Quaternary deposits in the western USA and elsewhere, such as soil development, weathering rinds on boulders at the surface or within the soil, and the progressive change in the weathering of surface boulders. To this latter group we can apply the Jenny (1941) soil equation, such that

$$\text{State of weathering} = f(T, C, P, V, R) \tag{1}$$

where

T = time
C = climate (principally precipitation and summer temperature)
P = parent material
V = vegetation
R = topography of the site

Even for simpler systems, such as the diagenesis of protein in the carbonate matrix of a

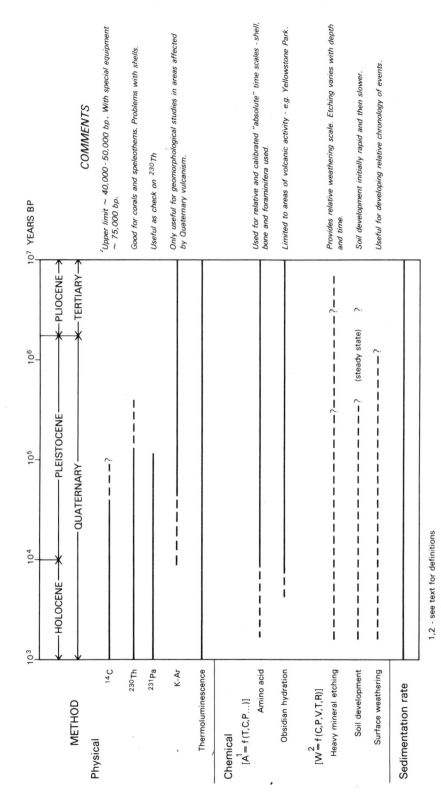

Fig. 18.1 Diagram illustrating the time span of some of the dating methods that can be applied to deposits greater than 10,000 years old

shell (amino acid method), the controls on the D- to L-amino acid ratios (A) can be expressed by a simplified version of the above equation:

$$A = f(T, C, P) \tag{2}$$

where T is time, C is climate (here primarily the integrated thermal histories in a shell deposition), and P is the particular amino acid assemblage for the taxa in question.

The third class of 'dating methods' is not involved with dating directly, but involves the correlation of a specific physical attribute of the sediment from a dated sequence to an undated one. This indeed is the traditional geological method of 'dating' by the lateral correlation of litho- and biostratigraphic units. In Quaternary studies the palaeomagnetic sequence established in potassium–argon dated volcanic rocks is used to 'date' deep-sea records which in turn possess a physical stratigraphy in the variations of the δO^{18} in carbonate fossils (Hecht, 1977) with distinctive patterns of fluctuation that permit the establishment of a stable isotope stratigraphy and, by inference, chronology (see papers in Cline and Hays, 1976). Of course, there is some overlap between this third group and the second. Thus, if a dated sequence of terraces can be established in one area, then the soil development of these terraces can be used to correlate, and hence date, other terrace sequences in the region, as long as factors C, P, V, and R are held constant (or nearly so). From the geomorphological point of view, the establishment of a chronostratigraphic framework is merely the initial stage in an investigation. Once the time-frame for a series of erosional and/or depositional events has been established, the way is now open for a series of studies on the *rates* of erosion or deposition. In turn, a general knowledge of rates of sedimentation can be used to establish a timescale (Fig. 18.1).

The use of any of the methods listed in Fig. 18.1 depends on a number of circumstances. In many parts of the world, potassium–argon, fission track, and obsidian hydration dating are not possible because they require suitable volcanic or igneous rocks. Thus, most of the dates that are produced by these methods are restricted to the active boundaries of the continental plate margins where collision and subduction have produced young rocks of Quaternary age. In a similar manner, the use of either the decay or growth of ^{14}C, ^{230}Th, and ^{231}Pa or the amino acid method requires that sediments preserve fossils. Again, the kilometres of barren Quaternary exposures far outweigh those that contain preserved datable materials. In areas of heavy rainfall and extensive leaching by groundwaters, much of the organic remains of plants and animals does not survive. Thus, the most useful group of methods may well be those that deal with the change of surface sediments and surface rocks through chemical and physical alterations. This group is, however, extremely intractable in terms of developing a suitable geochemical model that produces a 'date' for a particular depth of soil development or rind thickness (Porter, 1975, 1976). In that sense, one of the most exciting prospects is that of thermoluminescence (Fig. 18.1), which is used in a routine fashion in the USSR to date many of their middle Quaternary sequences, although an equivalent success story has yet to be forthcoming from the Western world.

Fig. 18.1 illustrates that the geomorphologist working in areas where sediments >10,000 years old occur has a large number of possible dating methods at his/her disposal. In contrast to research on Holocene events, we have lost the ability to use lichenometry, dendrochronology, and varve chronologies. We have, however, gained a large number of methods whose accuracy does not allow suitable separation of events within the Holocene, such as obsidian hydration, soil development, and potassium–argon dating. In this review we do not attempt to discuss all available methods, but limit ourselves to those with which we have some familiarity.

Physical Dating Methods

Radiocarbon Dating

Much has been written about the application of the radiocarbon method to dating between 10,000 bp and the upper limit of the technique. This limit varies—commercial laboratories can commonly date samples up to about 40,000 bp, although the counting errors are usually large. Conventional research laboratories with low backgrounds can push their limit back to just over 50,000 bp. Two laboratories (Groningen and the University of Washington) have elaborate isotopic enrichment systems that enable them to detect very low levels of ^{14}C activity and thus date samples to an upper limit of about 75,000 bp (e.g. Stuiver, 1978). However, it can be argued, with some justification, that the production of ^{14}C dates in the middle Wisconsin/Devensian time range has resulted in more confusion than enlightenment. Dates in this range have produced intense debate as to whether the sea level was close to present about 40,000 bp (Thom, 1973) or not. Stuiver (1977) has discussed the problems inherent in ^{14}C dates in the older part of their time range (essentially 7–15 half-lives from the death of the organism). The problems are largely concerned with the degree of sample contamination. Extremely small parts of modern or late Pleistocene contamination can easily cause a sample of last interglacial age to yield an apparent age between, say, 50,000 and 75,000 bp. This can be readily seen from Table 18.1. The opposite effect of contamination by old, dead carbon is not as significant (Table 18.2).

Table 18.1 Effect of varying degrees of sample contamination by *modern* carbon on the true sample age (from Polach and Golson, 1966)

True sample Age (years)	Apparent age after contamination by modern carbon (years)			
	1%	5%	20%	50%
5000	4950	4650	3700	2100
10,000	9800	9000	6800	3600
20,000	19,100	16,500	10,600	5000
30,000	27,200	21,000	12,200	5400
100,000	37,000	—	—	—

Table 18.2 Effect on true sample age of contamination by *old* carbon, *i.e.* carbon so old that all radioactivity has decayed (from Polach and Golson, 1966)

True sample Age (years)	Apparent age after contamination by old carbon (years)			
	5%	10%	20%	50%
500	900	1300	2200	6000
5000	5400	5800	6700	10,500
10,000	10,400	10,800	11,700	15,500
20,000	20,400	20,800	21,700	25,500

The requirements for a reliable date in the vicinity of 40,000 bp are (1) a large sample, (2) an uncontaminated sample, and (3) a laboratory with a low background count capable of counting the decay of the ^{14}C atoms over a period of weeks.

These requirements are not easily met. How does one know if a sample lacks contamination? In addition, by some refinement of Murphy's Law, critical samples are usually limited in size! Dating of small samples with conventional counting equipment is usually carried out in a 0.5-l counter, but this in itself usually limits the upper age to which dates can be pushed. At the University of Colorado, we have had considerable success in pre-processing a number of different types of sediment to extract very small amounts of organic material. By taking large samples and processing them by the methods outlined in Kihl (1975), we have had normal commercial laboratories successfully date samples where the concentration of organic material is close to 1%. The organic content and resulting dates for some of our samples are listed in Table 18.3. With the small 0.5-l counter, dates can be obtained on about 1 g of carbonaceous material.

However, these approaches are all exploring the limits of the conventional methods. A significantly new approach has recently been tested and involves the use of linear accelerators operating as mass spectrometers (either cyclotrons or tandem van de Graaff generators) (Nelson et al., 1977; Bennett et al., 1977; Gove, 1978). The method must still be considered to be in the exploratory stage, but certainly the initial results are extremely encouraging. The primary advantage of the new method is that rather than having to wait for ^{14}C β-decay (half of the ^{14}C atoms will decay by β-emission in ca. 5700 years), the accelerators count the number of ^{14}C atoms directly. The clear advantages are the very small sample size requirements and relatively short counting times. Bennett et al. (1978) report on a comparison between samples dated by the conventional β-ray counting method and those determined in the electrostatic accelerator at the University of Rochester, NY. In the latter case, the samples weighed only 3.5–15 mg, or about 10^3 times less than the conventional method requires. In addition, the actual counts of the ^{14}C ions accounted for only between 65 and 400 min; again there is a substantial saving of time over the β-ray emission method where, particularly for older samples, the counting time is measured in days. The quoted standard deviations in the comparison of the results from the two methods indicates that the β-ray method gives a standard deviation about half of that derived from the accelerator. Since both are derived from counting statistics, the errors could be reduced by increasing the number of counts (i.e. the time). With a sample about 40,000 years old, the standard errors in the two methods were virtually identical, and here the total run time in the accelerator was 400 min (Bennett et al., 1978).

The precision of accelerator radiocarbon dates can be expected to improve dramatically as equipment is designed and built specifically for this purpose. Dates up to about 100,000 bp are apparently possible, but it is well to remember some of the obvious drawbacks when very small samples are to be dated. These comments do not apply to massive material, such as a piece of wood, but they can apply if a series of small organic or carbonate fragments are used to make up the 3–15 mg sample. For example, a sample of foraminifera could easily be made up of a few individuals which have been reworked from older deposits. The same might apply to a sample of organic material where the direct count of the radiocarbon atoms is based on wind-disseminated pollen grains. In both cases, the samples may be of mixed ages. We shall return later to this problem when we discuss the utility of the amino acid method of relative and absolute age determination. It remains to be seen just how accessible these sophisticated facilities will be to the average researcher. In the USA there is currently an attempt to develop a network of regional facilities that would provide access to the system.

Additional Decay Methods

With the recent involvement of nuclear physicists in Quaternary dating through the linear accelerator method, additional potential dating techniques are being explored.

Table 18.3 ¹⁴C dates on samples with low organic content. Samples prepared by R. Kihl (INSTAAR)

| Sample | <2000 μm | | Organic matter | | Date bp |
	Original wt. (g)	Organic content (%)	Wt. <125 μm(g)	Wt. >125 μm(g)	
GRL-346-0 (QL-1179)	2100.0	16.39	2.1	91.0	$50{,}700\,{}^{+2000}_{-1600}$
GRL-358-0 (QL-1180)	2200.0	0.58	1.9	None	$42{,}400 \pm 800$
GRL-204-0 (QL-188)	1072.5	14.1	3.4	107.8	$50{,}400\,{}^{+1000}_{-\ 900}$
GRL-255-0 (DIC-482)	3216.9	3.8	2.5	11.0	$30{,}480\,{}^{+2800}_{-4300}$
GRL-126-0 (GAK)	1381.4	1.35	3.2	0.2	$12{,}180 \pm 240$
GRL-342-0 (GX-5527)	1345.0	0.43	2.1	None	2290 ± 170
GRL-332-0 (SI-3457)	476.2	4.8	1.0	None	3320 ± 80
GRL-248-0 (DIC-333, 402)	1382.1	8.4	1.5	83.7	>125 μm 2980 ± 190 <125 μm 3070 ± 75

Notes: GRL-346-0: date on >125 μm material only.
GRL-204-0: probably >125 μm material dated.
GRL-255-0: fraction dated uncertain.
<125 μm fraction: estimation of clay-humus fraction obtained from preparation procedure.
Organic matter content: loss on ignition.

Sources:

Sample	Location	Reference
GRL-346-0	Kivituibak Cliffs	Nelson
GRL-358-0	Kivituibak Cliffs	Nelson
GRL-204-0	Clyde Foreland	Miller
GRL-255-0	Mary Jane	Andrews
GRL-126-0	Devlin Park	Madole
GRL-342-0	Pangnirtung Fiord	Davis
GRL-332-0	Kingnait Fiord	Miller
GRL-248-0	Windy Lake	Miller

Madole date: published *J. Res. U.S. Geol. Surv.*, 1976, **4**, 163–169.
Davis date: received recently, not published, but a very good example of the method.

Initial studies have already been undertaken on the feasibility of using ^{10}Be to ^9Be ratios as age indices. ^{10}Be, like ^{14}C, is produced in the upper atmosphere by cosmic ray bombardment, but with a half-life of 1.5×10^6 years. ^{10}Be dating may allow the extension of absolute dating throughout the Pleistocene. However, there is no reservoir for ^{10}Be (such as the ocean-atmosphere reservoir for ^{14}C) and changes in ^{10}Be production in the upper atmosphere may mask the dating potential. Other promising isotopes are ^{36}Cl, with a half-life of 3×10^5 years, and ^{26}Al. The next 5 years may see some exciting advances in absolute dating by radioactive decay methods.

Uranium Series Dates

Uranium series dates have been determined on a surprisingly large variety of materials, namely coral, marine shell, peat, bone, soil, calcrete (caliche), speleothem carbonate, and deep-sea sediment. Reviews of the methods and discussions of problems are given in Broecker (1963, 1965), Ku (1976), Szabo (1969), and Kauffman *et al.* (1971).

Uranium series dating laboratories have been slow to cooperate, and there are few inter-laboratory checks (Harmon and Ku, 1976). There are no commercial laboratories, and this in itself suggests that the application of the principles is either (1) not that routine or (2) relatively expensive.

Uranium series methods have been applied most successfully to corals. Indeed, it is from the dating of raised reef corals on the islands of Barbados and New Guinea (Steinen *et al.*, 1973; Bloom *et al.*, 1974; Stearns, 1976) that much of the control on the dating of deep-sea oxygen isotope stratigraphy is obtained (Shackleton and Opdyke, 1973), with the familiar marine isotope stage 5e being correlated with the Barbados III Terrace, uranium series dated close to $125,000 \pm$ bp. Although these studies on global sea level changes are fundamental, it nevertheless remains true that the inshore waters of most of the world are not populated by corals, but by molluscs, and indeed, marine and land molluscs have traditionally formed a major cornerstone of Quaternary biostratigraphy in areas ranging from the Arctic and Antarctic to mid-latitudes. It is thus unfortunate that studies indicate that marine molluscs are not *always* suitable for providing reliable uranium series dates (cf. Kauffman *et al.*, 1971). Our own studies on the usefulness of uranium series dates on marine mulluscs have been carried out in cooperation with B. J. Szabo, USGS, Denver, Colorado (in Andrews *et al.*, 1975, 1976; Szabo, 1976). Szabo has dated about twenty-five mollusc samples from Arctic Canada, ranging in age from earliest Holocene to middle/early Pleistocene. Cross-checks on the age determinations were provided by ^{14}C dates, by amino acid ratios, and by general stratigraphy and position, the last two methods providing a relative chronology where dates were obtained at a single section. The results are still being analysed, but we can say the following:

1. about 15% of the samples could not be dated because of abnormalities (excessive uranium etc.);
2. a significant number, possibly 60%, provided dates that are of use to our investigations. If a trend is visible, it is that the uranium series dates (^{230}Th and ^{231}Pa) *underestimate* the true age of the sample;
3. that a combination of uranium series dates, combined with amino acid analyses of the same collection, is a powerful tool for Quaternary studies.

The amino acid ratios (see later) provide a stable relative chronology against which the 'absolute' uranium series dates can be compared. Fig. 18.2 illustrates the association between published amino acid and uranium series dates from eastern Baffin Island (data

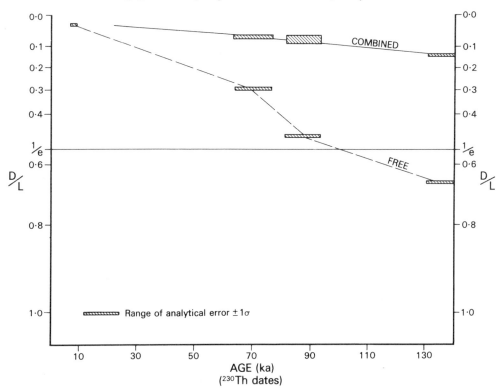

Fig. 18.2 Association between [230]Th dates and amino acid ratios (D: alloleucene; L: isoleucene) on marine molluscs from raised marine deposits on eastern Baffin Island, Canada (data from Andrews *et al.*, 1976; Miller *et al.*, 1977)

in Miller *et al.*, 1977; Andrews *et al.*, 1975, 1976). The dates of 115,000 and 130,000 bp are from a marine unit, the Cape Christian Member of the Clyde Foreland Formation (Feyling-Hanssen, 1976), which is equated with the climatic events of the last interglacial (Miller *et al.*, 1977) (Fig. 18.5). Such dates are certainly not unreasonable in light of most estimates of the date of the last interglacial of about 125,000 bp (Shackleton, 1969; Johnson and McClure, 1976; Ruddiman *et al.*, 1977). However, there is no doubt that uranium series dates on marine molluscs are potentially unreliable. Hopkins (1973), for example, has largely rejected such dates in his development of a chronology for the history of sea level in the Bering Sea region.

A major new departure in uranium series dating has gradually gathered force during the last 2–5 years. This is the dating of cave carbonate accretions (Harmon *et al.*, 1977; Thompson *et al.*, 1974, 1976; Ford *et al.*, 1972; Atkinson *et al.*, 1978). The method gives, possibly for the first time, a sense of chronology and climate on land (>50,000 BP) that is necessary to balance and weigh against the deep-sea stratigraphy. Carbonate rocks are relatively abundant on most continents; caves in these formations occur from high to low latitudes, and also at varying elevations within a region. Work on the age dating of cave carbonate deposits has been spearheaded by geomorphologists and geologists at McMaster University, Canada. Fig. 18.3 is from one of these studies, and indicates the chronology of growth of speleothems in the mountains of northwestern Canada (Harmon *et al.*, 1977). The use of frequency diagrams of radiometric ages for determining a pattern of Quaternary climatic events has been used by several workers (Wendland and

Bryson, 1974; Geyh and Rohde, 1972). In the case of ^{230}Th dates from the Rocky and Mackenzie mountains of Northwest Canada (Fig. 18.3) such a grouping suggests '. . . five distinct depositional (interglacial) episodes: (i) the Present to about 15 ka; (ii) 90–150 ka; (iii) 180–235 ka; (iv) 275–320 ka; and (v) somewhat older than 350 ka' (Harmon *et al.*, 1977, p. 2548). Although the authors rightly point to a general agreement between this chronology and an ocean δO^{18} record from core V 28–238 (Shackleton and Opdyke, 1973), nevertheless some of the differences between the records are of interest. For example, the deep-sea record would place the maximum glaciation during marine isotope stage 6 about 140,000–150,000 bp, thus suggesting an early deglaciation of the Rocky and Mackenzie mountains relative to the global (hence averaged) glacial response (Fig. 18.3). It is worth noting that in addition to being able to date speleothems by the ^{230}Th method, water extracted from the carbonate matrix can be used to determine the δO^{18} content of cave water (Duplessy *et al.*, 1971; Thompson *et al.*, 1976), which in turn can be used to develop an inductive glacial/climate model for correlation with other geological sequences.

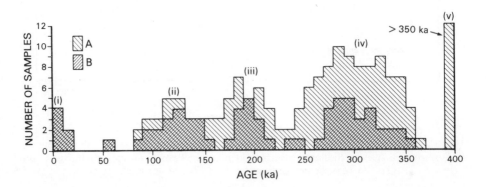

Fig. 18.3 The frequency distribution of speleothem dates from the Rocky and Mackenzie Mountains of Canada (from Harmon *et al.*, 1977, Figure 2) illustrating the non-random nature of the dates. The growth of speleothems is associated with interglacials. The histograms show (A) the number of samples whose age ±1 σ lies within the given 10 ka interval plus the number of samples whose interpolated or extrapolated growth period lies within that interval; and (B) the number of samples whose growth periods lie within the given 10 ka interval

Chemical Methods: Relative and Absolute Dating

Dating methods based on chemical alterations differ from physically based methods in the dependence of the reaction rates on various environmental parameters. For the simpler chemical reactions, the extent to which a particular reaction has progressed has been stated earlier to be a function of time, climate (primarily temperature), and the parent material, whereas the more complex reactions, such as rock weathering and soil development, are also dependent on vegetation and topography as well as additional climatic parameters. In most instances, temperature is the primary rate-controlling variable. The temperature variable is defined as the integrated thermal history and includes both magnitude (kelvin) and fluctuation (diurnal and seasonal) terms. In certain instances the moisture regime can be influential, as well as lesser variables such as environmental pH, water chemistry, and degree of continentality (primarily temperature range). For samples well in excess of 10,000 years old, it is frequently (if not always) difficult to assess the states of the various variables over time, with changing environmental conditions during glacial–interglacial cycles. Hence, the conversion from analytical data to absolute age is less precise than for some of the physically based methods.

An additional dependence for chemical reactions is on the nature of the system at t_0, when the clock began. For obsidian hydration, soil development, and rock weathering, this is the chemical composition and physical properties of the unaltered rock, whereas for amino acid studies, it is the nature of the unreacted proteinaceous material. Racemization in some pelecypod genera may be two to three times as fast as in other genera (Miller and Hare, 1975).

Obsidian Hydration Dating

Fresh obsidian glass, which contains 0.1–0.3% of water, is out of equilibrium and will, over time, hydrate to 3.5% of water to form perlite. The uptake of water by the glass changes the refractive index, induces strain, and appears visually as a surface rind. The simplified Jenny equation (equation 2), $A = f(T, C, P)$, holds for obsidian, where A = rind thickness, T = time since exposure, C = climate (integrated thermal history), and P = chemical composition of the glass.

The rate of obsidian hydration, like many first-order chemical reactions, is temperature dependent. Friedman *et al.* (1966) and Friedman and Long (1976) have shown that the activation energy of hydration is about 20 kcal, considerably lower than that for amino acid racemization (Fig. 18.4), and thus somewhat less temperature sensitive than amino acid racemization dating. Relative humidity is of little significance as the surface absorbs moisture until there is a layer one molecule thick, then hydration occurs. Hydration rates are, however, dependent on the chemical composition of the obsidian, and the rate constant must be calibrated for each obsidian type being used for dating purposes. In general, the higher the silica content, the faster the hydration occurs. The most suitable material for obsidian hydration dating is true obsidian (72–78% SiO_2). Dacite glass may be used but basaltic glass is unsuitable.

Obsidian rind thickness increases approximately as the square root of time. The obsidian date, determined from rind thickness, chemical composition, and temperature, reflects the time the surface was exposed to the atmosphere. To find the age of the associated flow, the rinds of 10–15 specimens must be measured. If the dates scatter, more samples are required. Material collected at 1–2 m depth is more suitable than surface samples, as obsidian in direct sunlight may reach anomalously high temperatures.

The useful time range for obsidian hydration dating may be as much as 10^6 years. Accuracy is seldom better than 10%, and more usually 20–30%, due to temperature uncertainties. When rind thicknesses are used as a simple correlation index, the accuracy is generally ±10%.

Tephra Superhydration.

Recent work in the infilling of ash vesicles by water has suggested that this process is similar to obsidian hydration and may be a useful Quaternary dating tool (Steen-McIntyre, 1975). The rate of superhydration is controlled by the chemical composition of the glass and such environmental parameters as temperature and groundwater chemistry.

A tephra shard exposed to the atmosphere hydrates, with the vapour moving towards the centre. Once the glass is completely hydrated, closed vesicles present in the centre of

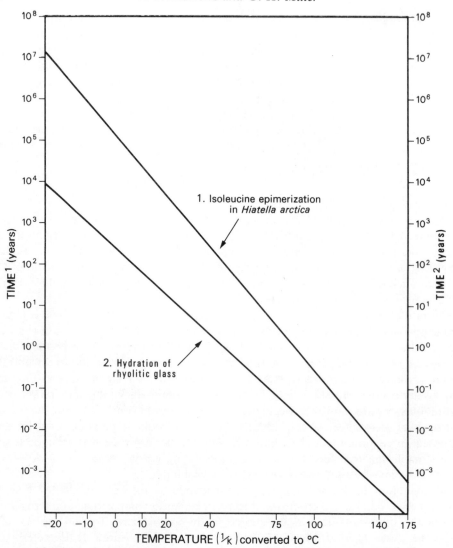

Fig. 18.4 Arrhenius plots for isoleucine epimerization in the pelecypod *Hiatella arctica* and the hydration of rhyolitic glass. Activation energies are 29 kcal for isoleucine epimerization and 20 kcal for obsidian hydration, the latter being less temperature sensitive then the former. (1) Time required for epimerization reaction to reach a value of $1/e$. (2) $1/k \times 10^2$, where k = diffusion constant for hydration

the shard will slowly fill with water. The filling of the vesicles is termed ash superhydration, and appears to be a useful tool for estimating the age of Pleistocene ash beds. It is less precise than obsidian hydration dates owing to the larger number of influential variables.

Amino Acid Geochronology

The time-dependent nature of protein diagenesis in fossil material was first noted only two decades ago by Abelson and his co-workers at the Geophysical Laboratory

(Abelson, 1955; Hare and Mitterer, 1967; Hare and Abelson, 1968). In the last decade the application of amino acid geochronology to Quaternary deposits has increased dramatically, and the method displays potential for being one of the main techniques for unravelling deposits formed between about 30,000 and 0.5–5 million years ago. Recent review articles are those by Schroeder and Bada (1976) and Williams and Smith (1977).

The method is based on the nature of amino acids forming complex protein chains in living organisms and their subsequent chemical alteration. Proteinaceous residue preserved from rapid biological decomposition by skeletal hard parts undergoes a series of chemical reactions including the first-order reactions, racemization, and peptide bond hydrolysis. Essentially all amino acids in the protein of an organism at death are in the L-configuration. As the protein chains are broken down through time, the L-isomers undergo interconversion to the D-configuration. This process is known as racemization, and is the primary tool in amino acid geochronology. Hydrolysis, the breaking of the peptide bonds linking amino acids in the protein chain, eventually releases free amino acids from the protein structure and is also broadly time dependent. The activation energy of these reactions (28–30 kcal for racemization, somewhat less for hydrolysis) indicates the temperature dependence of the reactions. For example, the time required to reach $t_{1/e}$ value (equivalent to a half-life) for the racemization of isoleucine in the pelecypod *Hiatella arctica* is 7.5×10^4 years at a constant temperature of $+10\,°C$ whereas the same ratio would be attained in 4×10^5 years at $0\,°C$ (Fig. 18.4).

The amino acid method can theoretically be applied to any proteinaceous material, although in practice only a few materials are suitable. To date, the method has been applied to fossil bone, shell (pelecypod and gastropod), foraminifera, teeth, hair, tusk, and organic residue in bulk sediment. Foraminifera appear to have the tightest matrix with molluscs only slightly less so. The solubility and complexity of bone protein makes this material only poorly suited to the amino acid method, but because of its local importance, much work has been undertaken on bone remains (Bada and Protsch, 1973; Hare, 1974; Bada and Helfman, 1975).

Amino acid analyses generally require only a few milligrams of material. The age limits range from *ca.* 0.5×10^6 years in warm climates ($+22\,°C$) to $\geqslant 10 \times 10^6$ years in Arctic regions ($-12\,°C$). In addition to providing chronological control, amino acid reactions can be used to resolve mixed population samples or, when suitable independent dating is available, to estimate the average diagenetic temperature since deposition. For example, by comparing amino acid ratios in shells deposited at the end of the last interglacial (if known by an independent dating check) with ratios in shells deposited at the start of the present interglacial, the average temperature of the last glaciation can be calculated and contrasted with the average post-glacial temperature. In an attempt to quantify the temperature dependence of the amino acid reactions we have analysed a series of *H. arctica* valves that were ^{14}C dated between 12,000 and 13,000 bp from a variety of thermal regimes. These data (Table 18.4) clearly show the effect that temperature has on the various reactions.

In addition to the standard enantiomeric (D- to L-) ratios in the protein hydroloysate, other amino acid reactions contain temporal information. Miller and Hare (1975) and Miller *et al.* (1977) have shown that the D- to L-ratios in the free amino acid fraction are especially suitable for age delimitation in arctic pelecypods deposited since the last interglacial. In addition, Miller and Hare (1975) showed that the proportion of free to peptide-bound amino acids increases with increasing geological age (see also Table 18.4).

Most amino acid studies are performed on samples beyond the range of ^{14}C dating.

Table 18.4 Amino acids in dated early post-glacial *Hiatella arctica* samples

Location	Mean annual Temperature (°C)	Asp	Glu	Ala	Val	Iso	Leu	Allo:iso (free)	Allo:iso (combined)
Washington	+10	0.917	0.89		0.85	0.85	0.77	0.27	0.078
Denmark	+7.7	0.96	0.94	0.81	0.92	0.93	0.89	0.21	0.053
Maine	+7.0	0.97	0.95	0.84	0.95	0.95	0.92	0.21	0.05
New Brunswick	+5	0.97	0.95	0.87	0.97	0.97	0.93	0.18	0.043
Anchorage	+2.1							0.16	0.034
Greenland	−10	0.98			0.985	0.988	0.979	<0.09	0.027
S. Baffin Is.	−7							N.D.†	0.024
N. Baffin Is.	−12	0.99	0.96	0.96	0.995	0.998	0.99	N.D.	0.020
Somerset Is.	−16	0.998	0.99	0.976	0.999	0.997	0.993	N.D.	0.018
Modern	—	1.00	1.00	1.00	1.00	1.00	1.00	N.D.	0.017
									(±0.001)

* All samples are between 12,000 and 13,000 bp except the samples from Somerset Island and N. Baffin Island which are *ca*. 9000 bp and S. Baffin Island which is *ca*. 11,000 bp.
† N.D. = not determined.

Because such samples nearly always have experienced at least one glacial–interglacial climatic shift, temperature reconstructions are rough estimates at best. Yet, as has been shown, the reactions are notably temperature sensitive. Perhaps the least ambiguous use of amino acid data is to circumvent the temperature dependence and use the ratios directly as relative age indices. In any geographic region for which it is reasonable to assume that the palaeoclimatic shifts affected the entire region uniformly, it is possible to apply the amino acid ratios directly as correlation and relative age indices. Thus the ratios can be used to correlate between disjunct strata as well as giving an indication of both the relative age, and the relative age differences between different fossiliferous strata. Miller *et al.* (1977) utilized this approach to subdivide fossiliferous glaciomarine units in Arctic Canada (Fig. 18.5). Coupled with other data (pollen, soils, radiometric data), direct application of amino acid ratios has been shown to be a powerful geochronological tool.

A second approach to ascribing absolute age to the enantiomeric ratios is known as the calibration method (Bada and Protsch, 1973; Bada and Helfman, 1975). The method requires an independently dated sample of an age such that its thermal history will be close to that of the sample under study. Amino acid ratios determined for the dated sample can be used to calculate the average diagenetic temperature for that sample (Fig. 18.2). This temperature is then applied to the undated sample and the age calculated from the amino acid ratios. The method generally requires extrapolation from a lower ratio to a higher ratio, and the assumption of linear kinetics for the racemization reaction is currently being strongly questioned (for bone, see Hare, 1974; for molluscan and foraminiferal remains, see Wehmiller and Hare, 1971; Bada and Schroeder, 1972; Mitterer, 1975; Mitterer and Kriausakul, 1977; Wehmiller and Belknap, 1978). However, a combination of non-linear kinetic models and independently dated samples should increase the precision of absolute dates derived from the amino acid reactions. An alternative solution involves delimiting two reactions for which the activation energies are sufficiently different that they can be used as simultaneous equations, with time and temperature as the two unknowns. Such an arrangement will allow the computation of both time and temperature directly from the amino acid ratios alone.

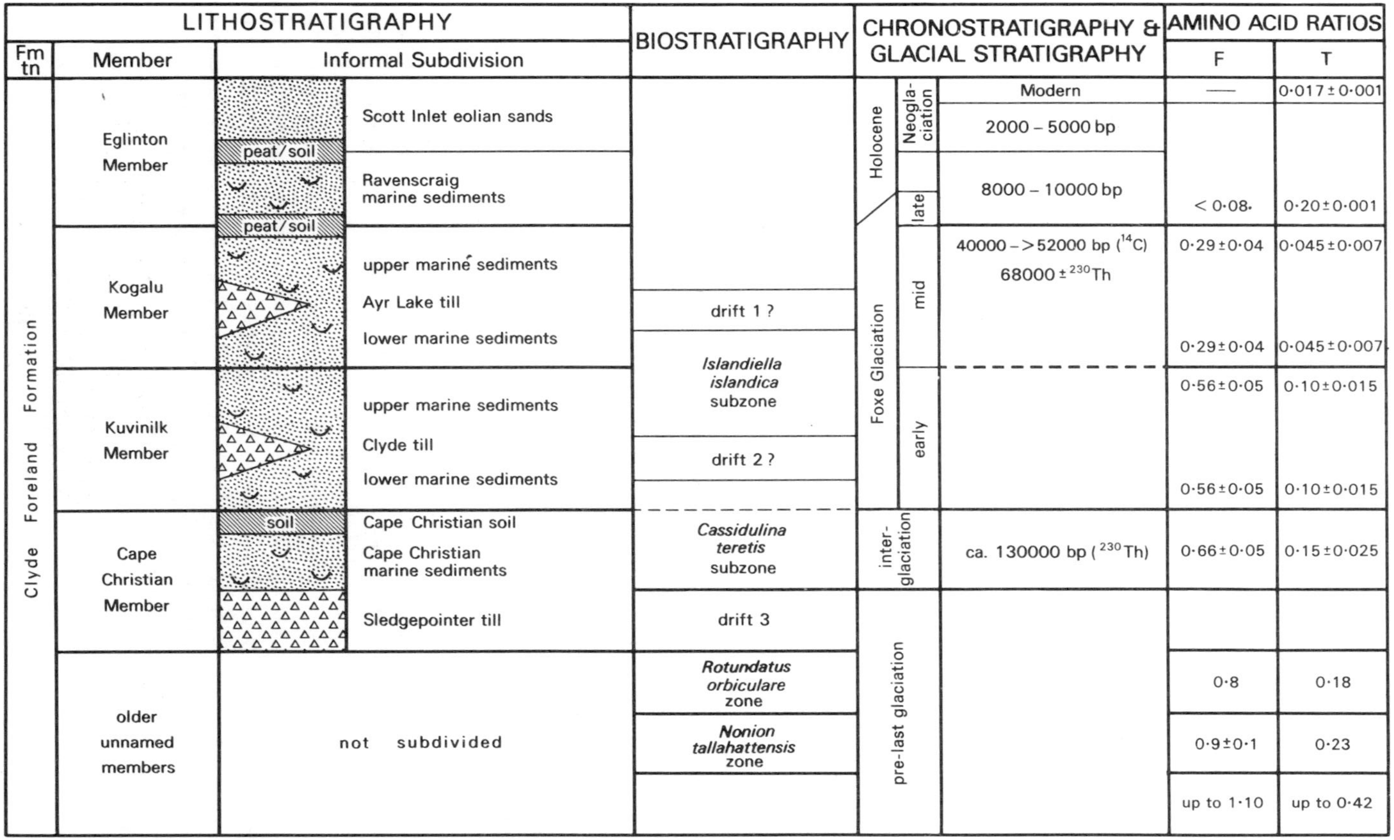

LITHOSTRATIGRAPHY			BIOSTRATIGRAPHY	CHRONOSTRATIGRAPHY & GLACIAL STRATIGRAPHY		AMINO ACID RATIOS	
Fmtn	Member	Informal Subdivision				F	T
Clyde Foreland Formation	Eglinton Member	Scott Inlet eolian sands		Holocene — Neoglaciation late	Modern	—	0·017±0·001
		Ravenscraig marine sediments			2000 – 5000 bp	< 0·08·	0·20±0·001
	Kogalu Member	upper marine sediments	drift 1 ?	Foxe Glaciation mid	8000 – 10000 bp	0·29±0·04	0·045±0·007
		Ayr Lake till					
		lower marine sediments	*Islandiella islandica* subzone		40000 – >52000 bp (^{14}C) 68000 ± ^{230}Th	0·29±0·04	0·045±0·007
	Kuvinilk Member	upper marine sediments		early		0·56±0·05	0·10±0·015
		Clyde till	drift 2 ?				
		lower marine sediments				0·56±0·05	0·10±0·015
	Cape Christian Member	Cape Christian soil	*Cassidulina teretis* subzone	inter-glaciation	ca. 130000 bp (^{230}Th)	0·66±0·05	0·15±0·025
		Cape Christian marine sediments					
		Sledgepointer till	drift 3	pre-last glaciation			
	older unnamed members	not subdivided	*Rotundatus orbiculare* zone			0·8	0·18
			Nonion tallahattensis zone			0·9±0·1	0·23
						up to 1·10	up to 0·42

Fig. 18.5 Relationship between the lithostratigraphy of raised marine sediments and tills on eastern Baffin Island, Canada, and amino-acid ratios and ^{14}C dates (from Miller *et al.*, 1977). Biostratigraphic zonations after Feyling-Hanssen (1976); amino acid ratios in the free (F) and total (T = free plus peptide bound) fractions

Radiocarbon Dating of Shell Protein

The dating of fossil carbonates by ^{14}C is limited by the exchange of younger carbon into the shell from carbonate and bicarbonate in ground water. These processes limit reliable carbonate dates to samples younger than 25,000–30,000 bp, although finite ages as old as 50,000 bp have been obtained. Thus, even with refined counting methods, carbonate ages can never be expected to reliably exceed 30,000–35,000 years owing to the natural contamination of the sample. A possible solution to this limitation combines amino acid analysis with the direct-counting method of ^{14}C dating under development. Miller and Hopkins (1979) have studied molluscs from western Alaska that were collected from a marine unit inter-bedded with pillow lavas. The lavas yielded a potassium–argon date of *ca.* 160,000 bp (Hopkins *et al.*, 1978). Amino acid analyses of the shells indicated that the heat of the associated lavas drove all of the reactions to completion in a very short length of time and destroyed the less stable amino acids. That these shells have remained in the natural environment for *ca.* 160,000 years without incorporating secondary amino acids testifies to the integrity of the carbonate matrix. The importance of this study is the demonstration that indigenous *organic* carbon in the shell matrix is free of contamination within the limits of detection. Thus, by extracting the amino acids from a fossil shell, and dating only the indigenous proteinaceous material utilizing the small sample requirements available with the linear accelerator techniques, it may be possible to obtain reliable ^{14}C dates from shell protein back to 60,000 bp or beyond.

Weathering Data As Relative Age Indices

Researchers in the Canadian Arctic (Isherwood, 1975; Locke, 1976, 1979; Birkeland, 1978; Foscolos *et al.*, 1977), in the Antarctic (Linkletter *et al.*, 1973; Ugolini and Bull, 1965; Everett, 1971), and in the western United States, (e.g. Birkeland, 1973; Carroll, 1974), have used the degree of soil development, thickness of weathering rinds on boulders (Porter, 1975, 1976), and the surface weathering of boulders as means of correlating one sequence to another, and as means of establishing a 'relative' chronology of Quaternary geomorphic events. These methods appear to be comparatively little used in Britain or Europe. In the previous section we noted that amino acid reactions are functions of time, temperature, and the genus of the material. Chemical processes are also involved in the development of soils and in the weathering of boulder surfaces. Indeed, we can generalize the factors that control these latter weathering processes by using the Jenny five-factor soil-forming equation (equation 1). In attempting to use weathering studies to establish chronosequences of geomorphic events, it is important to attempt to hold constant as many of the five factors in the equation as possible. Thus, if age is the prime concern of the study (T), then sites need to be chosen that have reasonably similar conditions for *C, P, V,* and *R*. In studies of glacial sequences it is common practice in the western USA and the Canadian Arctic to select sites on the crests of moraines. In areas of Baffin Island such sites are characterized by dry, wind-swept High Arctic vegetation. Soils are characteristically of the Polar Desert type, whereas at the base of the moraine, soils become more similar to Arctic Brown soils (Tedrow, 1977). Such a selection of sites results in factors *C, V,* and *R* being relatively constant. Most of the bedrock on Baffin Island is Precambrian granite and granite gneisses. Individual boulder lithologies can vary from biotite-rich granite gneisses which weather relatively easily to resistant fine-grained granites. As yet there is no reason to suspect that the homogenization of glacial erosion and deposition does not produce a relatively similar 'mix' of lithologies in the till matrix and in the proportions of the larger clasts. However, the mixing of lithologies does mean that in studying relative weathering sequences as a function of time, we are concerned with statistical problems that are much more severe than in either the amino acid or obsidian methods discussed previously. Specifically, the representativeness of a particular set of data does require careful forethought and planning because the climate control can be considered to operate at the regional rather than the micro-level, although the physical/chemical processes themselves operate on the rock at the molecular level.

In this review we present some examples of relative weathering studies. These are intended to illustrate both the opportunities and the problems that such studies provide. We consider some results of studies that have used (1) etching of heavy minerals in soils (2) thickness of weathering rinds, (3) soil development, and (4) weathering of surface boulders as age-dependent criteria in the establishment of regional chronosequences of geomorphic events. Although the interest in most of these studies has been directed toward a glacial stratigraphy and chronology, the techniques can be applied to any set of geomorphic surfaces and thus can be used in fluvial, marine, or desert studies. Approximate ages for the chronosequences may be determined by developing a calibration curve based on radiometrically dated sites.

1. Etching of heavy minerals. Some of the difficulties of relative weathering studies can be avoided if *P* (equation 1) is constant. Some workers in the USA have examined the change of heavy mineral grains in soils as a function of time (Bradley, 1965; Birkeland, 1974; Locke, 1976, 1979). The most common minerals used have been pyroxene and hornblende. In addition, several workers have used the depletion of certain heavy minerals (amphiboles and pyroxenes) compared to resistant minerals such as zircon and tourmaline (Ruhe, 1956) as another age-dependent criterion.

Locke (1979) has made the most systematic study. He developed a method for examining 100 hornblende grains per sample. On each grain the maximum amount of etching of the grain edge was measured in 6.5-μm increments and these measurements were then ranked in an ordinal classification from 0 (no etching) to 10. On samples from Baffin Island, Locke (1976, 1979) only measured etching up to class 4 (Maximum etching of 26 μm). Fig. 18.6 illustrates the final outcome of this study. The results indicate that the mean maximum etching depth (MMED) is a function of both depth in the soil profiles and time. The individual soil profiles were assigned to various glacial stratigraphic units on the basis of position, relationship to dated raised marine deposits, and to the characteristics of the soil profiles when compared to earlier studies (Dyke, 1977; Birkeland, 1978; Isherwood, 1975). In terms of the Baffin Island glacial stratigraphy, the following broad ages probably apply to the MMED profiles (Fig. 18.6):

Neoglacial	last 3000 years
Late Foxe stadial	8000–10,000 years
Middle Foxe stadial	60,000–80,000 years
Early Foxe stadial	90,000–100,000 years
Pre-Foxe events	>130,000 years

2. Weathering rind studies. Workers have noted that granites, basalts, and many other types of rock show progressive thickening of an outer oxidized rind on boulders which have been exposed to subaerial weathering. The actual chemical changes that occur within the weathering rind and at the weathering front are not well defined but appear to be dominated by processes involving oxidization of the parent minerals. Porter's (1975)

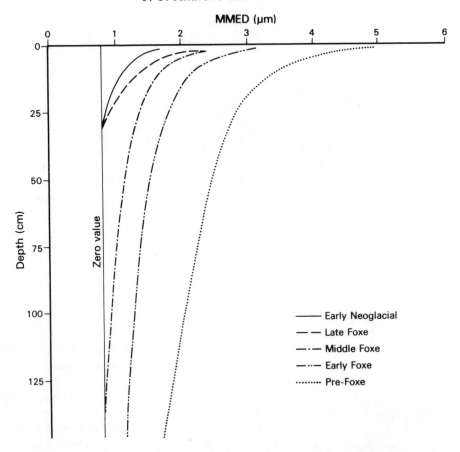

Fig. 18.6 Degree of etching of hornblende in soils of different ages from southern Cumberland Peninsula, Baffin Island (data and figure from W. W. Locke III, 1979)

work on basalts from the Northwest mountains of the USA is the most accurate work to date on the use of weathering rinds to develop a chronosequence of glacial deposits (Table 18.5).

Table 18.5 Weathering rind data on basalts from the Cascade Range, Washington State (from Porter, 1975, Table 103)

Rock-stratigraphic unit	No. of observations	Mean rind thickness and standard deviation (mm)
Lakedale Drift:		
Domerie Member	225	0.25 ± 0.04
Ronald Member	193	0.52 ± 0.06
Bullfrog Member	279	0.71 ± 0.12
Kittitas Drift:		
Indian John Member	287	1.05 ± 0.17
Swauk Prairie Member	413	1.10 ± 0.11
Thorp Drift	346	1.96 ± 0.24

If some radiometric dating control were available for some of these drift units, then it might be possible to develop a calibration curve that would relate rind thickness to age for those drifts which cannot be dated. However, it is not yet clear what form of curve might be expected. Birkeland (1973) used the principle of Occam's Razor and applied a linear curve to rind data from rock glaciers on Mt. Sopris, Colorado. However, as noted by Porter (1975, p. 104), other workers have suggested that the rate of rind development decreases logarithmically as a function of age (Černohouz and Šolc, 1966; Ollier, 1969). In the San Juan Mountains of Colorado, Andrews and Carrara (1973) attempted to develop a curve for the rate of weathering rind development by calibrating rind thickness against lichenometrically determined substrate age. An equation of the form

$$Age = a + bx^2 \tag{3}$$

was found to fit the data reasonably well (actual values were $a = 300$, $b = 2000$, and $x = $ rind thickness in mm).

Weathering rind studies deal with the progress of a micro-weathering front into a boulder. The method appears ideal for fine-grained volcanic rocks, such as basalts, as well as graywackes (Birkeland, personal communication, 1978), although it has also been traditionally used on rock types such as granites. Detailed studies, involving adequate sampling such as illustrated in Table 18.5, suggest that weathering rinds can be used to develop regional chronosequences. Inhomogeneities in bedrock lithologies may create scatter in the data, but it is worth noting that the standard deviations in Table 18.5 indicate a constant coefficient of variation which amounts to about ±10% of the mean. Rind studies (Madole, 1969) can also be carried out on clasts in soil profiles.

3. Soil development. Etching of heavy minerals and development of weathering rinds represent simpler geochemical systems than either the development of soil profiles or the weathering of boulder surfaces. Soil development, particularly the number of horizons and the thickness of the main pedogenic horizons, is used as an important time-dependent criterion in many studies in North America. This applies specifically to many mountain and northern areas where radiocarbon dating control is limited (or non-existent) and it can also be used to develop a geomorphological sequence for deposits that are beyond the limits of the radiocarbon dating method (*ca.* 40,000–50,000 bp). The studies of Birkeland (1974, 1978) and Foscolos *et al.* (1977) are examples that discuss the application of soil studies to problems of Quaternary geology and geomorphology.

Research at the University of Colorado on alpine and arctic soils indicates that the most useful age-dependent properties of soils are (i) thickness of the total solum (i.e. to the base of the Cox horizon), (ii) change in the intensity of 'redness' (Munsell colour charts) of the B horizon, and (iii) a number of parameters which reflect the increase in chemical alteration in the soil profile through time (Birkeland, 1975, 1978; Isherwood, 1975). In any dating or correlation technique it is important to ascertain what degree of similarity exists between studies performed by different individuals. Table 18.6 illustrates the depth to the Cox/Cn boundary on Polar Desert soils, Cumberland Peninsula, Baffin Island, Canada. The studies indicate substantial agreement and indicate that deposits from an early stadial of the last (Foxe) glaciation are distinct from mid- and late-stadial deposits. Since the rate of soil development is probably non-linear and may also be logarithmic (e.g. Birkeland, 1978), these data (Table 18.6) indicate that (i) there is a significant time interval between deposits of early and middle Foxe Glaciation or that (ii) there was a significant period of climatic amelioration between middle and early stadials [a 'soil-forming interval' (Morrison, 1967)].

Table 18.6 Comparison of depth of oxidation (cm) on soils of different ages from Cumberland Peninsula, Baffin Island.

Reference	Neoglacial (4000 bp)	Late Foxe Gl. (*ca.* 8000 bp)	Mid Foxe Gl. (60,000? bp)	Early Foxe Gl. (100,000? bp)	Pre-Foxe
Isherwood (1975) (Maktak Fiord)	5	22	25	80	80+
Andrews and Miller (1976)(Padle/Kingnait)	0	15	35	70	60+
Birkeland (1978) (Kingnait/Pangnirtung)	5	20		80	

Markos (1975) and Isherwood (1975) have used the ratio of plagioclase to quartz (P/Q) from X-ray diffractograms as an indicator of the rate of weathering with depth (in a single soil profile) and through time (comparison of different sites). The peak heights used were the plagioclase (002) reflection (28°) divided by the quartz (100) reflection (20.8°). If the ratio $(P/Q)_2$ is the ratio in the parent Cn horizon, then Isherwood (1975, p. 71) devised a weathering ratio, W:

$$W = \frac{(P/Q)_1}{(P/Q)_2} \tag{3}$$

where $(P/Q)_1$ is the ratio in the sample. With increasing age, W should decrease. For neoglacial soils $W = 1.0$. Fig. 18.7 illustrates the relationship between approximate age of the soils on moraines and W.

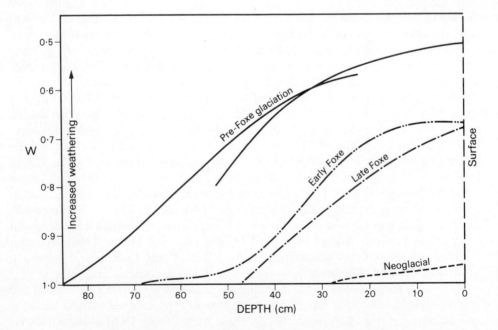

Fig. 18.7 Weathering index(W) based on plagioclase dissolution in the silt-sized fraction vs. soil depth for six Polar Desert Soils from northern Cumberland Peninsula (figure from Isherwood, 1975, Figure 3.8)

4. Surface boulder weathering. The distinction between fresh and weathered granite boulders has been used for many years as a criterion for subdividing the glacial deposits of the Sierra Nevada, Rocky Mountains, and Cordilleran mountains. Qualitative and quantitative weathering scales have been developed which have been used to discriminate between deposits. The technique used depends to a large extent on whether the differentiation is intended to deal specifically with deposits of Holocene age or whether there is a need to separate units of Holocene and Pleistocene age. Many different measurements have been used (e.g. Carroll, 1974; Birkeland, 1973; Dyke, 1977; Dugdale, 1972) and the following list merely illustrates the types of weathering that workers have argued to indicate some type of time-dependent change: (i) ratio of fresh to weathered surface boulders; (ii) number of boulders with weathering pits on their surfaces; (iii) height of positive relief features of boulders (i.e. quartz veins, feldspar crystals); (iv) number of boulders per unit area; and (v) degree of edge rounding on surface boulders. Again, these measurements can be used to define the weathering characteristics of a specific field unit and Porter (1976) has argued, rather persuasively, that these weathering characteristics can be used to differentiate (i.e. map) surface deposits of different ages. Such surfaces can be described as lithostratigraphic units.

Discussion

Although the latter part of this chapter has discussed so-called 'relative weathering' methods, it is worth emphasizing that perhaps the most interesting aspects of such work are the insights that they give us into the rates of chemical and physical processes. We judge this to be singularly important to geomorphological and geochemical studies. Chronology has been used nearly exclusively for developing a framework of events. These events might be episodes of repeated glaciation (e.g. Fig. 18.5), rise and fall of pluvial lakes, or other changes in the geomorphic regime of an area that result primarily in a depositional record. However, this framework of events represents a tremendous pool of resources for those interested in the rates of geomorphological processes over long timescales. The current emphasis on catastrophism as an important element in the creation of landscapes represents a vital challenge to the conventional geological mores which tend to interpret stratigraphic sections in terms of long-continued, low-amplitude changes. Our present world may best be seen through the binoculars of geology as comparable with conditions between 125,000 and 120,000 years ago. Shortly after, at 115,000 bp, the world had moved half way towards full glacial conditions. The rate of change of the world's climate, and hence geomorphic regimes, is difficult to imagine. If this scenario is indeed appropriate for our own world in the near future, it is of more than academic interest to increase by all possible means the accuracy and precision of dating methods that cover the Pleistocene Series (Fig. 18.1). The number of methods that can be applied widely during the critical time of the last interglacial/glacial transition are unfortunately small, and few have the necessary precision adequately to determine rates of change over intervals of 10^3 years. Chronology is one of the cornerstone of geomorphology, and researchers are urged to balance their studies of present geomorphic processes by an appreciation of rates of work over timescales of 10^4–10^6 years. For such an appreciation absolute and relative dating methods are required. This chapter has highlighted some of these methods.

Acknowledgements

Our involvement with dating relates to our cooperative research on the Quaternary geology and chronology of Arctic Canada. This work has been supported by the National

Science Foundation of the USA over the past 10 years and we gratefully acknowledge their support. Assistance and discussion on problems of dating Quaternary events have been held with many people over the last few years. We cannot mention all, but our own research has benefited particularly from the assistance of Drs. M. Stuiver, R. Stuckenrath, W. Blake, P. E. Hare, P. W. Birkeland, I. Freidman, D. Isherwood, W. W. Locke III, K. Pierce, and B. J. Szabo.

References

Abelson, P. H. (1955). Organic constituents of fossils. *Carnegie Inst. Wash. Yearb.*, **54**, 107–109.

Andrews, J. T., and Carrara, P. E. (1973). Ecological overview. Part I. The geomorphological and geological overview. In *The San Juan Ecology Project*, Colorado State University, Fort Collins, Rept. CSU-DWS 7052-Z, pp. 118–126.

Andrew, J. T., Feyling-Hanssen, R. W., Miller, G. H., Stuiver, M., Szabo, B. J., and Schlüchter, C. (1976). Alternative models of early and middle Wisconsin events, Broughton Island, Northwest Territories, Canada: toward a Quaternary chronology. In *Int. Geol. Correl. Program*, 73/1/24, IUGS/UNESCO (Eds. D. J. Easterbrook and V. Sibrava). Washington (Bellingham), Prague, Rept. No. 3, pp. pp. 28–61.

Andrews, J. T., and Miller, G. H. (1976). Quaternary glacial chronology of the eastern Canadian Arctic: A review and a contribution on amino-acid dating of Quaternary molluscs from the Clyde Cliffs. In *Quaternary Stratigraphy of North America* (Ed. W. C. Mahoney). Dowden, Hutchinson and Ross, Strondsburg, Pennsylvania, pp. 1–32.

Andrews, J. T., Szabo, B. J., and Isherwood, W. (1975). Multiple tills, radiometric ages, and assessment of the Wisconsin Glaciation in the eastern Canadian Arctic. *Arct. Alp. Res.*, **7**, 39–60.

Atkinson, T. C., Harmon, R. S., Smart, P. L., and Waltham, A. C. (1978). Palaeoclimatic and geomorphic implications of ^{230}Th/^{234}U dates on speleothems from Britain. *Nature, London.*, **272**, 24–28.

Bada, J. L., and Helfman, P. M. (1975). Amino acid racemization dating of fossil bones. *World Archaeol.*, **7**, 160.

Bada, J. L., and Protsch, R. (1973). Racemization reaction of aspartic acid and its use in dating fossil bones. *Proc. Nat. Acad. Sci. U.S.A.*, **70**, 1331–1334.

Bada, J. L., and Schroeder, R. A. (1972). Racemization of isoleucine in calcareous marine sediments: kinetics and mechanism. *Earth Planet. Sci. Lett.*, **15**, 1–11.

Bennett, C. L., Beukens, R. P., Clover M. R., Elmore, D., Gove, H. E., Kilius, L., Litherland, A. E., and Purser, K. H. (1978). Radiocarbon dating using electrostatic accelerators: dating of milligram samples. *Science*, **201**, 345–347.

Bennett, C. L., Beukens, R. P., Clover, M. R., Gove, H. E., Liebert, R. B., Litherland, A. E., Purser, K. H., and Sondheim, W. E. (1977). Radiocarbon dating using electrostatic accelerators: negative ions provide the key. *Science*, **198**, 508–510.

Birkeland, P. W. (1973). Use of relative dating methods in a stratigraphic study of rock glacier deposits, Mt. Sopris, Colorado. *Arct. Alp. Res.*, **5**, 401–416.

Birkeland, P. W. (1974). *Pedology, Weathering, and Geomorphological Research*. Oxford University Press, London, New York, 285 pp.

Birkeland, P. W. (1975). Soil development rates on tills in the Canadian Arctic compared with those in the mountains of the western U.S.A. *Abstr. Geol. Soc. Am.*, **7**, 1000.

Birkeland, P. W. (1978). Soil development as an indication of relative age of Quaternary deposits, Baffin Island, N.W.T., Canada. *Arct. Alp. Res.*, **10**, 733–747.

Bloom, A. L., Broecker, W. S., Chappell, J. M. A., Matthews, R. K., and Mesolella, K. J. (1974). Quaternary sea level fluctuations on a tectonic coast: new ^{230}Th/^{234}U dates from the Huon Peninsula, New Guinea. *Quat. Res.*, **4**, 185–205.

Bradley, W. C. (1965). Marine terraces on Ben Lomond Mountain, California. In *INQUA Guidebook for Field Conference 1*. Nebraska Academy of Science, Lincoln, Nebr., 148–150.

Broecker, W. S. (1963). A preliminary evaluation of uranium series in equilibrium as a tool for absolute age measurements on marine carbonates. *J. Geophys. Res.*, **68**, 2817–2834.

Broecker, W. S. (1965). Isotope geochemistry and the Pleistocene climatic record. In *The Quaternary of the United States* (Eds. H. E. Wright, Jr., and D. G. Frey). Princeton University Press, Princeton, pp. 737–754.

Carroll, T. (1974). Relative age dating techniques and a late Quaternary chronology, Arikaree Cirque, Colorado. *Geology*, **2**, 321–326.

Černohouz, J., and Šolc, I. (1966). Use of sandstone wanes and weathered basaltic crust in absolute chronology. *Nature, Lond.*, **212**, 806–807.

Cline, R. M., and Hays, J. D. (Eds.) (1976). Investigation of Late Quaternary paleoceanography and paleoclimatology. *Geol. Soc. Am. Mem.*, No. 145, 464 pp.

Coleman, S. M., and Pierce, K. L. (1977). Summary table of Quaternary dating methods, *Misc. Field Studies*, U.S.G.S., Map MF-904.

Dugdale, R. E. (1972). The Quaternary history of northern Cumberland Peninsula, Baffin Island, N.W.T. Part III. The late glacial deposits of Sulung Valley and adjacent parts of the Maktak trough. *Can J. Earth Sci.*, **9**, 366–374.

Duplessy, J. C., Labeyrie, J., Lalou, C., and Nguyen, H. V. (1971). La mésure des variations climatiques continentales. Application á la Période comprise entre 130,000 et 90,000 ans B.P. *Quat. Res.*, **2**, 133–161.

Dyke, A. S. (1977). *Quaternary Geomorphology, Glacial Chronology and Climatic and Sea-level History of Southwestern Cumberland Peninsula, Baffin Island, Northwest Territories, Canada.* PhD Thesis, Univ. Colorado, Boulder, 209 pp.

Everett, K. R. (1971). Soils of the Meserve Glacier area, Wright Valley, South Victoria Land, Antarctica. *Soil Sci.*, **112**, 425–438.

Feyling-Hanssen, R. W. (1976). A mid-Wisconsin interstadial on Broughton Island, Arctic Canada, and its foraminifera, *Arct. Alp. Res.*, **8**, 161–182.

Ford, D. C., Thompson, P., and Schwarcz, H. P. (1972). Dating cave calcite deposits by the uranium disequilibrium method: some preliminary results from Crowsnest Pass, Alberta. In *Research Methods in Geomorphology* (Eds. E. Yatsu and A. Falconer). Proc. Guelph Symp. Geomorphology, Guelph Univ., Canada, pp. 247–256.

Foscolos, A. E., Rutter, N. W., and Hughes, O. L. (1977). The use of pedological studies in interpreting the Quaternary history of Central Yukon Territory. *Geol. Surv. Canada Bull.*, No. 271, 48 pp.

Friedman, I., and Long, W. (1976). Hydration rate of obsidian. *Science*, **191**, 347–352.

Friedman, I., Long, W., and Smith, R. L. (1966). Hydration of natural glass and formation of perlite. *Geol. Soc. Am. Bull.*, **77**, 323–328.

Geyh, M. A., and Rohde, P. (1972). Weischelian chronostratigraphy, C^{14} dating and statistics. In *12th Int. Geol. Congr., Montreal*, Sect. 12, pp. 27–36.

Gove, H. E. (Ed.) (1978). *Proceedings of the First Conference on Radiocarbon Dating with Accelerators*. Univ. of Rochester, New York, 401 pp.

Grootes, P. M. (1977). Chronology of the early part of the last glacial in Northwest Europe. *Abstr. Geol. Soc. Am.*, **9**, 997–998.

Gustavsson, J. E., and Högberg, S. A. C. (1972). Uranium/thorium dating of Quaternary carbonates. *Boreas*, **1**, 247–274.

Hare, P. E. (1974). Amino acid dating of bone—the influence of water. *Carnegie Inst. Wash. Yearb.*, **73**, 576–581.

Hare, P. E., and Abelson, P. H. (1968). Racemization of amino acids in fossil shells. *Carnegie Inst. Wash. Yearb.*, **66**, 526–528.

Hare, P. E., and Mitterer, R. M. (1967). Nonprotein amino acids in fossil shells. *Carnegie Inst. Wash. Yearb.*, **65**, 326–364.

Harmon, R. S., Ford, D. C., and Schwarcz, H. P. (1977). Interglacial chronology of the Rocky and Mackenzie Mountains based upon $^{230}Th/^{234}U$ dating of calcite speleothems. *Can. J. Earth Sci.*, **14**, 2543–2552.

Harmon, R. S., and Ku, T.–L. (1976). The absolute limits $Th^{230}U^{234}$ dating method: preliminary results of the geochronological interlaboratory comparison project. *Abstr. Geol. Soc. Am.*, **8**, 903–904.

Hecht, A. D. (1977). The oxygen isotopic record of foraminifera in deep sea sediment. In *Foraminifera* (Eds. R. H. Hedley and C. A. Adams). Vol. 2, Academic Press, New York, pp. 1–43.

Hopkins, D. M. (1973). Sea level history in Beringia during the past 250,000 years. *Quat. Res.*, **3**, 520–540.

Hopkins, D. M., Silberman, M. L., and Yang, A. I. C. (1978). New data on the geochronology of St. Paul, Pribilof Islands, Alaska. In *Alaska: Accomplishments During 1977* (Ed. K. M. Blean). U.S.G.S. Circular, in press.

Isherwood, D. (1975). *Soil Geochemistry and Rock Weathering in an Arctic Environment.* PhD Thesis, Univ. Colorado, Boulder, 188 pp.

Jenny, H. (1941). *Factors of Soil Formation.* McGraw-Hill, New York, 281 pp.

Johnson, R. G., and McClure, B. R. (1976). A model for northern hemisphere continental ice sheet variation, *Quat. Res.*, **6**, 325–353.

Kauffman, A., and Broecker, W. S. (1965). Comparison of Th^{230} and C^{14} ages for carbonate materials from Lakes Lahontan and Bonneville. *J. Geophys. Res.*, **70**, 4039–4054.

Kauffman, A., Broecker, W. S., Ku, T. L., and Thurber, D. L. (1971) The status of U-series methods of mollusk dating. *Geochim. Cosmochim Acta*, **35**, 1155–1183.

Kihl, R. (1975). Physical preparation of organic matter samples for ^{14}C dating, *Arct. Alp. Res.*, **7**, 90–91.

Ku, T. L. (1976). The uranium-series methods of age determination, *Ann. Rev. Earth Planet. Sci.*, **4**, 347–379.

Linkletter, G. O., Bockheim, J., and Ugolini, F. C. (1973). Soils and glacial deposits in the Beacon Valley, southern Victoria Land, Antarctica. *N.Z.J. Geol. Geophys.*, **16**, 90–108.

Locke, W. W., Jr. (1976). *Etching of Hornblende as a Dating Criterion for Arctic Soils.* MSc Thesis, Univ. of Colorado, Boulder, 86 pp.

Locke, W. W., III (1979). Etching of hornblende grains in Arctic soils: an indicator of relative age and paleoclimate, *Quat. Res.*, **11**, 197–212.

Madole, R. F. (1969). Pinedale and Bull Lake glaciations in upper St. Vrain drainage basin, Boulder County, Colorado. *Arct. Alp. Res.*, **1**, 279–288.

Markos, G. (1975). Rates and kinetics of plagioclase dissolution in late Quaternary tills in Colorado and Wyoming, *Abstr. Geol. Soc. Am.*, **7**, 1190.

Miller, G. H., Andrews, J. T., and Short, S. K. (1977). The last interglacial/glacial cycle, Clyde Foreland, Baffin Island, N.W.T.: stratigraphy, biostratigraphy, and chronology. *Can J. Earth Sci.*, **14**, 2824–2857.

Miller, G. H., and Hare, P. E. (1975). Use of amino acid reactions in arctic marine fossils on stratigraphic and geochronological indicators. *Carnegie Inst. Wash. Yearb.*, **74**, 612–617.

Miller, G. H., and Hopkins, D. M. (1979). Degradation of molluscan shell protein by lava-induced transient heat flow, Pribilof Islands, Alaska: Implications for amino acid geochronology and radiocarbon dating. In *Recent Advances in the Biogeochemistry of Amino Acids* (Eds. P. E. Hare, K. King Jr, and T. C. Hoering). John Wiley & Sons, New York, in press.

Mitterer, R. M. (1975). Ages and diagenetic temperatures of Pleistocene deposits in Florida based on isoleucine epimerization in *Mercenaria. Earth Planet. Sci. Lett.*, **28**, 275–282.

Mitterer, R. M., and Kriausakul, N. (1977). Kinetics and mechanism of epimerization of isoleucine in fossil proteins. *Abstr. Geol. Soc. Am. with Programs*, **9**, 1097.

Morrison, R. B. (1967). Principles of Quaternary stratigraphy. In *Quaternary Soils* (Eds. R. B. Morrison and H. E. Wright, Jr.), In INQUA, VII Congr., **9**, 1–69.

Nelson, D. E., Korteling, R. G., and Stott, W. R. (1977). Carbon-14: direct detection at natural concentrations. *Science*, **198**, 507–508.

Ollier, C. D. (1969). *Weathering.* Elsevier, New York, 304 pp.

Pierce, K. L., Obradovitch, J. D., and Friedman, I. (1976). Obsidian hydration dating and correlation of Bull Lake and Pinedale glaciations near West Yellowstone, Montana. *Geol. Soc. Am. Bull.*, **87**, 703–710.

Polach, H. A., and Golson, J. (1966). Collection of specimens for radiocarbon dating and interpretation of results. Australian Institute of Aboriginal Studies, A.N.U., Canberra, Manual No. 2, 42 pp.

Porter, S. C. (1975). Weathering winds as a relative-age criterion: application to subdivision of glacial deposits in the Cascade Range. *Geology*, **3**, 101–104.

Porter, S. C. (1976). Pleistocene glaciation in the southern part of the North Cascade Range, Washington. *Geol. Soc. Am. Bull.*, **87**, 61–75.

Ruddiman, W. F., Sancetta, C. D., and McIntyre, A. (1977). Glacial/interglacial response rate of subpolar North Atlantic waters to climatic change: the record in oceanic sediments. *Phil. Trans. Roy. Soc. London, B*, **280**, 119–142.

Ruhe, R. (1956). Geomorphic surfaces and the nature of soils. *Soil Sci.*, **82**, 441–455.

Schroeder, R. A., and Bada, J. L. (1976). A review of the geochemical applications of the amino acid racemization reaction. *Earth Sci. Rev.*, **12**, 347–391.

Shackleton, N. J. (1969). The last interglacial in the marine and terrestrial records. *Proc. Roy. Soc. London, B*, **174**, 135–154.

Shackleton, N. J., and Opdyke, N. D. (1973). Oxygen isotope and paleomagnetic stratigraphy of equatorial Pacific core V28-238: oxygen isotope temperatures and ice volumes on a 10^5 year and 10^6 year scale. *Quat. Res.*, **3**, 39–55.

Shackleton, N. J., and Opdyke, N. D. (1976). Oxygen-isotope and paleomagnetic stratigraphy of Pacific core v23-239 late Pliocene to latest Pleistocene. *Geol. Soc. Am. Mem.*, No. 145, 449–464.

Stearns, C. E. (1976). Estimates of the position of sea level between 140,000 and 75,000 years ago. *Quat. Res.*, **6**, 445–449.

Steen-McIntyre, V. (1975). Hydration and superhydration of tephra glass—a potential tool for estimating age of Holocene and Pleistocene ash beds. In *Quaternary Studies* (Eds. M. M. Cresswell and R. P. Suggate). Royal Society of New Zealand, Wellington, N.Z., pp. 271–278.

Steinen, R. P., Harrison, R. S., and Matthews, R. K. (1973). Eustatic lowstand of sea level between 125,000 and 105,000 years BP: evidence from the subsurface of Barbados, West Indies. *Geol. Soc. Am. Bull.*, **84**, 63–70.

Stuiver, M. (1977). Recent developments in ^{14}C dating, *Abstr. Geol. Soc. Am.*, **9**, 1192–1193.

Stuiver, M. (1978). Radiocarbon timescale tested against magnetic and other dating methods. *Nature, Lond.*, **273**, 271–274.

Szabo, B. J. (1969). Uranium-series dating of Quaternary successions, Études sur le Quaternaire dans le Monde. VIII INQUA Congress, Paris, pp. 942–949.

Szabo, B. J. (1976). On dating marine shells by the uranium-series method. *Abstr. Geol. Soc. Am.*, **8**, 1132–1133.

Tedrow, J. C. F. (1977). *Soils of the Polar Landscapes*. Rutgers University Press, Rutgers, N.J., 638 pp.

Thom, B. G. (1973). The dilemma of high interstadial sea levels during the last glaciation, *Progr. Geog.*, **5**, 171–246.

Thompson, P., Schwarcz, H. P., and Ford, D. C., (1974). Continental Pleistocene climate variations from speleothem and isotopic data. *Science*, **184**, 893–895.

Thompson, P., Schwarcz, H. P., and Ford, D. C. (1976). Stable isotope geochemistry, geothermometry, and geochronology of speleothems from West Virginia. *Geol. Soc. Am. Bull.*, **87**, 1730–1738.

Ugolini, F. C., and Bull, C. (1965). Soil development and glacial events in Antarctica. *Quaternaria*, **7**, 251–269.

Wehmiller, J., and Belknap, D. F. (1978). Alternative kinetic models for the interpretation of amino acid enantiomeric ratios in Pleistocene mollusks: examples from California, Washington and Florida. *Quat. Res.*, **9**, 330–348.

Wehmiller, J., and Hare, P. E. (1971). Racemization of amino acids in marine sediments. *Science*, **173**, 907–911.

Wendland, W. M., and Bryson, R. A. (1974). Dating climatic episodes of the Holocene. *Quat. Res.*, **4**, 9–24.

Williams, K. M. and Smith, G. G. (1977). A critical evaluation of the application of amino acid racemization to geochronology and geothermometry. *Origins Life*, **8**, 91–144.

Timescales in Geomorphology
Edited by R. A. Cullingford, D. A. Davidson, and J. Lewin
© 1980 John Wiley & Sons Ltd

CHAPTER 19

Problems in radiocarbon dating the Chelford Interstadial of England

Peter Worsley

Department of Geography,
University of Reading

Introduction

One of the most significant advances in the last decade pertinent to the general problem of understanding landscape evolution in present-day temperate latitudes has been the reasonably finite determination of the duration of the Last-Glacial stage (Devensian/Weichselian/Wisconsin). As a result, it is now likely that this cold stage was about an order of magnitude greater than the duration of the present interglacial to date (i.e. it lasted from about 120 to 10 ka bp). If it is accepted as a working hypothesis that the patterns of vegetation change in each of the late Quaternary interglacials are similar (Turner and West, 1968), then we are currently approaching the late-post-temperate transition heralding the deterioration leading to another glacial stage. Perhaps, then, we may still generalize in the same terms about the relative importance in absolute time of the cold and temperate stages. It may thus follow that assessment of the impact of cold-climate processes on geomorphological development has to be made in the light of these two fundamentally different periods. Although slow and laborious investigations of the generally fragmentary terrestrial successions have managed to piece together an emerging picture which is consistent with this remarkable contrast in time, it was the study of the deep-sea floor records which initially provided the most convincing and complete evidence.

From the present standpoint, establishment of a timescale within the Last-Glacial stage prior to the ice advance maximum culminating about 18–20 ka bp is not easy. Radiocarbon dating techniques have been widely applied for the period back to about 40 ka bp but beyond that limit age determination becomes difficult. Nevertheless, it appears that in Britain a nearly continuous record of environmental changes can be deciphered back to almost 50 ka bp. Before then only one episode has a finite date—the Chelford deposits of supposed interstadial age. Numerical dating control on the pattern of environmental changes during the first half of the glacial stage is therefore almost absent. Thus the Chelford interstadial is important if the early Last-Glacial history of geomorphological change is to be understood, and its finite age is similarly crucial.

At the time of writing, sediments correlated with the organic beds at Chelford, Cheshire, have been recognized at Beetley and possibly at Wretton in Norfolk, and at Four Ashes in Staffordshire. Only the Chelford-area deposits have been the subject of ^{14}C dating. Currently the results of ^{14}C assays are available from an outcrop of very limited thickness and restricted geographical area together with another result from an adjacent locality which is probably an equivalent horizon. The results define a timespan between 25 and 65 ka bp but, on the basis of studies at many other localities, this timespan is known to cover a wide range of environmental conditions that are not recognized within the dated bed. The main aim of this contribution is to consider the problems connected with the dating of materials near to or possibly beyond the limit of the ^{14}C technique. This will be done in the context of the history of dating attempts on Chelford material. Another aim is to document in detail the dating of the oldest finitely dated horizon in Britain and what may well be the most intensively dated single bed of this age in the world. Hopefully this synthesis will contribute to the crusade against placing prime reliance upon ^{14}C dates in conflict with other evidence. It is submitted that in this instance at least, *contra* to Vita-Finzi (1973), 'the stratigraphic dog must wag the dating tail'.

Radiocarbon Dating

The principles of the ^{14}C dating technique have been outlined on many occasions and need not be repeated here. It will suffice to note several salient factors. Firstly, it must always be borne in mind that the usual approach has been to infer the amount of residual ^{14}C by short-term counts of its decay rate, for the absolute levels are beyond the capabilities of detection by classical analytical chemistry. Consequently, the result can be stated only in terms of probability. Usually it is quoted within limits of one standard deviation (s) on either side of the estimated value, a statement which can be made at the 68% confidence level. Although normally critical, this factor is relatively unimportant when comparing the various ^{14}C dates from Chelford. Secondly, it is now known that the level of ^{14}C in the biosphere has varied by up to 15%, necessitating a distinction between ^{14}C years and calendar years. This applies to the present interglacial, but values in the Last-Glacial stage are unknown and therefore will not be considered further. All the dates mentioned will be in conventional ^{14}C years bp (i.e. before AD 1950) calculated using the Libby half-life value of [14]C (5570 a) and the conversion in terms of the best known value ($\times 1.03$) will be ignored. Finally, the so-called date must always be regarded as a value derived from the ^{14}C level measured in the sample. This level need not be directly related to the level at the time of life due to contamination, which will be central to much of the following discussion.

International practice is for the various ^{14}C-dating laboratories to publish their results periodically in the form of short reports and accompanying date lists in the journal *Radiocarbon*, which was specifically instigated in 1960 for this purpose. Many laboratories follow this procedure but some important geological results remain unpublished long after they have been dated. A further complication is that the dates derived from the first decade of ^{14}C dating were never systematically published on a universal basis. This applies to some Chelford dates. Even though many are published in *Radiocarbon*, their retrieval is not easy without prior knowledge of the laboratory involved, so Table 19.1 summarizes all the available data from Chelford together with reference to the major published sources.

Table 19.1 Complete listing of the Chelford interstadial ^{14}C dates

Collector	^{14}C age (years)	Lab. ref. no.	Source
1. A. J. Whiteman	(1) >36,500	L-387A	Olson and Broecker (1961)
2. R. G. West	(2) >53,000	Gro-1292	de Vries (1958)
	>52,000	GrN-1292	Vogel and Zagwijn (1967)
	(3) 57,000		de Vries, personal communication, R. G. West (1958)
	59,000 ± 1000	Gro-1480	de Vries (1959)
	60,800 ± 1500	GrN-1475	Vogel and Zagwijn (1967)
		GrN-1480	Vogel, personal communication, P. Worsley (1966)
	60,500 ± 1500	GrN-1475	Grootes (1977)
3. G. S. Boulton and P. Worsley	(4) 39,800 ± 1500	Hv-737	Geyh, personal communication, G. S. Boulton (1965)
	(5) 41,300 ± 680	Hv-737B	Geyh, personal communication, P. Worsley (1967)
4. P. Worsley	(6) 32,850 ± 480	Hv-1978	Geyh, personal communication, P. Worsley (1968)
	(7) 30,770 ± 430	Hv-1979	Geyh, personal communication, P. Worsley (1968)
	(8) 26,200 ± 390	Hv-1978B	Geyh, personal communication, P. Worsley (1969)
	(9) $47,000 ^{+2300}_{-1800}$	Birm-157	Shotton *et al.* (1970)
	(10) >47,300	SRR-154	Harkness and Wilson (1974)
	(11) >48,700	SRR-155	Harkness and Wilson (1974)
	(12) $41,290 ^{+980}_{-880}$	SRR-156	Harkness and Wilson (1974)
	(13) >48,700	SRR-157	Harkness and Wilson (1974)
5. W. B. Evans	(14) >40,000	IGS-C14,25	Welin *et al.* (1972)

Chelford Stratigraphy

The organic exposures to be considered cropped out within a working sand quarry during the period 1955–73 at Farm Wood, Chelford, Cheshire (SJ 812731) (Fig. 19.1). Unfortunately, the sections have now been graded and it is unlikely that they will be exposed in the future as the old quarry is now a nature reserve. It was originally proposed (Shotton and West, 1969) that this locality be adopted as the stratotype for the Last-Glacial stage in Britain, although shortly afterwards the Four Ashes, Staffordshire, exposures were substituted for this choice (Mitchell *et al.*, 1973). Despite this, Chelford remains one of the very few successions in Britain with biogenic materials which post-date the Ipswichian interglacial and antedate the ice-advance maximum of about 20 ka. Observations over 15 years indicate that the organic bed forms an integral part of a sequence of mainly periglacial alluvial sediments which are unconformably overlain by glacial deposits *sensu stricto*. These two lithostratigraphic units have been named the Chelford Sands Formation and the Stockport Formation. The stratigraphy suggests that during the existence of severe periglacial environmental conditions associated with alluvial sand deposition there was a relatively short period of climatic amelioration during which a forest cover became established. In local pools within the forest,

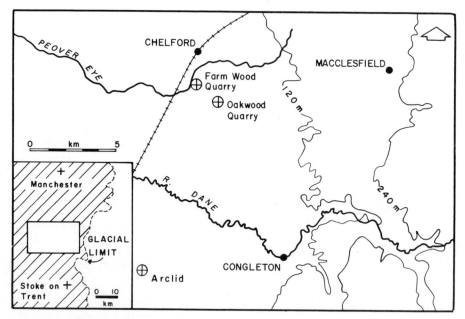

Fig. 19.1 Map of the Chelford area. Location of the three sites with interstadial deposits, Farm Wood and Oakwood near Chelford, and Arclid. The inset map shows the area in relation to the Last Glacial stage ice maximum

organic-rich muds accumulated, but the environment was unstable for it was periodically inundated by flood waters which apparently up-rooted many of the trees and redistributed much of the surface organic matter. Palaeoecological studies of the included biota have yielded a coherent interpretation of an ecosystem which closely parallels the modern boreal forest of southern Finland.

Following the abandonment of Farm Wood, a new quarry was opened about 3 km to the southeast at Oakwood. Fortunately for study purposes, the working technique was changed from lagooning as practised at Farm Wood to continuously pumping inflowing groundwater to permit essentially dry excavation. This resulted in full exposure down to bedrock and of particular importance was the discovery that the organic materials were almost exclusively contained within the fill of palaeochannels (Worsley, 1977). This finding permits a better appreciation of the Farm Wood palaeoecology *if* the basic assumption is made that the two exposures are directly linked beneath the ground surface. This possibility is supported by both the difference in absolute height data and the palaeochannel trend. Indeed, the known limited extent of the Farm Wood exposures is better understood in terms of this assumption. A channel setting for deposition of the organic material is consistent with the evidence suggesting periodic flooding and that more open country was not too far distant. The geological evidence at both Oakwood and Farm Wood indicates that the organic beds probably represent a period of short duration.

History of Collection and Dating

In the following account, the order of presentation will be determined by the date of field sampling. The dated material was collected on four separate occasions in the period 1956–67 by A. J. Whiteman, R. G. West, G. S. Boulton, and P. Worsley.

1. The first sample from Chelford to be obtained specifically for ^{14}C dating was collected by A. J. Whiteman in 1956, at a time when he was engaged in mapping the Nantwich geological map sheet for the Geological Survey. Chelford lay approximately 25 km northeast of the corner of this sheet. Whiteman's sample was submitted to the Lamont Laboratory, New York, the result of the assay being:

Wood   >36,500   L-387A

The result was important in showing clearly that the material was of at least mid-Last-Glacial stage in age. Therefore, in terms of the late Quaternary timescale then emerging, it was of some antiquity. Prior to the availability of the ^{14}C date, Whiteman's view was that the sand sequence might be as young as 18 ka or as old as the Pliocene.

2. Shortly after Whiteman's examination of the site, the locality was brought to the attention of I. M. Simpson, who was then mapping the Pleistocene succession in the Stockport area about 30 km to the north. Since his rocks had proved to be sterile biologically, but nevertheless seemed to correlate with the Chelford sequence, he elected to investigate in detail the immediate stratigraphy and soon saw the need to have the help of a palaeobotanist if the chronological status of the organic bed was to be successfully established. Work on the fossil flora was tackled by R. G. West, who concluded that the evidence seemed to indicate a possible age early in the Last-Glacial stage.

At approximately the same time, the late H. de Vries of Groningen University was specializing in techniques which would permit the determination of ages from organic materials containing extremely low levels of [14]C. Since no British Laboratory had this kind of capability arrangements were made for the Groningen Laboratory to attempt a dating. The material supplied came from an upright (*in situ*?) stump of *Picea* sp. in the uppermost bed of mud then exposed, and the stratigraphic position of this is shown in section D of Fig. 3 in Simpson and West (1958). In a paper on low-level counting results, de Vries (1958) reported the result of his first Chelford assay:

Wood   >53,000   Gro-1292

Thus the ^{14}C data were consistent with the stratigraphic evidence. Within the constraints imposed by the background counts and errors in the sample counts, de Vries's apparatus was operating at its practical limit. In order to overcome this problem, de Vries was also working on an alternative approach—that of isotopic enrichment of the [14]C. The enrichment process was undertaken at the Laboratory for Mass Spectrography in Amsterdam where carbon monoxide derived from the sample was passed through thermal-diffusion columns and the degree of enrichment was detected by the O^{18} abundance in the CO. This technique was not without difficulties, the principal ones being the necessity for a large sample (*ca.* 500 g), the large volumes of gas to be handled, and the long preparation time (1–2 months). Haring *et al.* (1958) described their enrichment programme and also reported the first geological date resulting from the new technique. This was from material collected from the Amersfoort Interstadial sequence at the type site, and its ^{14}C age was given as:

64,000 ± 1800   Gro-1397

It was concluded that this was necessarily a *minimum* date because of the difficulties arising from infiltration by more modern humus.

This Amersfoort sample was followed in the counter by one from Chelford, and in April 1958 de Vries was able to give the preliminary result in a letter to R. G. West. This was:

Wood   57,000

It should be emphasized that this was a *preliminary* date and was given as an indication of the sample age; hence the probability from the long-term average and the errors arising from both the enrichment and degree of enrichment were not given. This value was published in a footnote to Simpson and West (1958). For at least a decade afterwards this result was extensively cited in the literature, sometimes accompanied by the laboratory reference number which rightly belonged to the first Groningen Chelford count (Gro-1292). In reality it is not a true Groningen date at all.

In a review paper, published posthumously, on ^{14}C measurement and application de Vries (1959) announced the final date as:

Wood   59,000 ± 1000   Gro-1475/1480

It appears that this result has been completely overlooked by British workers since up to the present no citation is known in the literature.

In 1965 the author was trying to seek clarification of the Chelford dating results. The then Head of the Groningen Laboratory, J. C. Vogel, revealed that the results of samples dated in the late-1950s were in need of slight revision because some of the constant values used in the original calculations required modification. One factor involved the reference standard formerly used by Groningen (recent wood). Later this was abandoned in favour of the now universal standard—US National Bureau of Standards oxalic acid based on age-corrected ^{14}C activity of AD 1890 wood. In 1966 the author was notified (Vogel, personal communication) that the preliminary date of 57,000 was recalculated as:

60,800 ± 1500   GrN-1480

and this value was incorporated in a diagrammatic representation of the East Cheshire Quaternary stratigraphy by Worsley (1966). Finally, Vogel and Zagwijn (1967) gave most of the 'old' de Vries geological dates in revised form, and these included those from Chelford:

>52,000   GrN-1292
60,800 ± 1500   GrN-1475

All of these revised dates and all subsequent dates from Groningen based on the international standard have the laboratory code GrN rather than Gro of the earliest results. Also, if separate measurements on the same gas preparations were made, each count received a unique laboratory reference number. Thus the enriched gas (isotopic enrichment of 8.12) was counted twice and hence received two reference numbers GrN-1475 and GrN-1480. The resulting date in both cases is based on the average value of the two counts and where two reference numbers existed for the same gas the lowest

Fig. 19.2 ^{14}C–dated *in situ* tree stumps. The upper photograph (a) shows a stump of unknown species exposed in 1965 rooted above a peat bed (Hv–737B). The lower photograph (b) shows an *in situ* stump (*Pinus sylvestris* group) overlain by a peat bed. Three methane and four benzene preparations derived from the wood of this tree have been ^{14}C dated, plus a single gas sample from the peat

was adopted for publication. Thus, despite the range of calculated age values, only two 'dates' on Chelford materials have been determined at Groningen.

3. Early in 1965, G. S. Boulton and the author were collaborating on an alternative interpretation of the classic tripartite stratigraphy (Boulton and Worsley, 1965). In connection with this, a field discussion was held at Farm Wood, Chelford. It had been reported that several tree stumps *in situ* had been exposed recently and on this occasion a convincing example was located overlying a bed of felted peat (Fig. 19.2a). Peat and wood were collected for dating and these were submitted to the [14]C Laboratory of the Lower Saxony Geological Survey in Hannover, West Germany. At that time the laboratory was attempting to perfect a method of finite dating beyond 50,000 without sample enrichment and in the light of the Groningen results a comparative dating from the same horizon was opportune.

Later that year the results of two measurements on this material were reported (M. A. Geyh, personal communication):

41,300±680   Hv-737
39,800±1500   Hv-737B

These two results were very surprising since there was no stratigraphic evidence to indicate that the ^{14}C ages should be significantly different from those already determined. Besides the age divergence, a more serious problem related to the conflict in the palaeoenvironmental reconstructions between Chelford and sites in the Midlands, notably Upton Warren and Fladbury, which had yielded similar dates. Furthermore, the Upton Warren material had been dated independently by both Groningen and Yale with an encouraging degree of consistency. Hence the simplest explanation appeared to be that the Hannover dates had been influenced by contamination from younger materials and that this should be the favoured working hypothesis.

4. The last phase of collecting and dating activity commenced in the late summer of 1967. During a routine visit to observe the progressive removal of the sands, the author was fortunate to find an excellent exposure of an undoubted *in situ* tree (see Fig. 19.2b). At 0.5 m above the water level of the lagoon lay a stratum including broken and rolled material from trees but without any peat. This seemed to be a flood facies. A thin (20 mm) felted peat cropping out 1.5 m above the water could be traced continuously for 50 m and in the centre of this the *in situ* stump was located. The peat appeared to have accumulated concurrently with the growth of the tree and, as such, was a palaeosol. However, no evidence of pedogenic development could be detected, suggesting that the time available for the operation of soil forming processes was short. No other tree material was found along the exposure and, whilst appreciating the dangers of interpreting a limited two-dimensional section, the lack of other tree debris at this horizon could indicate that the tree density was low.

Only 0.75 m of the the tree bole remained in the position of life. It had a diameter of 0.3 m and subsequent thin section examination of the wood structure revealed that the tree was a member of the *Pinus sylvestris* group. The stump had very little bark adhering to it, and that which remained lay in protected recesses associated with the branching roots. There was a predominantly horizontal root system and, after careful excavation, one root could be traced for over 2.4 m from the bole. Generally the roots were exceedingly shallow in depth, this being in marked contrast with the previous tree. This contrast is probably accounted for by the fact that in the original example the stump lay above the main organic bed, which could have served as a moisture source, whilst the reverse stratigraphic relationship held in the latter case. The entire stump was removed from the section and conserved as potential dating material.

The tree and allied land surface were buried by well sorted sands which did not disturb the organic materials, suggesting the tree did not die through catastrophic causes. Immediately overlying the broken-off stump was a thicker felted peat (>0.2 m). This cut cleanly across the bole and extended for at least 50 m on either side. As far as the exposures permitted, this particular peat appeared to be the main organic horizon in the north-eastern quarry sections. Laterally the peat bed became thinner and it also became gently involuted, this being ascribed to post-depositional compaction. A quantity of the main peat bed above the stump was collected for dating purposes. Above this bed no further organic material was detected.

In view of the doubts concerning the Hv-737 results and an assurance that more good and stratigraphically reliable materials were now available, the Hannover laboratory was prepared to make an independent check of the Chelford ^{14}C date. For the first time two samples from Chelford were assayed which were undoubtedly of different ages since they were superposed in the field. Sub-samples of the wood and peat yielded the following ages in May 1968:

| Peat | $30,770 \pm 430$ | Hv-1979 |
| Wood | $32,850 \pm 480$ | Hv-1978 |

Clearly these results were even more anomalous, on face value being some 10 ka younger than the previous Hannover dates. Interestingly, the two new dates revealed the correct stratigraphic order of the samples. Further, the laboratory commented that in their experience wood and peat react differently to contamination and therefore it was unlikely that this latter cause was the explanation for the difference from previous dating results. In the light of the problem of reconciliation, the laboratory resolved to date a humic acid extract from the wood as an independent check. In the event insufficient humic acid could be obtained, so another wood sub-sample was dated. This yielded:

| Wood | $26,200 \pm 390$ | Hv-1978B |

The laboratory suggested that there must be a geological explanation for the divergence between the original and later Hannover dates, i.e. they were not from the same stratigraphic level. Owing to ambiguity in translation it was originally understood that the Hv-1978B date was obtained from a count on the humic acid extracted from the wood. Unfortunately, this error, for which the author takes responsibility, has been quoted in *Radiocarbon* (Shotton *et al.*, 1970).

At the time, the dating results from Groningen and Lamont (three assays) were consistent in indicating a true date of at least 60 ka and probably an organic bed of restricted temporal status. On the other hand, the five Hannover assays, if accepted, gave a range of 26–41 ka, suggesting an organic complex covering a timespan perhaps equivalent to an interglacial in duration. Since (a) the same tree had yielded ages of both 26 and 31 ka, and (b) there were serious problems in reconciling the palaeoecological implications of forested conditions during a period when other sites in the English Midlands indicated polar desert, the explanation clearly lay with the likelihood that contamination by younger materials was influencing the results.

In order to contribute directly to the clarification of the British Last-Glacial stage (Devensian), the University of Birmingham Geology Department had established its own ^{14}C laboratory in 1966. Accordingly, it was designed and constructed with the aim of achieving the oldest possible finite dates (provided that the samples warranted it). In practice, this has had a limit at 49 ka. What may be termed the 'Chelford dilemma' was naturally of direct interest to the Birmingham dating programme, especially since the coleopteran fauna had been studied at the department (Coope, 1959). Another sub-sample of the 1967 materials was submitted for dating, and through the cooperation of F. W. Shotton this material was given especially rigorous pre-treatment and four separate humate extractions were made prior to the gasification of the sample. The sample count time occupied nearly 3 days. The result was:

Wood $47,000^{+2300}_{-1800}$ Birm-157

It is important to appreciate the meaning of the count data upon which this particular reported age was calculated. Since the age is finite, the count rate of the sample less that of the background is greater than 4σ, for the Birmingham practice is to define age limits by the 4σ criterion (99.9% probability that if the same gas was counted under the same conditions the results would fall within the limits of the experimental error). In this case this was only marginally so ($4\sigma = 0.2768$ counts per minute; sample activity $= 0.2782$ counts per minute) and, if either the background or sample counts had been about 17 h less, would have exceeded one quarter of the count and the age would have had to be given as >47 ka. More critically, the same conclusion would also have applied if the correction for atmospheric pressure fluctuations had been in error in the third decimal place.

There is little doubt, therefore, that after thorough pre-treatment the sample was registering a very low level of ^{14}C activity. If it is *assumed* that the Groningen finite date is approximately correct and that both the 1957 and 1967 collected wood samples are effectively of the same geological age, then a residual contamination after pre-treatment in the Birmingham gas preparation would be sufficient to explain the difference. Further, the higher count rates which must have been registered at Hannover can only have derived from a contaminant rather than the original wood in the sample.

In the early 1970s, N. R. Page was advocating that ^{14}C age determination should be considered more important than conventional stratigraphy (Page, 1972). He expressed interest in Chelford results since he was curious about the wide range of dates derived from a restricted outcrop, a range that was inconsistent with his interpretative framework. Learning of the continued existence of part of the tree stump collected in 1967, he requested a sample. With the support of the Institute of Geological Sciences he arranged for the newly established Scottish Universities' Research and Reactor Laboratory at East Kilbride to undertake further assays.

The East Kilbride approach was to try to date various fractions prepared from the wood sample in order to assess the possible effect of potential contamination on the previously reported age determinations. Another point worth noting is that the East Kilbride ^{14}C counts are made by liquid scintillation counting rather than by gas-proportional counting. To evaluate the contamination hypothesis the laboratory counted four different fractions, namely untreated wood, humic free wood, humic extract from the former, and cellulose (Harkness and Wilson, 1974). The results were as follows:

untreated wood	>47,300	SRR-154
humic free wood	>48,700	SRR-155
humic extract	$41,290^{+980}_{-880}$	SRR-156
cellulose	>48,700	SRR-157

The remarkable result was that all three wood samples yielded dates beyond the limits of finite dating with the apparatus in use, which, as can be seen, was >47 or 48 ka. Of particular interest, in view of the dating history of the material collected in 1967, was that the untreated wood gave the same 'infinite' age as the specially treated preparations (the humic-free wood and the cellulose). These data indicate that the collected material was as near ideal as is likely to be encountered with sediments of such antiquity. Furthermore, it seems probable that all of the dated Chelford material is in a similar condition. Consequently, in this case the degree of pre-treatment would appear to have no significant influence upon the amount of residual ^{14}C in the material. However, the date from the humic extract at 41 ka is not surprising since such extracts almost invariably indicate contamination by younger materials. The most important aspect of the East Kilbride results is that the strong suspicion held throughout that the original Groningen determinations were valid is vindicated. None of the evidence available suggests that there is a fundamentally different age to the various organic beds which constitute the interstadial sequence.

5. For many years the existence of sub-surface organic-rich materials within Chelford-type sands has been known from borehole evidence at Arclid (Fig. 19.1), about 25 km southwest of Chelford. In 1969 W. B. Evans of the Institute of Geological Sciences obtained a sample of wood from the screens at the Taxmere Quarry plant which in all probability was derived from the bed revealed by the boreholes. This was submitted to the ^{14}C Laboratory of the Swedish Geological Survey in Stockholm. The assay yielded:

Wood   >40,000   IGS-C14/25 (St-3273)

which lends some support to the suspected correlation with the Farm Wood bed.

Discussion

It could be argued that in the absence of radiocarbon dating information, the stratigraphic evidence merely indicates that the organic materials are of interstadial character, antedating an ice advance over the locality, but precise correlation with a specific glacial stage is not possible. In this view the residual ^{14}C in all the samples measured would be the product of contamination by more modern organic matter of infinitely old materials.

This possibility is a real one and has been apparent from the earliest days of the ^{14}C dating attempts. It is relevant to recall that the second sample to be subjected to the enrichment process by de Vries and then introduced into the counter was carbon dioxide gas derived from anthracite which theoretically was totally deficient in ^{14}C. However, he was able to detect some very low-level activity which corresponded with a date of 73 ka. A further example is the dating of the humus extracted from the Amersfoort Wood sample previously mentioned (64 ka). This yielded an age of 42 ka and hence had acquired some more recent humus after burial, forcing the conclusion 'because of possible infiltration, all dates are more or less minimum dates' (Haring *et al.*, 1958). Support for this attitude came from van der Hammen *et al.* (1967), who commented on the Amersfoort result: 'due to the great effect of the slightest contamination with recent carbon on samples in this age range the figure must be considered a minimum age. Only when several Early Glacial samples have been measured will it be possible to arrive at a trustworthy date for this period'. Most recently, Grootes (1978) has stated that laboratory contamination was present at Groningen during the first decade of enrichment dating and consequently this may have affected the validity of the results. *If* therefore, the ^{14}C data are only able to demonstrate a minimum age of early Last-Glacial stage, what can positively be concluded about the chronological status of the Chelford organic deposits?

Firstly, there is a good match of the pollen spectra from Chelford with those from the interstadial deposits at Brørup in west Denmark. Here it should be recalled that the Brørup sequence occupies a basin in the lower parts of which is an Eemian interglacial sequence. This succession is overlain, in turn, by two interstadial beds. Hence there is little doubt that the Brørup interstadial is of early Last-Glacial stage age. Andersen (1961) has compared his detailed Brørup pollen diagram with that from Chelford and found that the respective records were similar and, hence, that the climatic inferences were consistent. He thus concluded that the correlation between the two 'seems highly probable indeed'. The oldest finite ^{14}C date from Brørup is:

59,100 ± 700   GrN-1470

The second line of reasoning relates to the type site for the Devensian Stage at Four Ashes. As commented earlier, this locality supplanted Chelford as the stratotype since it contained a much more elaborate succession of organic-rich beds seemingly representative of many of the various environments which existed prior to the ice-advance maximum about 20 ka. Studies of the beetle faunas by Morgan (1973) and pollen analysis by Andrews and West (1977) have revealed that a Chelford-type organic bed (site 10) lay immediately above the same unconformity as another bed which carried an interglacial assemblage. This relationship suggests either an early glacial stage age or, less likely, a pre-interglacial age for the material with strong Chelford affinities. Also lying stratigraphically higher were lenses with 'Upton Warren Interstadial Complex' faunas and some of these had ^{14}C dates of mid-Devensian age.

Thirdly, the Chelford ^{14}C data may be assessed in terms of the gross succession in the Chelford area. The *assumption* that the Chelford Sands are an integral sedimentary unit carries with it the implication that a specific type of environment occurred during their deposition. This was interrupted by the deposition of organic materials as can be judged by the stratigraphy. It is known that the deposition of the sands was followed by glaciation of the region and that this probably occurred between 20 and 25 ka. On the other hand, the base is formed by bedrock, or a patchy till whose chronological status is uncertain. However, taking the British evidence as a whole, it would seem that an early Devensian glaciation of Cheshire is unlikely, and thus the commencement of sand deposition could be related to the onset of climatic deterioration at the end of the last interglacial about 120 ka. Hence the maximum possible duration for the periglacial environment accompanied by alluvial sand transport is some 100 ka. The interstadial beds lie in the middle of the succession and if a constant deposition rate is *assumed* then the organic material grew and accumulated about 70 ka. It is evident that this estimate is crude, but nevertheless it is consistent with the overall conclusions derived from other approaches.

The restricted geological evidence available therefore suggests that the Chelford interstadial is an early Last-Glacial stage event. Its precise absolute age remains uncertain at present since it is exceedingly difficult to distinguish between genuine, residual, low-level ^{14}C activity and that derived from post-depositional infiltration. Clearly the age lies close to or beyond the currently practical limits of ^{14}C dating. However, the future looks promising, since following just over a decade of virtual dormancy in the publication of enriched ^{14}C dates a sudden change occurred in 1978. Immediately after the completion of a draft of this account two papers were published simultaneously by Grootes (1978) and Stuiver *et al.* (1978). Both concerned technical improvements in low-level counting techniques using thermal diffusion enrichment and proportional carbon dioxide counters enabling the sources of contamination to be identified better. This permits the extension of the ^{14}C timescale back to 75 ka. In the present context the paper by Grootes is particularly important since it reports 19 new ^{14}C dates between 56 and 73 ka obtained from samples collected in the western European mainland. On face value these permit the identification of a close succession of three interstadials in the early part of the Last-Glacial stage, each defined in ^{14}C years. These are called Amersfoort, Brørup, and Odderade. The correlative on stratigraphic and palynological grounds of the type Brørup of Denmark at the Amersfoort (Netherlands) locality is considered to commence at $64,400 \pm 800$ and the succeeding Odderade at $60,500 \pm 600$. A forthcoming evaluation by Grootes of the early de Vries enrichment results is in preparation. He has kindly commented that in his opinion the Chelford date of 60.5 ka (GrN-1475) is a few thousand years too young and that it probably represents a date of the second Brørup Interstadial. Two assessments are possible utilizing two different assumptions: (a) if the same contaminating activity as in the anthracite carbon dioxide were present (this gas immediately preceded the first geological enriched date) then the true age would be 62.7 ka; (b) if the contamination was the same as the first geological date (Amersfoort) the true age would be 64.2 ka. Hence, if all factors are considered, the date gives a reasonable indication of the true sample age. Hopefully a new age determination will be possible utilizing the improved enrichment processes, for some of the peat collected at Farm Wood in 1967 is still available and excellent material is constantly being exposed at the Oakwood Quarry, Chelford. Also, recent developments involving a radically different approach to ^{14}C dating have emerged. These involve the direct counting of ^{14}C concentrations by the use of a cyclotron (Muller, 1977) or a van de Graaff accelerator (Nelson *et al.*, 1977) as high-energy mass spectrometers, with the potential of deriving finite 'dates' back to about 100 ka. However, the contamination problem remains the same as for conventional ^{14}C decay counting.

Conclusion

The ^{14}C data reviewed are presented in diagrammatic form in Fig. 19.3, plotted with the 2*s* confidence limits in order to emphasize the inescapable timespan characteristic of a so-called 'date'. Although the total assemblage gives clear support for regarding the ^{14}C age of the Farm Wood bed as at least 60–65 ka, this conclusion was less certain in 1969. In retrospect that year can be seen as the critical 'watershed', for then the first independent check on essentially the same material was made by another laboratory. Thus the Birmingham assay, Birm-157, demonstrated that Hv-1978 must reflect the presence of some laboratory contaminant in the gas preparation. Following this revelation, geological explanations for the age divergence invoking derivation and recycling of the wood and peat were no longer necessary, although they were not excluded, and it became more probable that the 'interstadial' was of restricted duration. The most dramatic vindication of the view that the material was 'old' in ^{14}C terms had to await the East Kilbride work, for then it became apparent that even the raw sample straight from the field without any pre-treatment was undoubtedly 'old'. Thus the pioneer work of de Vries and his colleagues in the very low-level counting and enrichment techniques and their assays on the Chelford material still retain considerable value.

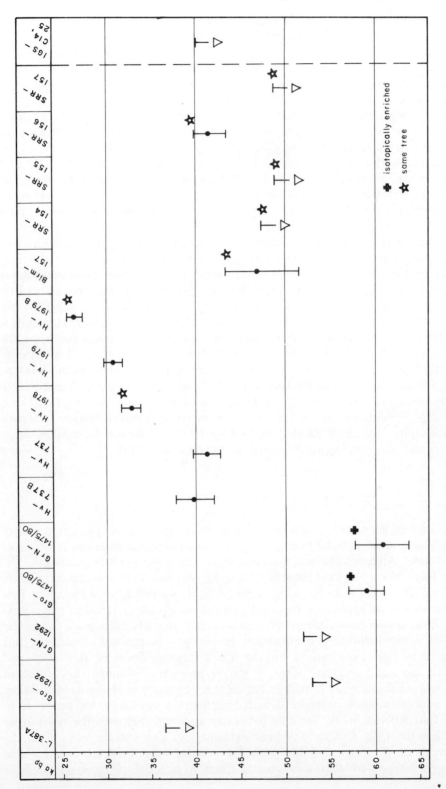

Fig. 19.3 Plot of the Cheshire Chelford interstadial ^{14}C dates. Plot of all the reported ^{14}C dates on material from the organic bed at Farm Wood Chelford together with one (extreme right-hand side) from Arclid. Note that the uncertainty ranges are ±2 s and that in reality there are only two dates from the Groningen laboratory

Acknowledgements

Grateful thanks are extended to the many workers who have contributed to the Chelford dating programme. Discussions at various times with G. S. Boulton, G. R. Coope, F. W. Shotton, and R. G. West have been particularly helpful. The manuscript was critically reviewed by W. Blake, Jr., D. T. Holyoak, and D. A. St.-Onge. P. M. Grootes both reviewed the account and added greater insight into the initial development of the enrichment technique. The author's work at Chelford has been supported by the British Natural Environment Research Council and the University of Reading. The account was prepared whilst he was employed by the University of Ottawa.

References

Andersen, S. T. (1961). Vegetation and its environment in Denmark in the early Weichselian glacial (last glacial). *Dan. Geol. Unders. Raekke 2*, **75**, 175 pp.

Andrews, R., and West, R. G. (1977). Appendix. Pollen analysis from Four Ashes, Worcs. *Phil. Trans R. Soc., B*, 280, 242–246.

Boulton, G. S., and Worsley, P. (1965). Late Weichselian glaciation of the Cheshire–Shropshire Basin. *Nature, Lond.*, **207**, 704–706.

Coope, G. R. (1959). A Late Pleistocene insect fauna from Chelford, Cheshire. *Proc. R. Soc., B*, **151**, 70–86.

Grootes, P. M. (1977). *Thermal Diffusion Isotopic Enrichment and Radiocarbon Dating Beyond 50,000 years BP*. PhD Thesis, University of Groningen, 221 p.

Grootes, P. M. (1978). Carbon-14 time scale extended: comparison of chronologies. *Science*, **200**, 11–15.

van der Hammen, T., Maarleveld, G. C., Vogel, J. C., and Zagwijn, W. H. (1967). Stratigraphy, climatic succession and radiocarbon dating of the Last Glacial in the Netherlands. *Geol. Mijnbouw*, **46**, 79–95.

Haring, A., de Vries, A. E., and de Vries, H. (1958). Radiocarbon dating up to 70,000 years by isotopic enrichment. *Science*, **128**, 472–473.

Harkness, D. D., and Wilson, H. W. (1974). Scottish Universities Research and Reactor Centre radiocarbon measurements, II. *Radiocarbon*, **16**, 238–251.

Mitchell, G. R., Penny, L. F., Shotton, F. W., and West, R. G. (1973). A correlation of Quaternary deposits of the British Isles. *Geol. Soc. Lond. Spec. Rep.*, No. 4, 99 pp.

Morgan, A. V. (1973). Late Pleistocene environmental changes indicated by fossil insect faunas of the English Midlands. *Boreas*, **2**, 173–212.

Muller, R. A. (1977). Radioisotope dating with a cyclotron. *Science*, **196**, 489–492.

Nelson, D. E., Korteling, R. G., and Stott, W. R. (1977). Carbon-14: direct detection at natural concentrations. *Science*, **198**, 507–508.

Olson, E. A., and Broecker, W. S. (1961). Lamont natural radiocarbon measurements, VII. *Radiocarbon*, **3**, 141–175.

Page, N. R. (1972). On the age of the Hoxnian interglacial. *Geol. J.*, **8**, 129–142.

Shotton, F. W., and West, R. G. (1969). Stratigraphical table of the British Quaternary. *Proc. Geol. Soc. Lond.*, 155–157.

Shotton, F. W., Blundell, D. J., and Williams, R. E. G. (1970). Birmingham University radiocarbon dates, IV. *Radiocarbon*, **12**, 385–399.

Simpson, I. M., and West, R. G. (1958). On the stratigraphy and palaeobotany of a late-Pleistocene organic deposit at Chelford, Cheshire, *New Phytol.*, **57**, 239–250.

Stuiver, M., Heusser, C. J., and Yang, I. C. (1978). North American glacial history extended to 70,000 years ago. *Science*, **200**, 16–21.

Turner, C., and West, R. G. (1968). The subdivision and zonation of interglacial periods. *Eiszeitalter Gegenw.*, **19**, 93–101.

Vita-Finzi, C. (1973). *Recent Earth History*. Macmillan, London & Basingstoke.

Vogel, J. C., and Zagwijn, W. H. (1967). Groningen radiocarbon dates, VI. *Radiocarbon*, **9**, 63–106.

de Vries, H. (1958). Radiocarbon dates for upper Eem and Würm-interstadial samples. *Eiszeitalter Gegenw.*, **9**, 10–17.

de Vries, H. (1959). Measurement and use of natural radiocarbon. In *Researches in Geochemistry* (Ed. P. J. Abelson). Wiley, Chichester, pp. 169–189.

Welin, E., Engstrand, L., and Vaczy, S. (1972). Institute of Geological Sciences Radiocarbon dates, II. *Radiocarbon*, **14,** 140–144.

Worsley, P. (1966). Some Weichselian fossil frost wedges from east Cheshire. *Mercian Geol.,* **1,** 357–365.

Worsley, P. (1977). The Cheshire–Shropshire Plain. In *Wales and the Cheshire–Shropshire Lowland* (Ed. D. Q. Bowen), Xth INQUA, Norwich, pp. 53–64.

Timescales in Geomorphology
Edited by R. A. Cullingford, D. A. Davidson, and J. Lewin
© 1980 John Wiley & Sons Ltd

CHAPTER 20

The age and geomorphological context of a Norfolk palaeosol

Allan Straw

Department of Geography,
University of Exeter

Evidence for the presence in former interglacials or interstadials of plant and animal communities at least as complex as those which have developed in Flandrian time has been forthcoming from many sites in the British Isles, but much of this evidence has accrued from bog, lacustrine, and estuarine sediments surviving from these periods. The former existence of complex ecosystems demands that concurrent soil formation should have been as advanced then as in the Flandrian, certainly in the interglacials, but few such soils have survived or at least have so far been discovered. Most soils were destroyed by subsequent glacial or periglacial erosion and their constituent materials dispersed and incorporated in tills, heads, aeolian sands, and fluvial, estuarine, and marine sediments. However, those which have survived and been discovered acquire a potentially important role in clarifying the timescale of geomorphological events not only of the local area but sometimes further afield.

One such relict soil (Fig. 20.1) survives in north-west Norfolk and was exposed for some years up to 1974 as a consequence of gravel extraction in the floor of a dry valley at Docking Common (TF 790357) at 60 m OD. Developed at depth within flinty 'valley gravels', the soil was exposed, conveniently for a three-dimensional appraisal of its pedogenic character, along about 70 m of a right-angled section.

This paper discusses briefly the geomorphic situation of the palaeosol and associated gravels and also the timescales that must be considered in determining not only the age of the soil but the timespan of events recorded at the site.

Stratigraphy

Beneath the palaeosol, a *Lower Gravel* at least 6 m thick (Fig. 20.4) consists largely of poorly sorted gravel and sand. The gravel fraction (Fig. 20.5; Table 20.1), composed almost entirely of angular and sub-angular flints up to 10 cm long, is incorporated in a sand matrix largely of quartz grains and flint chips. Although layering within the gravel is indistinct, bedding is imparted to the deposit as a whole by frequent intercalation of

Fig. 20.1 The palaeosol at Docking Common. Horizons 1, 2, 3 (with bird nest-holes) above spade;
horizons 4 and 5 separated by a highly irregular iron-pan discernible to left of spade

many lenses and seams of silty fine sand, which vary in thickness from a few centimetres
to as much as 50 cm (Fig. 20.2). Particle-size analysis (Fig. 20.5; Table 20.1) and
stratigraphic situation point to aeolian transport and deposition of these silty sands.
Intraformational involutions frequently contort both the gravel and sand layers.

The *palaeosol* survives across the floor of a former 50 m-wide depression in the surface
of the Lower Gravel (Fig. 20.4) and displays five horizons differentiated by texture,
structure, mineral composition, and colour (Tables 20.1 and 20.2; Fig. 20.5). The
uppermost horizon of compact sand and silty sand incorporates thin seams and lenses
containing diffused organic matter, and overlies an indurated horizon of silty sand
showing pronounced streaking of secondary iron compounds. A third horizon, gravelly
and bleached in appearance, passes diffusely into another eluviated but somewhat
stronger-coloured horizon of flint gravel. The latter has an abrupt irregular contact with
the lowest horizon which comprises heavy concentrations of illuviated iron oxides.

Fig. 20.2 Stratigraphy of the Docking Common deposits, viewed to the north-east. The lower gravel, with silty sand layers and involutions, is overlain on left by the palaeosol (with holes). The latter is covered in part by the upper gravel and is destroyed by involutions as it rises near to the surface

Fig. 20.3 Deep involutions affecting the upper gravel and palaeosol horizons on the north-west face of Docking Common quarry

Table 20.1 Textural variation and sorting of deposits at Docking Common quarry

Deposits			No. of samples	Clay (<2 μm)	Silt (2–63 μm)	Sand (0.063–2 mm)	Gravel (>2 mm)	Sorting indices, $\frac{1}{2}(\varphi 16-\varphi 84)$
Silt layers			7	12–20	46–76	12–36	0–2	2.0–3.5
Lower gravel			7	—	1–13	37–42	49–58	2.9–3.4
Upper gravel			4	—	3–7	41–50	48–55	3.0–3.3
Palaeosol	1	a	2	—	8–10	86–89	3–4	1.0
		b	2	11–13	38–47	40–47	2	3.0
		c	2	11–14	32–35	48–49	5–6	2.9
	2		2	6–7	22–25	61–63	6–7	1.9–2.1
Horizons	3		2	—	10–12	69	19	2.7–2.9
	4		2	—	7	35	58	3.0–3.4

Although the highest horizon appears to consist of fluvially reworked soil materials and may therefore be regarded as a sedimentary unit, the lower and original albic and spodic horizons are clearly developed within the upper part of the Lower Gravel, and the marked irregularity of the iron-pan interface between horizons four and five is a pedogenic and not a sedimentary feature (Fig. 20.1).

Three metres of *Upper Gravel* overlie the palaeosol across the former shallow depression eroded in the Lower Gravel. Similar to the latter in general sedimentary characteristics, flint size and shape, and degree of sorting, the Upper Gravel is caught up in complex involutions (Figs. 20.2–20.4). These penetrate deeply enough not only to involve the uppermost layers of the surviving palaeosol but also, in passing into the Lower Gravel beyond the confines of the depression, to have destroyed here the palaeosol where it undoubtedly once existed (Fig. 20.2). One 3 m-long ice-wedge cast, 30 cm wide at the top, originated in the Upper Gravel to pierce the palaeosol and terminate in the Lower Gravel.

Geomorphology

The Docking Common gravels occupy the floor of the headward portion of a wide shallow dry valley that trends south-east from Docking. Field observations indicate that the lower layers of gravel rest directly on chalk. South-east of the quarry an old marl pit at a slightly higher level (TF 796354) reveals thin glacial till overlying chalk, and southwards augering confirms chalk beneath faint spur-tip benches between small tributary dry-valleys (Fig. 20.4).

The flanks of the main valley are underlain by chalky glacial till, the base of which is hidden by the higher gravel layers. The till, variously greyish and brownish white in colour, consists mainly of pieces of chalk and flint with a few far-travelled igneous and sedimentary rocks in a matrix of clayey and sandy crushed chalk. Overlying the till, especially around Docking and on the higher ground west of the valley, are bedded sandy and flinty outwash gravels which eventually contributed much material towards the younger Docking Common gravels. The contrasting attitudes of these older and younger gravels demonstrate unequivocally that excavation of the valley presumably under a dominantly fluvial regime was an intervening event.

Table 20.2 Characteristics of palaeosol horizons

Horizons	Texture, compaction, structure	Munsell colour	Thickness (cm)
1 (reworked)	Compact, weakly cemented, contorted layers and lenses of bedded sand and silty sand with a few angular flints. Some contain diffused organic matter, others are well sorted, consistent with fluvial deposition. Secondary iron concentrated selectively along bedding planes. Well defined though irregular upper and lower contacts sometimes with iron-pan (less than 5 mm). Frequently above iron-pans are thin (less than 2 cm) gleyed zones.	Very dark brown (10 YR 2/2) to yellowish brown (10 YR 5/4). Gleyed areas: grey (10 YR 5/1, 6/1)	15–60
2 (albic)	Moderately indurated silty sand containing a few small flints and a few thin (less than 5 mm) seams of grey clay. Pronounced lateral streaking imparted by selective deposition of secondary iron along planes deriving from a fragipan structure. Upper contact occasionally contorted; sharp but transitional lower contact.	Generally pale yellow (2.2 Y 7/4) to yellowish red (5 YR 5/8)	15–20
3 (albic)	Mainly friable unbedded sand, becoming more gravelly near base, with angular flints generally less than 3 cm across. Gradational lower contact.	Pale olive (5 Y 6/3)	10–30
4 (albic)	Sandy, amorphous flint gravel with angular and sub-angular flints to 10 cm across, and a few rounded quartzite pebbles. Abrupt, irregular, frequently 'piped' lower contact.	Brown (7.5 YR 5/4) to pale brown (10 YR 6/3)	18–100
5 (spodic)	Sandy flint gravel cemented by heavy concentration of illuviated iron oxides forming a dense irregular pan within the highest part of the Lower Gravel.	Dark reddish brown (2.5 YR 2/4, 3/4, 3/6)	1–60

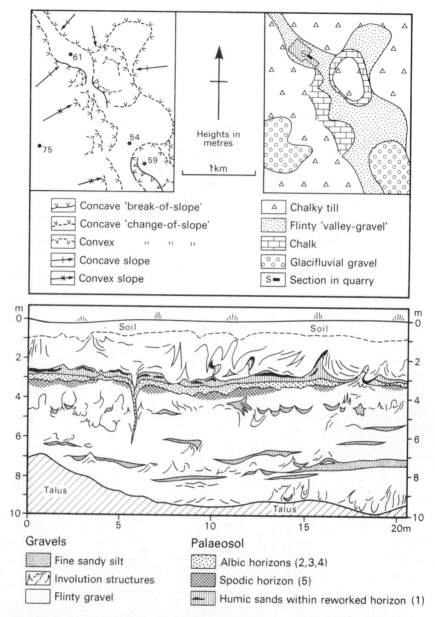

Fig. 20.4 Site, situation and diagrammatic section of the gravels and palaeosol exposed in Docking Common quarry. The section summarizes features of the exposure which are illustrated in more detail in Figs. 20.1, 20.2 and 20.3

The Lower Gravel constitutes the bulk of the valley floor deposits, and both the fact and manner of aggradation point to a change in transportation processes. The profusion of angular flints and the poorly sorted nature of the gravel suggest soliflual processes operative on the side-slopes of the valley while snow-melt water achieved some transport and rearrangement of material along the valley floor. The numerous involution horizons within the Lower Gravel and the contained seams of aeolian silty fine sand (Fig. 20.2 and 20.4) confirm prevailing cold conditions and an upwards-migrating permafrost table

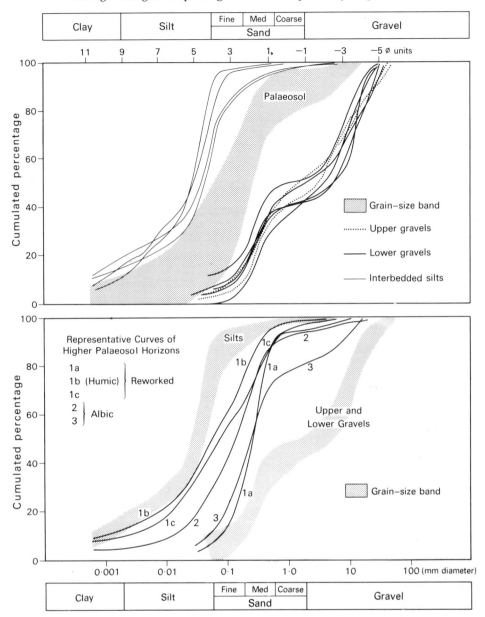

Fig. 20.5 Particle-size curves for Docking Common gravels and palaeosol

during deposition. Deposits very similar in composition and sedimentary character have been described at Welton-le-Wold within the Lincolnshire Wolds by Alabaster and Straw (1976).

Aggradation of the Lower Gravel was followed by an erosional phase manifested by the shallow 50 m-wide depression in the gravel surface. The linear trace of the depression suggests erosion by running water during a time when slope solifluction was negligible and permafrost was probably degrading, but excavation appears to have ceased through desiccation when the depression was about 3.5–4 m deep.

Pedogenesis succeeded cessation of fluvial activity within the depression. The palaeosol is continuous across the depression floor and there are strong indications that formerly it extended over and beyond the flanks of the depression onto areas now forming the present land surface. The podsolic character of the palaeosol confirms not only a free-draining condition over the valley floor but also a more temperate environment and presumably a closed vegetation cover.

The upper reworked horizons of the palaeosol indicate a brief period of fluvial activity before accumulation of the Upper Gravel within the depression. Such activity may reflect a general rise in water table, but more probably snow-melt over a seasonally frozen surface, because the Upper Gravel confirms a rapid return to niveo-soliflual and niveo-fluvial processes similar to those which prevailed during deposition of the Lower Gravel. The eventual re-establishment of permafrost within this potentially highly permeable material is witnessed by both the long ice-wedge cast and the slightly younger, deeply penetrating involutions.

In summary, the sequence of events was as follows:

1. Deposition of the chalky tills and outwash gravels of north-west Norfolk.
2. Formation of the Docking Common valley.
3. Aggradation of the Lower Gravel under cold climatic conditions.
4. Fluvial erosion of a 50 m wide depression within the Lower Gravel to a depth of almost 4 m.
5. Formation of the palaeosol.
6. Reworking of the uppermost palaeosol horizons giving way to deposition of the Upper Gravel within the depression under renewed cold climatic conditions.
7. Development of the ice-wedge cast and involutions.
8. Flandrian pedogenesis.

Timescales

Three timescales may be considered in respect of stages 3–7 of this sequence.
1. The chalky tills of north-west Norfolk are regarded by some workers as of Anglian age (Banham *et al.*, 1975; Shotton *et al.*, 1977). If the Upper Gravel is a Devensian deposit, then perhaps about 300,000 years are available for valley formation, gravel aggradation, and palaeosol development. A simple orthodox correlation might place valley formation in the Hoxnian, the Lower Gravel in the Wolstonian, and the palaeosol in the Ipswichian.
2. Straw (1965, 1967, 1973) ascribes the north-west Norfolk tills and outwash to the Wolstonian. This interpretation would reduce the timescale effectively to the order of 50,000 years, and would permit reference also of both the Lower Gravel and the palaeosol to the Devensian.
3. The cold–temperate–cold environmental stages indicated by the Lower Gravel–palaeosol–Upper Gravel sequence might also be taken to represent the 'Late Glacial' oscillation recorded in pollen zones I, II, and III, the palaeosol representing perhaps the Allerød phase. A timescale of less than 3000 years need then be envisaged.

Discussion

The long timescale, whereby the Lower Gravel is referred to the Wolstonian, is not well supported by the evidence. Valley formation in the Ipswichian interglacial would be restricted at best to the shallow palaeosol depression. Reference of the Lower and Upper Gravel to two separate Glaciations would seem to ignore the similarity of the two phases of sedimentation that occurred at Docking Common. It must be noted, however, that Ipswichian interglacial deposits beneath cryoturbated gravel are known near the Fenland margin at Wretton (Sparks and West, 1970) and at Tattershall (Girling, 1974). The palaeosol at Docking Common contains no pollen by which comparison with these deposits might be made, but humic material from the uppermost reworked horizon has on ^{14}C assay yielded finite dates of 19,300 ± 300 (Birm-350) and 24,000 ± 550 years bp (Birm-412).

The short timescale seems inadequate on several grounds. The ^{14}C dates, if reliable, provide an absolute minimum age of the palaeosol which is considerably older than the Allerød or Bölling interstadials. Moreover, the conditions which produced permafrost at this dry site necessary for the formation of the ice-wedge cast and the deep involutions in the Upper Gravel would seem to have been far too intense to ascribe to a Zone III environment (Sparks *et al.*, 1972; Maarleveld, 1976).

The medium timescale accords best with the evidence available. Lithologically similar, the Lower and Upper Gravels no doubt derive from identical source materials, and they comprise a broadly homogeneous unit within a valley of simple form that was excavated after the last glacierization of the area. Geomorphologically these depositional stages are separated only by minor channelling of the Lower Gravel and by palaeosol formation, whereas the period of valley formation prior to deposition of the Lower Gravel would seem to require a considerably longer time. It must also be remembered that the Docking Common valley is a headward portion, albeit relatively shallow, of the Wensum system most of which is incised deeply into the Chalk across central Norfolk. Formation of both the palaeosol and the depression in which it survives might be accommodated within one or more of the earlier Devensian interstadials. Such a probability is supported by the finite ^{14}C dates, for the older date provides a minimum age only for the palaeosol. No long break is envisaged between the existence of an intact soil profile and the redeposition after reworking of the organic matter. Redeposition was no doubt occurring while erosion of topsoil upvalley was proceeding.

Regional Correlation

An intensely cold period in eastern England in the Late Devensian is confirmed in eastern Holderness, where tills of the Drab–Purple complex were probably emplaced soon after about 18,250 years bp (Penny *et al.*, 1969). It can reasonably be assumed that this cold phase is represented at Docking Common by the Upper Gravel and its structures.

Evidence is not forthcoming from eastern Holderness for cold periods earlier in the Devensian, but quarry sections at Kirkby-on-Bain and Tattershall in the Bain valley in Lincolnshire reveal intraformational cryogenic structures in flinty and chalky fluviatile gravels in which finer grained sediments with organic matter have been ^{14}C-dated between 30,800 and 44,300 years bp (Girling, 1974).

At Wretton in west Norfolk, Ipswichian interglacial deposits are overlain by Early Devensian cryoturbated gravels of the River Wissey (Sparks and West, 1970), which incorporate horizons with involutions, ice-wedge casts, and ground-ice structures.

One other line of evidence is available. Catt and Penny (1966) claim that ice reached north Norfolk during the post-18,250 bp. Devensian advance. However, two advances of

Devensian ice separated by a considerable period of weathering and denudation have
been demonstrated in east Lincolnshire, the second of these being less extensive than the
first and associated with fresher morainic and glacifluvial features (Straw, 1957, 1961,
1969). Suggate and West's (1959) demonstration of a complete Late-Glacial sequence in
a kettle-hole in the second advance moraine at Aby Grange (TF 429798) near Alford
supports the view that the eastern Holderness advances after 18,250 bp may be
correlated more certainly with the second, and not the first, Lincolnshire advance (Fig.
20.6).

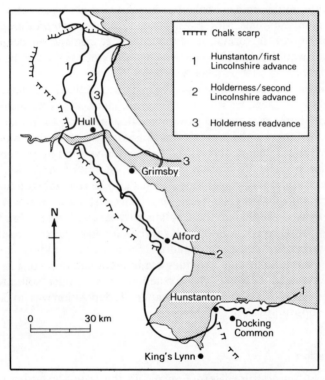

Fig. 20.6 Devensian ice limits in eastern England

It was during the first advance that Devensian ice pressed into the Fens as far as the
Stickney moraine, reached north Norfolk (Straw, 1960), and impounded pro-glacial
'Lake Fenland'. On Kirkby Moor (TF 225630) east of Woodhall Spa in Lincolnshire,
deltaic sands deposited on the margin of 'Lake Fenland' at 20–26 m OD by the
contemporary River Bain are older than the lower lying fluviatile gravels at Kirkby-on-
Bain and Tattershall. The maximum advance of Devensian ice into Lincolnshire and to
north Norfolk would seem to have been earlier than 45,000 years bp.

Evidence does exist, therefore, in Lincolnshire and the Fenland area for periods of
cold in the early part of the Devensian sufficiently intense and prolonged to account for
both the aggradation and the structural disturbance of the Lower Gravel at Docking
Common.

Conclusion

It has been shown that in its geomorphological context the age of the palaeosol at Docking Common can be considered with reference to three timescales. The geomorphic sequence reveals phases of erosion and deposition controlled by alternating and contrasting environmental conditions. Neither the long nor the short timescale accommodates satisfactorily all of the geological and geomorphological circumstances. Application of the medium timescale causes no problems of interpretation, and an attempt has been made to demonstrate that the occurrence of an intensely cold phase early in the Devensian Glaciation is not special pleading only to explain the characteristics of the Lower Gravel but is a phenomenon witnessed by fluvial and glacial deposits over a much wider area of eastern England.

The age of the palaeosol cannot be determined more precisely than middle Devensian and older than 24,000 years bp, but its degree of development certainly merits more detailed examination in terms of contemporary environmental conditions than it has been possible to present in this paper.

References

Alabaster, C., and Straw, A. (1976). The Pleistocene context of faunal remains and artefacts discovered at Welton-le-Wold, Lincolnshire. *Proc. Yorks. Geol. Soc.*, **41**, 75–93.

Banham, P. H., Davis, H., and Perrin, R. M. S. (1975). Short field meeting in north Norfolk. *Proc. Geol. Assoc.*, **86**, 251–258.

Catt, J. A., and Penny, L. F. (1966). The Pleistocene deposits of Holderness, east Yorkshire. *Proc. Yorks. Geol. Soc.*, **35**, 375–420.

Girling, M. A. (1974). Evidence from Lincolnshire of the age and intensity of the mid-Devensian temperate episode. *Nature, Lond.*, **250**, 270.

Maarleveld, G. S. (1976). Periglacial phenomena and the mean annual temperature during the last glacial time in the Netherlands. *Biul. Peryglac.*, **26**, 57–78.

Penny, L. F., Coope, G. R., and Catt, J. A. (1969). Age and insect fauna of the Dimlington silts, east Yorkshire. *Nature, Lond.*, **224**, 65–67.

Shotton, F. W., Banham, P. H., and Bishop, W. W. (1977). Glacial–interglacial stratigraphy of the Quaternary in Midland and eastern England. In *British Quaternary Studies: Recent Advances*. Clarendon Press, Oxford, pp. 267–282.

Sparks, B. W., and West, R. G. (1970). Late Pleistocene deposits at Wretton, Norfolk. I. Ipswichian interglacial deposits. *Phil. Trans. Roy. Soc., B*, **258**, 1–30.

Sparks, B. W., Williams, R. B. G., and Bell, F. G. (1972). Presumed ground-ice depressions in East Anglia. *Proc. Roy. Soc., A*, **327**, 329–343.

Straw, A. (1957). Some glacial features of east Lincolnshire. *East Midland Geog.*, **1**, 41–48.

Straw, A. (1960). The limit of the Last Glaciation in north Norfolk. *Proc. Geol. Assoc.*, **71**, 379–390.

Straw, A. (1961). Drifts, meltwater channels and ice margins in the Lincolnshire Wolds. *Trans. Inst. Br. Geog.*, **29**, 115–128.

Straw, A. (1965). A reassessment of the Chalky Boulder Clay or Marly Drift of north Norfolk. *Z. Geomorphol.*, **9**, 209–221.

Straw, A. (1967). The Penultimate or Gipping Glaciation in north Norfolk. *Trans. Norf. Norw. Nat. Soc.*, **21**, 21–24.

Straw, A. (1969). Pleistocene events in Lincolnshire: a survey and revised nomenclature. *Trans. Linc. Nat. Union*, **17**, 85–98.

Straw, A. (1973). The glacial geomorphology of central and north Norfolk. *East Midland Geog.*, **5**, 333–354.

Suggate, R. P., and West, R. G. (1959). On the extent of the Last Glaciation in eastern England. *Proc. Roy. Soc., B*, **150**, 263–283.

Timescales in Geomorphology
Edited by R. A. Cullingford, D. A. Davidson, and J. Lewin
© 1980 John Wiley & Sons Ltd

CHAPTER 21

Rates of erosion in the Little Colorado valley, Arizona

R. J. Rice

*Department of Geography,
University of Leicester*

In its lower middle course, that is, between the settlement of Leupp and the confluence of Hopi Trail Canyon (Fig. 21.1), the Little Colorado flows across the north-eastern margin of the San Francisco volcanic field (Moore *et al.*, 1976). This field has been intermittently active since at least early Pliocene times, and on several occasions extrusive volcanic materials have either invaded the contemporaneous valley floor or terminated a short distance therefrom. The lava flows were classified by Colton (1936) into five major age-groups, based on the surface modification they have suffered. More recently this relative chronology has been supplemented and amplified by the application of potassium–argon dating techniques (Damon *et al.*, 1974), with the result that it is now possible to obtain a much better idea of the rate at which certain geomorphic changes have been occurring. It is the purpose of this paper to review the inferences that can be drawn from the disposition of the radiometrically dated rocks. Following an introductory section on the regional setting, attention will first be directed to downcutting along the axis of the main river, and secondly to concurrent changes in selected tributary catchments. Conclusions from this part of the study will then be employed as a basis for discussing two further topics, namely, the long-term constancy of the erosion rates and the identifiable effects of Quaternary tectonism.

Regional Setting

Between Leupp and Hopi Trail Canyon, the Little Colorado drains a broad upland depression with heights generally in the range 1300–1450 m. The valley is bounded to the east and north-east by the prominent cuesta known as the Ward Terrace, to the south-west by the San Francisco volcanic peaks, and to the west by the 2000-m Coconino plateau. Apart from the relatively recent igneous extrusions, the bedrock geology consists almost entirely of a Permo-Triassic sedimentary sequence whose main components may be summarized as follows:

Name	Approximate thickness (m)	Lithological characteristics
Chinle formation { Petrified Forest member	300	Mainly variegated mudstones and fine siltstones, with a few thin sandstone horizons.
Shinarump member	25	Predominantly pale red and grey sandstones and conglomerates, but with a few interleaved beds of mudstone.
Moenkopi formation	115	A complex sequence of reddish brown mudstones, siltstones, and sandstones, with lenticular beds of gypsum. Thinly bedded in the main but occasional massive sandstones.
Kaibab limestone	100	Variably bedded limestones, sandy limestones, and calcareous sandstones, with occasional layers of chert.

A gentle regional dip towards the east-north-east is interrupted west of the Little Colorado by a complex system of large monoclines. The two main members in the area under review are the Coconino Point and Black Point monoclines with respective maximum downthrows to the east of 610 and 200 m. Further structural complication is provided by a series of minor domes and basins, together with numerous faults; with a few notable exceptions the latter have throws limited to under 30 m.

The floor of the Little Colorado valley constitutes part of the Painted Desert and receives an average annual precipitation of about 150 mm. The wettest season is usually the summer, with a substantial proportion of the rain falling in the form of summer thunderstorms. Although summer temperatures are high with a July mean normally over 25 °C, the winters are cold with a January mean only about 1 °C above freezing point. Meteorological records for the settlement of Cameron indicate that frost can be expected for about 118 days per annum. The prevailing climatic conditions support a true desert flora on the lowest ground, but, as rainfall increases with altitude, so firstly grasses and then juniper and pinyon-pine come to dominate the slightly higher regions. The most elevated peaks, of course, support the Canadian, Hudsonian, and Arctic–Alpine life forms as originally defined in this area by the classic work of Merriam (1890).

Rate of Downcutting by the Little Colorado

Dated rock samples from four different extrusions provide information relevant to the rate of downcutting by the trunk river. In two cases very fluid basaltic lavas actually invaded the contemporaneous valley floor, thus yielding a direct indication of the height of the river at the time of the vulcanicity. In two other cases the evidence is less direct since the volcanic rocks are restricted to tributary catchments, yet the former level of the main river may still be estimated with considerable confidence. The location of the four cases is indicated on Fig. 21.1 and each merits brief individual description.

(i) *Black Point flow.* At present this flow, dated at 2.39 ± 0.32 Ma (Damon, 1965), forms a capping only a few metres thick to a ridge which rises abruptly above the plateau

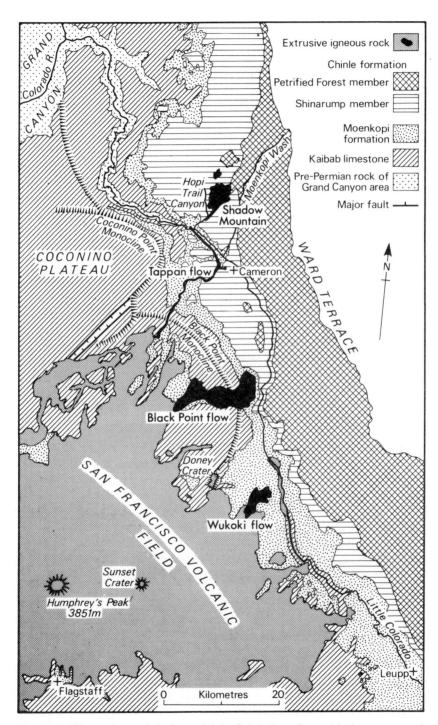

Fig. 21.1 The geology of the lower Little Colorado valley, with the outcrops of the volcanic rocks on which the present paper is based shown in black

formed by the flat-lying Kaibab limestone west of the Black Point monocline. At its expanded terminus, situated above the steeply plunging strata deformed by the monocline, the lava rests upon a sheet of gravel. The composition of the gravel is consistent with its being an alluvial deposit of the Little Colorado, and as it lies 204 m above modern alluvium its presence implies downcutting by that river at a mean rate of 85.4 m Ma^{-1} for the last 2.39 Ma. Confirmation that the Little Colorado was flowing at this high level when the lava entered the valley comes from patches of gravel scattered across the summit of the basalt. As Colton (1936) deduced, these were almost certainly laid down when the river resumed its flow and spilled across the barrier blocking its old route.

(ii) *Tappan flow*. The Tappan lava, dated at 0.51 ± 0.079 Ma (Damon *et al.*, 1974), entered the Little Colorado valley at a point where the river was flowing in a deep canyon across the outcrop of the Shinarump conglomerate. The basalt filled the canyon to its brim, thus necessitating the cutting of a completely new canyon parallel to the old one. The difference in height between the floor of the old lava-filled canyon and the modern alluvium is 48 m, yielding a mean rate of incision of 94.1 m Ma^{-1} for the last 0.51 Ma.

The Tappan flow is particularly instructive as an indicator of the temporal variability that the long-term average may conceal (Rice, 1977). The lava at its maximum is 40 m thick, with the result that the Little Colorado would have had to incise its bed by that amount before reaching its pre-eruptive level. However, after approaching within about 4 m of that level, a major aggradational phase supervened which carried the river back up to the height of the lava dam. This permitted the river to migrate laterally and meant that, in places, a second totally new canyon had to be excavated. In other words, during the last 0.51 Ma the Little Colorado may have deepened its valley by 48 m but it has actually sawn down through at least 124 m of resistant Shinarump and Moenkopi sediments.

(iii) *Wukoki flow*. This lava, dated at 0.87 ± 0.14 Ma (Damon *et al.*, 1974), spread as a thin sheet across a smooth pediment, carved from Moenkopi sediments, that declines at a low angle towards the axis of the Little Colorado valley. The flow terminated 2.5 km short of the river, but extrapolation of the regular surface of the pediment suggests a former valley floor about 85 m above that of the present day. Of course, the trunk river could conceivably have been incised below the level of the pediment, but this incision, if any, seems likely to have been slight since there is no indication of any dissection of the surface on which the lava rests. The Wukoki flow is therefore interpreted as implying a mean rate of downcutting of 97.7 m Ma^{-1} for the last 0.87 Ma.

(iv) *Shadow Mountain extrusion*. Material extruded from this vent on the right bank of the Little Colorado includes both basaltic lavas, dated at 0.62 ± 0.23 Ma, and abundant tephra (Damon *et al.*, 1974; Condit, 1974). The latter are primarily responsible for the main cone which rises 210 m above the surrounding plateau. The lavas do not reach closer than 5.5 km to the Little Colorado, so that any relationship with the trunk river must be established via the two south-flowing tributaries of Moenkopi Wash and Hopi Trail Wash. The lower reach of the valley drained by Moenkopi Wash has been so severely gullied that it retains few deposits of any significance to the present study. However, on the western slopes 3 km upstream from the Little Colorado confluence lies a group of large, rounded basalt cobbles which must be the residuum of a former terrace gravel. They are sited 37 m above the modern valley floor and signify that the drainage must have flowed at least as high as this subsequent to the Shadow Mountain eruption. The evidence along Hopi Trail Canyon is both more complete and more definitive (Fig. 21.2). Terrace fragments incorporating basalt debris are extensively preserved on ledges

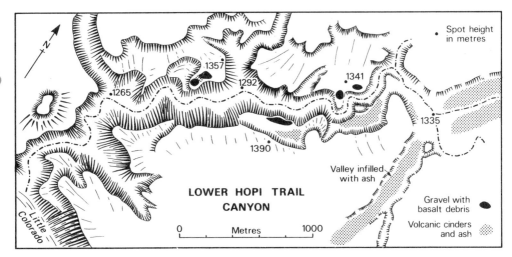

Fig. 21.2 The distribution of Shadow Mountain tephra and basalt-bearing river gravels along the flanks of lower Hopi Trail Canyon. The altitudinal relationships are shown in more detail as part of Fig. 21.4

high above the canyon floor. Particular importance attaches to the most elevated of such fragments, since these again will indicate the minimum level to which the drainage must have reached in post-eruptive times. In the case of Hopi Trail Canyon crucial supplementary evidence is provided by the tephra, since the lowest elevation at which such air-borne ejectamenta occur denotes the minimum depth to which erosion must have proceeded by the time of the eruption. In practice the highest basalt-bearing gravel occurs at almost exactly the same level as the lowest tephra, thus defining with considerable precision the height of contemporaneous Hopi Trail Wash. Unfortunately, close to the Little Colorado, erosion has destroyed much of the evidence, leaving a gap of almost 2 km to be bridged by extrapolation (Fig. 21.4). On this basis the level of the trunk river is estimated to have been 70 m higher than today, yielding a mean rate of incision of 112.9 m Ma^{-1} for the last 0.62 Ma.

From Fig. 21.3 it appears that all four cases discussed above accord with a long-term downcutting by the trunk river at a mean rate of about 95 m per million years. As already pointed out, this figure conceals undoubted shorter term fluctuations, but there is no reason to suppose that there has been any secular acceleration or deceleration in the rate of river incision.

Variations in Drainage Incision Along Tributary Washes

A lava flow will frequently preserve not only part of the main valley floor but also a section of the contemporaneous tributary wash down which it moved. The Tappan basalt, for instance, flowed about 45 km along a well defined tributary valley before entering the canyon of the Little Colorado. New washes subsequently carved along the edge of the lava permit an assessment of the changes in elevation suffered by the local

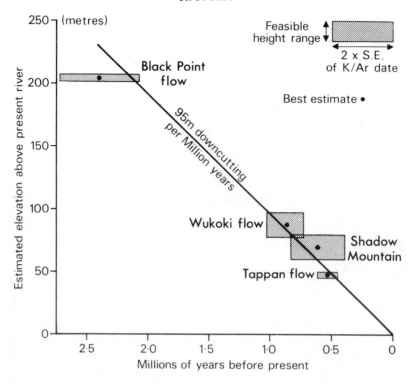

Fig. 21.3 A plot of age against elevation above present river level of the four
dated extrusions described in the text

drainage during the last 0.51 Ma. As shown by Fig. 21.4, the floors of the modern washes
lie within 1–2 m of the one originally invaded by the Tappan flow (Rice, 1977).
Moreoever, the absence of an alluvial cover over much of the basalt precludes any deep
alluviation. In other words, while the trunk river has lowered its course by 48 m and
carved down through over twice that thickness of solid rock, the elevation of one of its
tributaries has fluctuated within a range of less than 15 m, with most of that figure
representing no more than the incision required for the wash to return to its pre-eruptive
level.

The disposition of both the Wukoki and Black Point flows is also consistent with the
thesis that the trunk river has incised its valley much more than its immediate tributaries.
This is particularly clear in the case of the Black Point flow which, at its terminus, caps a
ridge standing over 200 km above the Little Colorado, but 13 km to the west stands only
40 m above adjacent washes. The fact that the lava caps a ridge obviously implies
inversion of the local relief, but it is not now possible to reconstruct in any detail the
topography as it existed at the time of the eruption. More instructive in that respect is the
Shadow Mountain extrusion where the tephra buried the contemporaneous relief over a
wide area. Abundant cinders borne more than 5 km southwards from the main cone
completely filled a substantial valley that was tributary to Hopi Trail Canyon (Fig. 21.2).
The form of this valley is easily reconstructed from exposures that result from dissection
by post-eruptive washes, and it can be shown that the old valley floor was graded to a
level only 1 m or so above the present drainage. This conclusion is supported by a
number of other patches of cinders preserved in re-entrants at and about the level of the

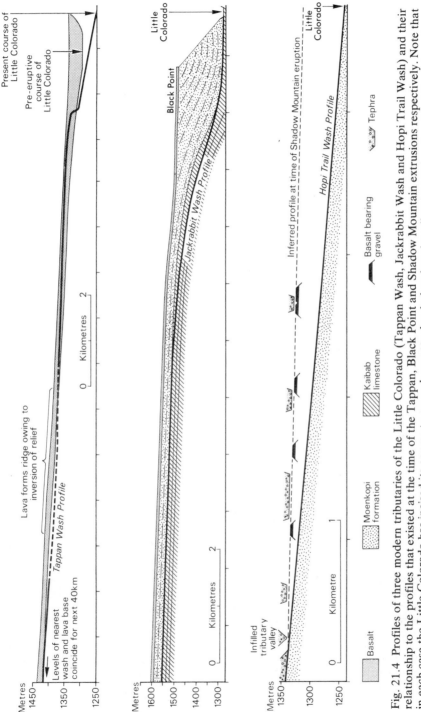

Fig. 21.4 Profiles of three modern tributaries of the Little Colorado (Tappan Wash, Jackrabbit Wash and Hopi Trail Wash) and their relationship to the profiles that existed at the time of the Tappan, Black Point and Shadow Mountain extrusions respectively. Note that in each case the Little Colorado has incised its course to a much greater depth than has the tributary wash only a few kilometres above the point of confluence

modern washes. Moreover, the evidence of both tephra and basalt-bearing gravels along the length of Hopi Trail Canyon points unequivocally to a much gentler gradient for that drainage line at the time of the eruption than at present (Fig. 21.4).

The Influence of Bedrock Lithology

So far attention has been confined almost exclusively to linear incision by the drainage net, where it has been shown that the downcutting by the tributaries has often lagged far behind that of the trunk river. However, in attempting to explain the morphological evolution of the region as a whole cognizance must obviously be taken of contrasts in bedrock lithology. For purposes of discussion the rock types cropping out in the study area may be divided into four major groups:

(a) *Limestone*. Many of the most striking landforms of the lower Little Colorado valley are developed on the outcrops of the Kaibab limestone. Where those limestone beds are horizontal, extensive and largely undissected plateaux are found. The ridge capped by the Black Point flow rises above such a limestone plateau. The core of the ridge is composed almost entirely of Moenkopi sediments, with the bounding concave break of slope coincident with the top of the limestone. The inversion of relief responsible for converting the Black Point flow into a ridge-top capping has therefore been achieved by the stripping of the Moenkopi sediments from the top of the limestone; yet once the limestone was exposed (and it is difficult to conceive that this did not occur nearly 2 million years ago), further downwearing seems to have been a few metres at the most. Also indicative of the importance of stripping back of the Moenkopi sediments is the almost perfect conformity between structure and surface form where the limestone is deformed by the Black Point monocline. Stripping on this scale could only be achieved where there is a massive contrast in the resistance to erosion of the two rock types involved.

A further indication of the slow pace of denudation on the Kaibab limestone is afforded by the persistence of ancient forms with little loss of morphological detail (Fig. 21.5). For instance, fault scarps that are demonstrably older than the Tappan lava have suffered little degradation and at most have receded a few metres from the surface trace of the fault. Equally instructive is the preservation of ancient segments of river channel. A good example is provided by a shallow gravel-floored trench incised into the limestone 4 km south of the Black Point flow. Both the dimensions of the trench and composition of the gravel are consistent with this being an abandoned course of the Little Colorado. Its floor lies 170 m above modern alluvium, and the inferred rate of downcutting at 95 m

---

Fig. 21.5 Diagrams, drawn primarily from air photographs, of the topographic forms preserved on the outcrop of the Kaibab limestone. Because of the clean stripping of the Moenkopi sediments from the limestone, the contours that have been generalized from topographic maps may be regarded as indicating the form of both the surface relief and the geological structure. (A) The Burro Channel situated above the level of the Tappan lava and well to the west of the current edge of the Moenkopi sediments; the faults shown are all marked by prominent scarps, most of them apparently fault scarps *sensu stricto* although a few could owe their origin to stripping of the Moenkopi formation from the top of the dislocated limestone. (B) The Needmore Channel incised into a rising slope of Kaibab limestone and standing above the level of the nearby Tappan lava. (C) A short but broad channel segment lying 170 m above the present level of the Little Colorado. South of the channel, tensional stresses in the limestone have produced a series of deep cracks with virtually no relative displacement of the two sides of the fissures. (D) The Doney Channel as identified by Breed (1969)

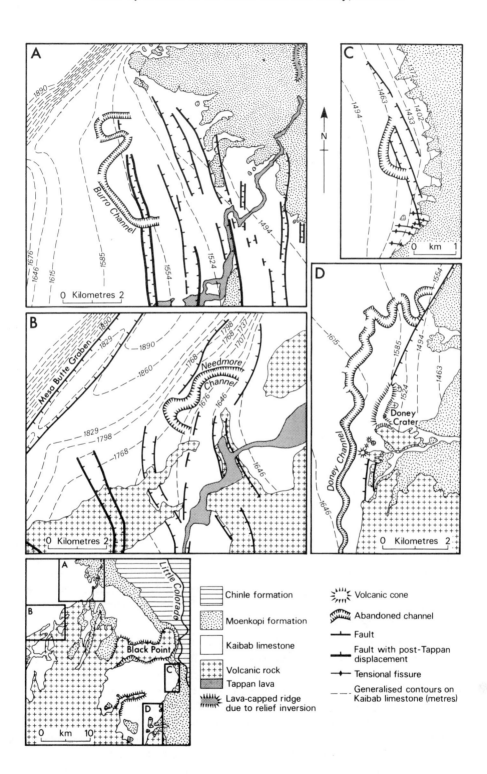

Ma⁻¹ suggests that the channel may be about 1.8 Ma old. There are at least three further instances where abandoned segments of tributary valleys are extant. In each case precise dating is difficult, yet there can be no doubt regarding the antiquity of the feature. Breed (1969) has described the 13 km-long Doney channel and has deduced from its relationship to the volcanic suite that it dates back at least to Pliocene times. Further west the elevation of the Needmore and Burro channels demonstrates that they must be older than the nearby Tappan lava; that they are very substantially older is indicated by the fact that they are remnants of an ancient drainage net, developed in part on a former cover of Moenkopi sediments, that had already been destroyed even before the Tappan flow entered the area.

(b) *Siltstone and mudstone.* Implicit in the preceding paragraphs is the view that parts of the Moenkopi succession are subject to relatively rapid erosion. These are undoubtedly the finer-grained beds, and it can be shown, for instance, that even where buttressed by interbedded sandstones the edge of the Moenkopi formation has been eroded back 275 m since emplacement of the Tappan lava (Rice, 1977). Moreoever, where traversing the less resistant parts of the Moenkopi outcrop the Tappan basalt today snakes across the landscape as an isolated ridge owing to relief inversion (Fig. 21.5A). However, it is the Petrified Forest member of the Chinle formation that has certainly been subject to the most speedy denudation. The outcrop characteristically consists of broad, low-angled pediments occasionally surmounted by steep-sided residuals. The pediments floor a broad vale that, north of Cameron, must have been excavated to a depth of about 200 m since the Black Point lava invaded the main valley. The rapid erosion of the unresistant sediments has left little evidence regarding stages in the denudation history, although Condit (1974) points out that on the eastern and northern margin of Shadow Mountain a tributary of Moenkopi Wash has cut down 10 m below the level of the volcanics dated at 0.62 Ma.

(c) *Sandstone and conglomerate.* In terms of resistance to erosion these beds generally occupy an intermediate position between the limestone and the finer-grained sediments Near the head of Hopi Trail Canyon an old meander loop excavated from a massive sandstone is still discernible although it must be at least as old as the Shadow Mountain extrusion; in the same vicinity are other indications that landforms fashioned from the Shinarump beds have not been radically altered during the last 0.62 Ma. On the other hand, the freshness of such features as fault scarps is noticeably less than on the Kaibab limestone, and the rim of the Little Colorado canyon upstream from the confluence of Hopi Trail Wash appears to have receded as much as 100 m since emplacement of the Tappan lava on the valley floor. In the latter case, however, it is difficult to eliminate the possibility that much of the erosion is due to lateral shifting by the trunk river rather than to normal slope-forming processes.

(d) *Volcanic rocks.* The lavas have invariably proved very resistant to erosion. This is demonstrated by the inversion of relief associated with both the Black Point flow and also parts of the Tappan flow. Although superficial irregularities such as spatter cones and pressure ridges have been smoothed away by erosion on the surface of the Black Point flow, they are still evident on the Tappan flow. Moreover, in many places the edge of the Tappan lava appears to have been but little modified since consolidation. The same conclusion is drawn by Condit (1973) in a study of the Shadow Mountain lavas; he comments that most of the present edges appear to represent close to the original maximum extent of the flows since vesicular textures and characteristic marginal jointing systems are still preserved.

Temporal Variability in the Erosion Rates

It has been shown in the previous sections that, during the last 2.39 Ma, parts of the Little Colorado basin have been denuded at a fast rate, whilst others have remained relatively intact. It can scarcely be doubted that, during the same period, substantial climatic changes have taken place. Updike and Péwé (1974), for instance, have identified the deposits of two separate glaciations on the San Francisco peaks, probably referable to the Illinoian and Wisconsinan periods. Although phases of aggradation are known to have affected the Little Colorado (Rice, 1974), these have not yet been satisfactorily related to climatic fluctuations. It is pertinent however, to enquire how far the inferred secular erosion rates accord with what is known of current processes since the latter might be revealed as unrepresentative of the long time interval being considered in this paper.

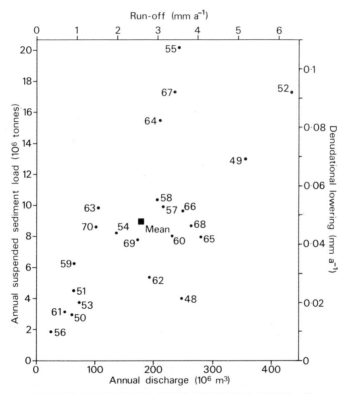

Fig. 21.6 A plot of water and suspended sediment discharge at the U.S. Geological Survey gauging stations at Cameron during the years 1948–1970. The complex relationship between these two variables is indicated, for instance, by the sediment discharge in 1948 amounting to only one fifth of that in 1955 with approximately the same total run-off. In calculating the denudational lowering represented by the suspension load a mean rock density of 2.7 g cm^{-3} has been assumed (data from relevant Water Supply Papers of the U.S.G.S.)

Water- and sediment-gauging stations maintained by the US Geological Survey on the Little Colorado at Cameron provide basic data on the contemporary rate of erosion. Fig. 21.6 shows that the relationship between water and suspended sediment discharge is complex, but whatever the cause of the apparent variability, the figures still indicate an overall denudation rate of 0.0477 mm a^{-1}. This value, of course, applies to the whole catchment upstream from Cameron and any comparison with the long-term downcutting achieved by the Little Colorado needs to be treated with caution. It is not known from which parts of the catchment most of the suspension load is derived, but published analyses of water samples collected at intervals over the period of gauging show an average of 63% of the transported sediment to be of clay size (<0.002 mm). That the outcrop of the Petrified Forest member probably makes a disproportionate contribution is suggested by the measurements of Colbert (1956), who found that steep slopes north of Cameron cut in that member are currently receding at 5 mm a^{-1}.

It would be valuable to have information regarding the solution load of the Little Colorado but, despite publication of a few chemical analyses, the data are totally inadequate for any view to be formulated, for instance, on the current rate of limestone solution. On the other hand, the present depth of runoff at 2.7 mm a^{-1} is so small that, even if the water were totally saturated, the solutional lowering of any limestone surface would still be extremely slow. The conclusion must be that, whilst the low runoff rate may severely limit chemical denudation of the limestone, the same discharge is still capable of carrying huge quantities of fine-grained sediment. The old aphorism 'too thick to drink, too thin to plough' is certainly applicable to the waters of the Little Colorado, with sediment concentrations commonly in excess of 50,000 mg l^{-1} and sometimes even surpassing 200,000 mg l^{-1}. In summary, there is no reason to suppose, from the evidence of current measurements, that both the rate and the pattern of denudation as inferred from the old lava flows are not continuing at the present day.

Quaternary Tectonism

In a region where assessment of geomorphic change is being based upon extrusive volcanic activity, it is natural to seek possible effects of earth movements. There is no doubt that significant crustal instability has occurred since emplacement of the Black Point flow. Near the Doney channel a segment of lava that must approximate in age to the Black Point flow has been let down over 15 m between a pair of closely spaced parallel faults. Such graben structures are typical of much of the tectonic movement that has occurred during the last 2.39 Ma. Condit (1974) has described two graben dislocating rocks of the Shadow Mountain extrusion and locally exhibiting a displacement of at least 20 m. Just west of Cameron the Tappan lava is affected by a pair of faults that have lowered the igneous rock by 34 m, whilst further south several smaller dislocations have been similarly active in the last half-million years (Rice, 1977). Although obviously younger than the rocks which they affect, these faulted structures are not easy to date precisely. Condit (1974) argues that around Shadow Mountain the lava was apparently still fluid when movement occurred so that faulting was penecontemporaneous with the vulcanicity. Yet the Tappan lava appears to have had a new river channel scored across its surface before movement was complete, so that at least some of the displacement is more recent than the extrusion (Rice, 1977). That the whole region remains tectonically active to this day is indicated by relatively frequent earthquake tremors (Lange, 1965; Sturgul and Irwin, 1971).

Barrington and Kerr (1963) claim that Cenozoic vulcanicity in northern Arizona may have generated hydrothermal solutions which, by dissolving the Kaibab limestone, caused several circular collapse structures to develop in the overlying Moenkopi and Chinle formations. This explanation of a number of collapses in the vicinity of Cameron appears preferable to any which invokes sinkhole formation by meteoric water. A characteristic of the limestone is the limited karstification it has suffered. Although there are a few sinks and known caverns, the most distinctive surface features of the limestone plateaux are long, vertical-sided fissures that in at least one case extend to a depth of 80 m (Colton, 1938). The angular, sub-parallel walls of the fissures suggest that they are basically structural rather than erosional, although some degree of modification by solution seems probable. That the limestone contains large volumes of voids is indicated by the presence of 'blowholes' which inhale or exhale according to the prevailing pressure relationships. A detailed investigation showed one such system of blowholes to have a volume of at least 2×10^8 m^3 and to be interconnected over a distance of almost 40 km (Sartor and Lamar, 1962). At first sight it might seem that these subterranean voids are complementary to the slow surface lowering of the limestone, with most of the solutional activity being concentrated underground. However, the very limited development of traditional karstic landforms, allied to the primary structural control exhibited by so many surface features, suggests that tectonism is as important as groundwater solution in explaining details of the present morphology.

It should be pointed out that it is easier to detect the effects of localized dislocations, such as those discussed above, than patterns of regional warping. Barnes (1974) contends that the widespread graben structures reflect a radial tensile stress field related to a dominant compressive stress from the south-west. He argues that in late Pleistocene times many of the major structures have experienced continuing uplift. In the author's view, nothing in the present study is at variance with this thesis, and indeed it seems likely that the continued rapid downcutting by the Little Colorado is an expression of adjustment to this sustained tectonic elevation. On the other hand, it is most improbable that warping by itself can explain the very low gradient assumed, for instance, by the reconstructed Hopi Trail drainage at the time of the Shadow Mountain eruption; at most, tectonic movement would seem to be a very minor contributory factor in such cases.

Conclusions

Evidence provided by radiometrically dated lavas permits a number of inferences to be drawn regarding the rate and nature of denudation in the lower Little Colorado valley during the last 2.39 Ma:

(1) Despite minor reversals owing to temporary aggradational phases, the trunk river has continued to incise its course at a mean rate of 95 m Ma^{-1}.

(2) Away from the trunk river the rate of drainage incision has often been substantially less. In part this might be explained by local geological contrasts as, for example, where lava appears to have restrained the migration of a rejuvenation head up Tappan Wash. On the other hand, there are cases, such as along Hopi Trail Canyon, where the geological differences appear inadequate to explain demonstrable variations in the depth of stream incision.

(3) The rate of denudational lowering of the landscape has varied enormously according to the nature of the outcropping rock. Limestone and basaltic lava have both proved exceptionally resistant, still retaining minor surface forms of great

antiquity. The contrast with the finer-grained sedimentaries has been such that even the youngest dated lava has been subject to local relief inversion.

(4) The denudation has been accompanied by a crustal instability which assumes its most obvious form in a series of long, narrow graben, but which probably involves broader patterns of uplift and depression.

(5) The progressive deepening of the valley, with downcutting by the trunk river and more limited erosion by the tributaries, might be held to favour preservation of old 'erosion surfaces'. In that respect the present study can be said to support those earlier workers such as Childs (1948) and Cooley (1962), who have identified ancient pedimented surfaces and, from such evidence, endeavoured to reconstruct the erosional history of the basin. On the other hand, the contrast in erosion rates on different rock types promotes extensive stripping of lithological interfaces which, in a region of low dips, can simulate old erosion surfaces. In the author's view the importance of this element in the present landscape has often been inadequately acknowledged.

Acknowledgements

The author gratefully acknowledges financial assistance towards the cost of field work from the University of Leicester. He is also much indebted to Mr. W. J. Breed of the Museum of Northern Arizona for introducing him to the area and for discussing many of the geomorphological problems it presents.

References

Barnes, C. W. (1974). Interference and gravity tectonics in the Gray Mountain area, Arizona. In *Geology of Northern Arizona* (Eds. T. N. V. Karlstrom, G. A. Swann and R. L. Eastwood). Geological Society of America, Flagstaff, Arizona pp. 442–453.

Barrington, J., and Kerr, P. F. (1963). Collapse features and silica plugs near Cameron, Arizona. *Geol. Soc. Am. Bull.*, **74**, 1237–1258.

Breed, W. J. (1969). A Pliocene river channel in Wupatki National Monument, Arizona. *J. Ariz. Acad. Sci.*, **5**, 177–181.

Childs, O. E. (1948). Geomorphology of the valley of the Little Colorado River, Arizona. *Geol. Soc. Am. Bull.*, **59**, 353–388.

Colbert, E. H. (1956). Rates of erosion in the Chinle formation. *Plateau*, **28**, 73–76.

Colton, H. S. (1936). The basaltic cinder cones and lava flows of the San Francisco volcanic field. *Mus. N. Ariz. Bull.*, **10**, 49 pp. (Revised Edition, 1967).

Colton, H. S. (1938). The exploration of limestone solution cracks. *Mus. N. Ariz. Mus. Notes*, **10**, 29–32.

Condit, C. D. (1973). *The Geology of Shadow Mountain, Coconino County, Arizona*. Unpublished MS Thesis, Northern Arizona University.

Condit, C. D. (1974). Geology of Shadow Mountain. In *Geology of Northern Arizona* (Eds. T. N. V. Karlstrom, G. A. Swann and R. L. Eastwood). Geological Society of America, Flagstaff, Arizona, pp. 454–463.

Cooley, M. E. (1962). Geomorphology and the age of volcanic rocks in north-eastern Arizona. *Ariz. Geol. Soc. Digest*, **5**, 97–116.

Damon, P. E. (1965). K–Ar dates for volcanism adjacent to the Colorado River, *Ann. Prog. Rep. to U.S. Atom. Energy Comm.*, No. COO–689–50, pp. 38–43.

Damon, P. E., Shafiqullah, M., and Leventhal, J. S. (1974). K–Ar chronology for the San Francisco volcanic field and rate of erosion of the Little Colorado River. In *Geology of Northern Arizona* (Eds. T. N. V. Karlstrom, G. A. Swann and R. L. Eastwood). Geological Society of America, Flagstaff, Arizona, pp. 221–235.

Lange, A. (1965). Local seismic monitoring, Kaibab area, Arizona. *Stanford Res. Inst. Rep.*, pp. 71–76.

Merriam, C. H. (1890). Results of a biological survey of the San Francisco Mountain region and the desert of the Little Colorado, Arizona. *North America Fauna*, No. 3, 1–396.

Moore, R. B., Wolfe, E. W., and Ulrich, G. E. (1976). Volcanic rocks of the eastern and northern parts of the San Francisco volcanic field, Arizona. *J. Res. U.S. Geol. Surv.*, **4,** 549–560.

Rice, R. J. (1974). Terraces and abandoned channels of the Little Colorado River between Leupp and Cameron, Arizona. *Plateau*, **46,** 102–119.

Rice, R. J. (1977). The geomorphology of the Tappan lava flow near Cameron, Arizona. *J. Ariz. Acad. Sci.*, **12,** 131–139.

Sartor, J. D., and Lamar, D. L. (1962). Meterological–geological investigations of the Wupatki blowhole system. *Rand Corp. Mem.*, RM-3139-RC.

Sturgul, J. R., and Irwin, T. D. (1971). Earthquake history of Arizona and New Mexico, 1850–1966. *Ariz. Geol. Soc. Digest*, **9,** 1–22.

Updike, R. G., and Péwé, T. L. (1974). Glacial and pre-glacial deposits in the San Francisco Mountain area, northern Arizona. In *Geology of Northern Arizona* (Eds. T. N. V. Karlstrom, G. A. Swann and R. L. Eastwood). Geological Society of America, Flagstaff, Arizona, pp. 557–566.

Timescales in Geomorphology
Edited by R. A. Cullingford, D. A. Davidson, and J. Lewin
© 1980 John Wiley & Sons Ltd

CHAPTER 22

Timescales of landform development on tropical shields—A study from Sierra Leone

Michael F. Thomas

Department of Earth and Environmental Science,
University of Stirling

The tropical cratonic areas of the world afford unique opportunities for the study of long-term landform development. In West Africa, for example, the last major orogeny took place in the late Precambrian (600–550 Ma) and is represented in Sierra Leone by the Rokelides (Allen, 1968; Dillon and Sougy, 1974; Fig. 22.1), while the last known glacial interruption occurred in the Ordovician (Furon, 1960; Reid and Tucker, 1972). As a result, there exists for many areas the possibility of a continuity of landform development over timespans unparalleled in many of the classic areas for geomorphological study

It must not be thought however, that such areas have been tectonically inactive or that energy inputs into the geomorphic systems have been few or minor. It has long been known (Furon, 1960; King, 1961) that the African continent has been deformed into a series of domes and basins and that rifting and vulcanism is associated with these structures (King, 1970). It is also now accepted that the coastline of Africa was formed during the Mesozoic as the super-continent of Gondwanaland finally broke up and drifted into its separate components (Ladd *et al.*, 1973; Le Pichon and Fox, 1971). These events have been associated with the formation of essentially simple structures of large dimensions, and many geomorphologists would claim that this has not only permitted the survival of ancient relief, but also allows inter-regional correlations between the denudation chronologies of different parts of the continent and even between continents (King, 1962). However, such attempts are not without difficulty, because the prolonged sub-aerial evolution of the exposed basement areas, together with the infrequency of transgressive interruptions, has left little stratigraphic evidence upon which to build a conventional denudation chronology.

In the view of some geomorphologists this is compensated for by the extent and state of preservation of erosion surfaces which, it is held, form a readily identifiable series from the high remnants of ancient plateaus to the recently formed glacis extending from contemporary hillslopes (King, 1962; Michel, 1973). However, few studies have considered how different elements of the relief have come to survive, apparently little affected by erosion. Neither has there been an adequate discussion of the functional behaviour of different geological formations within the denudation system. Expressed differently, insufficient attention has been given to the theories of landform development as they might be applied to crystalline terrains in the tropics, and in particular there has been no penetrating study of differential erosion as the foundation of the dynamic equilibrium concept of Hack (1960, 1977). In this study some of these questions will be explored in the context of landform development over long timespans on the West African craton, using field areas in Sierra Leone for exemplification.

The Geological Framework

A zone of emergent Basement Complex crystalline rocks extends from the Guinée–Sierra Leone border eastwards to the Voltaian scarp in Ghana, embracing not only Sierra Leone but also eastern Guinée, Liberia, Côte d'Ivoire and much of Haute Volta. Over most of Sierra Leone this basement falls within the Liberian Age Province (*ca.* 2700 Ma) which, close to the eastern border of Liberia, has been reworked to form the Eburnean Age Province (*ca.* 1900 Ma) (Hurley and Rand, 1973). This cratonic area is made up of a granitised basement of infra-crustal rocks, containing narrow zones of supra-crustal schists and amphibolites (the Kambui Schists). Late Liberian Age granitoids intrude older basement rocks and give rise to striking relief features. During the late Precambrian, a geosyncline formed along the southwestern edge of the older craton, culminating in the Rokelide Orogeny which belongs to the Pan-African Age Province (*ca.* 600 Ma), (Allen, 1968). This zone is marked in Sierra Leone by the Rokel River Group, which are mostly mudstones and associated volcanics, and the Marampa Schists. Whatever relief was formed in this episode appears to have been largely eliminated by the onset of Cambrian and Ordovician sedimentation.

In the far north of Sierra Leone, The Saionya Scarp Series represents the southernmost tip of the great Palaeozoic Basin of Tauodeni, which covers western Guinée, Mali, and much of Mauritania, while the Voltaian Basin of Ghana represents a comparable area of downwarping to the east. Thin basal conglomerates have been considered as Cambrian, but most of the formation is regarded as Ordovician and contains tillites, mudstones, arkosic rocks, and major doleritic intrusive masses (Haughton, 1963; Reid and Tucker, 1972). These rocks form a prominent escarpment overlooking the basement rock, where they tongue into northern Sierra Leone (Fig. 22.1 and 22.2).

It is at this stage that we must consider the early landform development of this area. The Taoudeni and Voltaian Basins are thought to have been downwarped during the Hercynian earth movements (Furon, 1960), and the older surfaces of planation recognized in Guinée by Michel (1973) are found preserved on and by these sedimentary formations. The association of quasi-horizontal sedimentary formations, and associated sills of intrusive rocks, with the appearance of extensive surfaces of erosion is striking and is a feature also of King's type areas in Natal (King, 1962, 1972).

Geologists have said little about any former extension of these Palaeozoic sediments across the intervening basement areas. Although Hubbard (1967) has adduced evidence for this which is discussed below, most workers consider the present outcrop to represent shallow shelf conditions or to have been faulted (McFarlane *et al.*, 1980).

After the Palaeozoic sedimentation and the ensuing warping and possible faulting of the basement rocks, the next major crustal disturbance appears to have been a part of the late Karroo (220–180 Ma) upheavals that led to widespread basic intrusive activity. In this area, the Freetown Basic Igneous Complex (Wells, 1962; Umeji, 1975) is dated to

Sierra Leone -
Geology

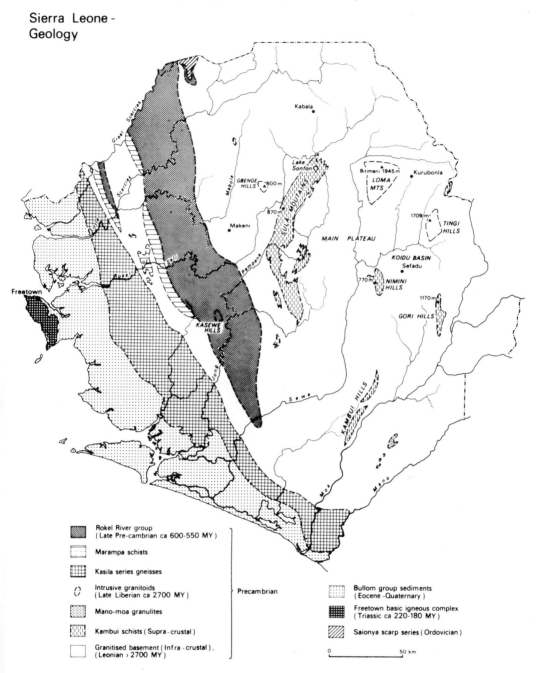

Fig. 22.1 Sierra Leone—Geology (compiled from several sources including Allen (1968), Hawkes (1970) and A. McFarlane and others, 1980)

this event along with many doleritic dykes and sills. The Freetown Peninsula today stands out as one of the most prominent landforms in West Africa, the hills rising to more than 850 m within 5 km of the coast, yet separated by 150 km from hills of comparable altitude inland. This remarkable feature appears to have excited no comment from

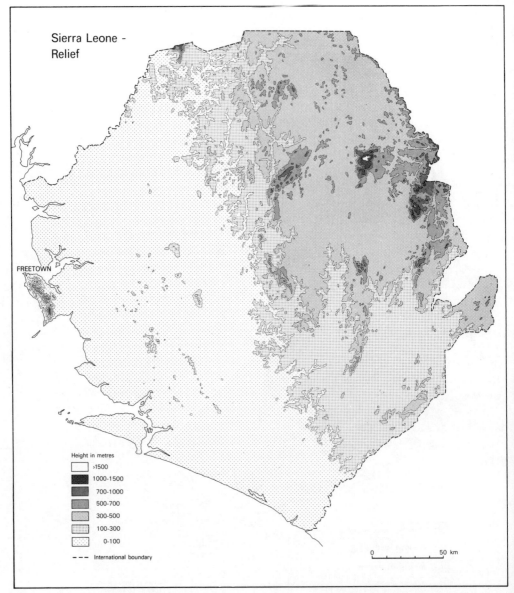

Fig. 22.2 Sierra Leone—relief (compiled from the 1:500,000 map of Sierra Leone published by the Directorate of Overseas Surveys for the Government of Sierra Leone)

workers reconstructing the erosion history of this area (Hall, 1969; McFarlane *et al.*, 1980).

The first opening of the North Atlantic probably commenced towards the close of this activity (Ladd *et al.*, 1973; Le Pichon and Fox, 1971). This event gradually brought into existence the present coastline of Africa and must have led to major changes in the course of denudation of the continent, re-orientating and rejuvenating drainage lines and eventually leading to the establishment of a humid tropical climate. Widespread evidence, from the early Tertiary sediments within the inland, continental basins of northern and western Africa, shows clearly that humid tropical, lateritizing conditions had become established, probably during the Upper Cretaceous or Palaeocene (Millot, 1970; Dillon and Sougy, 1974). Millot (1970) also refers to an earlier period of lateritic weathering during the Lower Cretaceous. The sedimentary record (McMaster *et al.*, 1970; Bezrukov and Senin, 1970; Machens, 1973) also indicates that gentle basining occurred all along the West African continental shelf. It is almost certain that this was accompanied by renewed epeirogenic uplift of the basement inland. The Cretaceous sea, although transgressive in Senegal and in Nigeria and north Africa, appears not to have invaded the area of Sierra Leone.

A kimberlite volcanic episode took place during the Cretaceous (*ca.* 92 Ma according to Bardet and Vachette, 1966), and it is from this event that fragmentary evidence concerning the early geomorphic evolution of the area comes. The kimberlites survive today in the form of small pipes and numerous narrow dykes (Grantham and Allen, 1960). Comparison of these features with the model of a kimberlite pipe presented by Hawthorne (1973) from studies in southern Africa indicates that these features must have undergone deep erosion since the Cretaceous. The order of magnitude for this erosion could be in excess of 1000 m, although any attempt at precision from available evidence would be unjustified. The pipes contain sedimentary and volcanic xenoliths (Hubbard, 1967), which indicates a sedimentary cover in north east Sierra Leone during the Cretaceous. It is not known to which formation the xenoliths belong; the choice appears to be between the Rokel River Series, exposed 100 km to the west and south-west, and the Saionya Scarp Series, forming an escarpment 200 km to the north-west. However, Hubbard (1967) does not rule out the possibility of a distinct volcanic cycle having occurred in this area. The fact that the Rokel River Series forms a lowland tract which passes unconformably beneath the Saionya Scarp Series argues against the survival of this formation on the emergent basement as late as the Cretaceous. The Saionya Scarp Series, however, still forms a striking escarpment, nearly 700 m high in the north of the country, and it is possible that its present position is a result of scarp retreat initiated by Mesozoic uplift of the basement. The direction and rate of this retreat are difficult to reconstruct from existing evidence, although the distance of the Palaeozoic outcrop from the kimberlites indicates a rate of 2 km Ma^{-1} (2 mm a^{-1}) which is not unreasonable (Young, 1974).

The Cenozoic Era in Sierra Leone was marked by shallow sedimentation, leading to the formation of the Bullom Group of sands and clays, thought to date from the early Tertiary (Eocene ?) to the Quaternary, though very little is known about them. They form a broad coastal plain west of the Kasila Series and form a wedge of sediment no more than 120 m thick below the coastal plain, though they are much deeper off-shore (Hawkes, 1970; McMaster *et al.*, 1970).

The Geomorphic Framework

A comparison of the geology with the relief of Sierra Leone is instructive. A broad coastal lowland varies in width from 50 km in the south-east to 150 km in the north-west and corresponds in width and trend with the Rokel River Group of rocks and with the coastal sediments (Bullom Group). The inner edge of this coastal plain is not much over 100 m in height and its surface is punctuated here and there by residual hills, the most prominent of which are the Kasewe Hills (500 m), consisting of Precambrian volcanic rocks. Only the Freetown Peninsula, with its hills rising to more than 850 m, interrupts the gradual decline of altitude towards an estuarine and lagoonal coastline.

In contrast, the eastern half of the country is varied in relief. Reference is often made to a 'Main Plateau' dominating the north-eastern part of the country, and generally around 400 m above sea level (Dixey, 1922; Hall, 1969; McFarlane *et al.*, 1980). The transition to this plateau from the coastal plain is abrupt in the centre of the country, where the Sula Mountains form an elevated rim, but in the south, where the drainage runs parallel with the trend of the basement rocks, there is deep dissection along the Sewa and Moa river systems (Figs. 22.1 and 22.2).

Groups of hills rising above this plateau fall into two principal groups: the duricrusted ridges formed by the Kambui Schists, attaining heights of around 700–800 m, and bornhardt groups composed in the main of porphyroblastic granites, within which the metasomatic growth of large potash feldspar porphyroblasts appears to have occurred after the formation of the granitic or granodioritic matrix (Marmo, 1956, 1971). One of these groups, the Loma Mountains, rises to form the highest elevation in West Africa (Bintumani, 1945 m). This mountain, however, is capped by a dolerite sill (Dixey, 1922; Daveau, 1971) which is likely to be early Mesozoic in age. The neighbouring Tingi Hills rise to over 1700 m, and it is suggested by both Daveau (1971) and McFarlane *et al.* (1980) that both masses have been block faulted with the intervening zone behaving as a graben. No firm date for such an event has been offered, but McFarlane *et al.* (1980) consider that a late Palaeozoic to early Mesozoic date is likely. Other granitoid masses are less elevated, the Gbenge Hills barely reaching 700 m, for instance, despite their equally bold and massive bornhardt forms.

Exceptional to all these features is the Freetown Peninsula, which is a layered basic igneous complex of early Mesozoic age (220–180 Ma). Its relief is peculiar in its isolation, and the crescentic form of the hill mass indicates a seaward extension, now eroded or foundered (Krause, 1964). No evidence of local faulting has so far been adduced.

Geomorphic Evolution and the Survival of Palaeoforms

Published interpretations of the relief of Sierra Leone have postulated a sequence of erosion surfaces to correspond broadly with each major topographic level (Dixey, 1922; Hall, 1969; McFarlane *et al.*, 1980). Faulting is used to explain the elevation of the highest areas, while 'local' planations are advanced to account for small areas of intermediate level, between the Main Plateau and the Coastal Plain Surface in the south east (Hall, 1969). The details are outlined in Table 22.1. In a study of adjacent areas of Guinée, Michel (1973) comes to similar conclusions and offers regional correlations with other parts of West Africa. Essentially, Michel argues for three major planations: the first taking place in the Jurassic, and surviving as isolated remnants of the 'Labé Surface' in the Futa Djalon Mountains (1100–1200 m); the second during the Cretaceous forming the 'Dongol Sigon Surface' (850–950 m); and the third in the early Tertiary, producing the extensive 'Fantofa Surface' of the Mandingo Plateau (550–650 m). Local planations in the Pliocene were followed by glacis[1] development during the Quaternary (Table 22.1). In Sierra Leone, the early Tertiary surface is considered to be equivalent to the Main Plateau and to belong to the 'African Surface' (King, 1950, 1962) recognized elsewhere on the continent, while the extensive, duricrusted summits of the schist belts are designated as the 'Nimini Surface' and considered by Hall (1969) and by McFarlane *et al.* (1980) to be pre-Eocene in age, and to correspond with a sub-Bullom laterite found in boreholes near Freetown. This connection remains conjectural, however.

The questions which this study will attempt to discuss concern the recognition of supposedly ancient palaeoforms, and the criteria used to argue an age for them. More broadly, the problems of linking concepts of planation with differential erosion underlies much of the discussion (Hack, 1960, 1977), and the aim is not simply to test the validity of landform histories, but to place such an analysis within a functional study of landform environments, to assess the consequences of denudation over varying timescales.

The problem of the survival of palaeoforms has been discussed by Twidale (1976, p. 91), who concludes that 'in humid regions paleoforms do not long survive; in arid zones they may'. The survival of ancient forms in the Sahara has been remarked by Rapp (1975) in a review of fundamental work by Beuf *et al.* (1971), who were able to demonstrate the survival intact of large areas of Ordovician, glaciated pavement, exposed by removal of Silurian rocks. However, Sierra Leone is humid tropical and has probably experienced this type of climate with minor interruptions since the Upper Cretaceous at least. In such environments, the geochemical evolution of weathering profiles and duricrusts forms a major component of the long-term evolution of landscapes. Twidale (1976) refers to the importance of duricrusted surfaces, and they have frequently been taken to represent ancient surfaces of advanced planation.

A major problem in reconstructing landform histories is to establish a datum from which a sequence of events is subsequently seen to take place. This problem is particularly acute on the emergent shield topographies of the world. It is solved logically, but without verification, by the supposed formation of a supra-continental, Gondwana Surface of advanced planation, which was virtually complete at the onset of Continental Drift in the Jurassic (*ca.* 180 Ma) (King, 1950, 1962). However, even if such a surface once existed very widely in Africa, its survivals today are few and uncertain, and the identification of high altitude massifs as remnants of such a surface is fraught with difficulties. Thus the Jos Plateau of Nigeria, once considered part of this surface (Pugh and King, 1952; King, 1962), is known now to comprise granites intruded during the late Jurassic (*ca.* 160 Ma), and it is possible that a residual, hilly relief has persisted in this area since the lower Cretaceous (Thomas, 1978b).

In Sierra Leone, the kimberlite event (*ca.* 92 Ma) may afford the only known clue to the nature of the landsurface as far back as the Cretaceous, when, it has been suggested, a sedimentary cover may have extended as far as the Koidu area (Hubbard, 1967), where the kimberlite dykes and small pipes represent a root zone perhaps as much as 1000 m below the Cretaceous landsurface. Overlooking the Koidu Basin, the Nimini Hills form a duricrusted plateau rising 350 m above the adjacent granites with their kimberlitic intusions. The 'Nimini Surface' was considered to be Cretaceous by Hall (1969), and therefore, by implication, the lowering of the Koidu granite surface since the Cretaceous can only have been of the order of 350–450 m, if we assume that the duricrusted hills retain their ancient levels. However, if there was a cover, perhaps of as much as 500 m of Ordovician sediments and volcanics, then the total depth of erosion since the kimberlite eruptions comes closer to that predicted by Hawthorne's (1973) model of a kimberlite pipe. This erosion can have been achieved in two ways: firstly, by the removal, laterally, of the sedimentary cover, and secondly, by the differential erosion, vertically, of the underlying basement.

The Ages of Duricrusts

The association of duricrusts with ancient palaeoforms in tropical latitudes has been established for certain areas, notably parts of Australia, and widely assumed elsewhere (Twidale, 1976). However, McFarlane (1971, 1976) has graphically emphasized the problems and pitfalls of attempting to reconstruct the so-called 'Buganda Surface' in

Table 22.1 Regional Landform Correlations for West Africa

Geological time scale	Ma bp	Principal geological and climatic events	Planation surfaces and	
			Senegal/Guinée/Haute Volta Altitude (m)	Côte d'Ivoire/Nigeria Altitude (m)
HOLOCENE	0.006	Minor oscillations to present day	Second Valley Fill[1]	Alluviation[3,4]
	0.008	Drier		
	0.009	Wet		
	0.10			
	0.012	Dry—minimum sea level		
	0.025	Wet	First Valley Fill[1]	
	0.040			
Upper		Dry	Low Glacis[1]	Lower Slope[3,4]
	0.060			
PLEISTOCENE		Wet		
	0.10			
	0.12	Dry	Middle Glacis[1]	Middle Slope[3] 130
Middle	0.5	(climates uncertain)		
Lower	0.7		High Glacis[1]	High Glacis[3] 200
	2.4	Uplift—dissection		
PLIOCENE		Local planation	Local planation[1]	'Cuirasses[3] Ferrugineuses' 300
	7	Detrital sedimentation ('Continental Terminal')		
MIOCENE	26	Epeirogeny, faulting, differential erosion		
OLIGOCENE	38	Bullom Group sedimentation Transgression		
EOCENE	54			
PALAEOCENE		Extensive planation Humid climate established	'Fantofa Surface'[1] 550 (Mandingo Plateau) 650 (Bandiagara Plateau)[2] 600	'Cuirasses[3] Bauxitiques' 500 ('High Plains',[2,5] N. Nigeria)
	65	Transgression in Senegal		
Upper	92	Kimberlites in Sierra Leone	'Dongol Sigon Surface'[1] 850 (Futa Djalon Mtns.) 950	
CRETACEOUS		Epeirogeny, doming, faulting Transgression in Senegal		
Lower	136	'Continental intercalaire'	? ? ?	? ? ?
			'Labe Surface,[1,2] 1100 (Futa Djalon Mtns.) 1200	(Jos Plateau[5]) 1300 1450
JURASSIC	c180	'Younger Granite' episode in Nigeria/Niger, intrusion of Freetown Basic Igneous Complex, doming, faulting of extensive planation surface		
	190			
TRIASSIC	225			
PERMEAN	280	Domes and basins during Hercynian earth movements		
CARBONIFEROUS	345			
DEVONIAN	395			
SILURIAN	430			
ORDOVICIAN	500	Deposition of Saionya Scarp Series—glaciation		
CAMBRIAN	570	Planation—unconformity		
PRE-CAMBRIAN	600	Rokelide Orogeny ('Pan-African Orogeny')		

[1]After Michel (1973). [2]After Lamotte and Rougerie (1961). [3]After Grandin and Delvigne (1969). [4]After Avenard (1973). [5]After Pugh and King (1952). [6]After Dixey (1922). [7]After Hall (1969). [8]After Daveau (1971). [9]After Grandin and Hayward (1975). [10]After McFarlane et al. (1978).

Broken horizontal lines indicate the periods of most widely accepted extensive planations in West Africa. If the correlations of King are followed then the 'Jurassic' surface may be 'Gondwana' and the 'Palaeocene' surface would be the 'African Surface'.

depositional phases	Sierra Leone—proposed framework for interpretation		
Sierra Leone (published sources) Altitude (m)	Depositional/ weathering phases	'Acyclic' systems —continuous	Geologically controlled 'planations'
Recent flat deposits[7]	Successive cut/fill episodes		
High terraces (R. Sewa)[7]	Early valley fill		
'Bullom Surface'[10] 0–40 (mainly depositional)	Low Glacis (Koidu basin) Bullom Surface		
Middle Glacis[9] 70 (Freetown Peninsula) Erosion platforms[6] 140 160 210	Middle Glacis (Freetown and Kasewe Hills) High Glacis (Kasewe Hills— fragmentary)		
'Coastal Plain Surface'[6,10] −100 'Cuirasses Ferrugineuses'[9] 350 (Freetown Peninsula) Local planations in S.E. Sierra Leone:[7] 'Tongo Surface' 220 'Koidu Surface' 400	Nimini/Sula/ 150 Kasila Duricrusts 770		
'Main Plateau Surface'[7] 400 (Koinadugu Plateau)[6] 500 'Cuirasses Bauxitiques'[9] 550 (Freetown Peninsula) 'Sula Surface'[10] 600 'Nimini Surface'[10] 700 (Nimini and Sula Hills) 800			
? ? ? 'Loma Surface'[8,10] 800+ (High summits in Sula Mtns., at 800 m, surface faulted to 1200 m in Tingi Hills and 1800 m in Loma Mtns.) 1800 (High surface in Nimba 1600 Mtns.) 1800	? ? ?	?	?

Column annotations ('Acyclic' systems —continuous):

→ Progressive stripping of early Paleozoic (Saionya Scarp Series) cover
↑ Increasing humidity of climate leading to continuous laterization/duricrusting
↑ Epeirogeny/Planation—Epeirogeny, progressive dissection/differential erosion
—Deep weathering and bauxitization below plateaus

↑ Epeirogeny/Planation

Early planation and Paleozoic deposition

Column annotations (Geologically controlled 'planations'):

↑ Rokel River Group sediments maintained at low altitude by areal erosion
↑ Isolation of Koidu, Tongo, and other 'basins' by resistant rock bars
→ Block faulting creates persistent relief differences

→ Possible block faulting creates persistent relief differences

Uganda from the correlation of remnant duricrusted hills. This and much other work makes it necessary to consider the mode of formation of the duricrust or laterite profile, before questions about 'age' can be answered with any meaning.

Notwithstanding such problems, there have been several discussions concerning the ages of duricrusts in Sierra Leone. Wilson and Marmo (1958) and McFarlane *et al.* (1980) based their pre-Eocene age for the Nimini-Sula crusts on a long distance correlation with sub-Bullom Group laterites found in boreholes near Freetown. On the other hand, Gaskin (1975) attempted to calculate an age for the duricrusts on the Tonkolili Ironstones in the southern Sulas, using hypothetical rainfall-infiltration rates and silica extraction by stream water, based on contemporary measurements, together with depth/composition profiles taken from detailed boreholes. He arrived at a range of ages from 43 Ma (infiltration 1524 mm a^{-1}) to 64 Ma (1015 mm a^{-1}), which accords with a Palaeocene–Eocene age for profiles with a total depth of decomposition of 115 m. This approach presents many difficulties. Firstly, any assumption concerning average infiltration rates during long time periods can only be conjectural. Secondly, the rate of removal of solutes by this water over the same period may not approximate to the calculations based on contemporary records. One reason for this latter difficulty is that the dilute nature of the water found in deeply weathered rock is partly a function of the prior weathering of the rock, and cannot be taken as a guide to past conditions. Nevertheless, an age much younger than the early Tertiary seems unlikely, given the depths of weathering and crust formation and the degree of relief development in these hills (350–450 m). Indeed, it might be argued that the duricrusts are much older, having been covered by the Ordovician rocks which may have persisted across this area in the Cretaceous. If, on the other hand, the duricrusting began with the removal of the sedimentary cover, it might be necessary to suggest the more recent (43 Ma) age for the Sula Mountain duricrust, and the Nimini profiles would necessarily be older.

In the Côte d'Ivoire, Grandin and Delvigne (1969) recognized two surfaces of wide extent, represented by 'cuirasses bauxitiques' at around 500 m and 'cuirasses fer-rugineuses' at 300 m. The bauxitic crusts are considered to be part of the African Surface and more ancient than the ferruginous crusts because of their more advanced weathering stage and present altitude. More recently, Grandin and Hayward (1975) have sought to extend this interpretation to Sierra Leone, where in the Freetown Peninsula they describe a 'surface bauxitique' on hills and spurs at 530 m and a 'surface ferrugineuse' at levels around 300 m. A correlation is thus sought between geochemical evolution, altitude and age of the landsurface, an approach commonly used in Europe (Bakker, 1967; Nieuwenhuis, 1971; Verague, 1977) to distinguish between saprolites of different composition. This evidence is discussed below.

In the absence of ferruginous or bauxitic crusts, there is little evidence, apart from relative or absolute altitude, on which to base speculation about landsurface age. An area of subdued granite relief, such as that containing the kimberlites around Koidu, may be regarded as a 'local' planation related in this case to the slightly higher Main Plateau developed elsewhere, and therefore presumed to be of Tertiary origin (Hall, 1969). However, it is also possible to regard the landsurface as essentially 'young', in the sense that few if any relics of ancient forms and deposits are preserved. In this view, the striking feature of the Koidu basin is the strong structural control over its altitude relative to the Nimini Hills schist belt, and the detailed lithologic control over its internal morphology.

This observation embodies an apparent paradox, for while many workers draw attention to the simple, regular arrangement of 'surfaces' on the African continent, rising inland from warped or faulted coastal margins (King, 1962; McFarlane *et al.*, 1980), it is also widely observed that structural and lithologic controls can be discerned in the major outlines as well as the finer details of the relief (Thomas, 1968; Twidale, 1976; Hack, 1960, 1977). The manner in which ancient forms are preserved in one case and destroyed in another is not always well understood, and while Twidale (1976) gives examples of the preservation of palaeoforms under a variety of conditions, there are many puzzling anomalies, some of which can be glimpsed from the different depths of erosion into the kimberlites of southern Africa as recorded by Hawthorne (1973).

This paradox might be regarded as a result of using different spatial and temporal scales, the broad outlines of the relief having been determined by widely spaced cycles of erosion during remote periods of geological time, while the morphologic detail is evolving in response to differential erosion at the present day (Schumm and Lichty, 1965). However, this explanation only partially succeeds, because individual duricrusted summits or bornhardts may legitimately be regarded as being of ancient origin, while major escarpments appear 'fixed' in their positions by lithologic and structural determinants. Similarly, the preservation of plains under arid conditions (Twidale, 1976) hardly accounts for the extensive surfaces of central and western Africa which have long histories of humid or sub-humid climates. The survival of ancient relief in remote interiors of the continental landmasses (Twidale, 1976) is a predictable response to headward erosion of rivers from coastlines which in this case came into being with the opening of the Atlantic in the early Mesozoic, but the close structural control over this activity begs the question, and returns the argument to the nature of differential erosion.

The purpose of the rest of this study is to enquire into the field evidence from Sierra Leone concerning the nature of morphogenesis under different conditions, and to interpret this evidence in terms of the survival of palaeoforms and the timescale of landform development in selected areas.

Morphogenetic Environments in Sierra Leone

Four contrasting environments have been selected for study:
1. Duricrusted surfaces forming summit levels on the schist belts and high bevels in the Freetown Peninsula (Grandin and Hayward, 1975).
2. The positive relief of porphyroblastic granite masses such as the Loma and Tingi Hills, where the summit culminations consist of bare rock domes (bornhardts), and iron crusts have formed only within intermontane basins (Thomas, 1978a).
3. The negative relief of granite basins such as Koidu, etched into the main plateau surface, and where duricrust is fragmentary and seldom forms summit outcrops.
4. Hillslope/piedmont zones around the Freetown and Kasewe Hills where active morphogenesis takes place in a scarp or hillslope environment.

Duricrusted Upland Surfaces

Duricrusted surfaces in the Kambui Schist belts and on the hills of the Freetown Basic Igneous Complex (Fig. 22.1) have been attributed to different geological ages as discussed above. The criteria used may be briefly summarized: (i) long-range stratigraphic correlation; (ii) inter-regional comparisons based on relative height and position in the landscape; (iii) calculation of rate and depth of weathering; and (iv) geochemical evolution of the crusts measured in terms of relative enrichment of alumina. A further criterion which may prove valuable is (v) the measurement of remanent magnetism. This has recently been used to provide an early Tertiary date for deep weathering in eastern Australia (Pillans, 1977). Other recent research in Senegal (Nahon and Lappartient,

1977) has used the stratigraphic method, allied to radiometric dating of lavas, to analyse the complexities of geochemical evolution of iron encrusted profiles.

Such complexities of evolution, together with the influence of rock mineralogy over crust composition, make comparisons between different field areas difficult. In particular, the distinction between bauxitic (or allitic) crusts and ferruginous (or ferrallitic) deposits attempted by Grandin and Hayward (1975) creates serious problems.

Laterites from Sula Mountain amphibolites were analysed by Wilson and Marmo (1958), who found them leached of most of their silica to depths of 4 m (SiO_2 less than 5%) and variously aluminous or ferruginous according to the underlying rock (Al_2O_3 25–50%, Fe_2O_3 20–60%; see Fig. 22.3). The high degree of leaching, the visible preservation of details of rock structure, and their elevated site associated with deep dissection, all suggest comparison with the 'primary laterites' described by Harrison (1933) and Bleackley (1964) from similar deposits in Guyana. Given that separation of South America from Africa began in the Mesozoic, a parallel development in the two areas may have taken place. However, these duricrusts do not fall into the allitic province (Dury, 1969; Fig. 22.3), and duricrusts from ironstones within the same formation, not unnaturally, were found to offer prospects as iron ore deposits (Gaskin, 1975). On the other hand, feldspathic gneisses forming part of a discontinuous ridge in the Kasila Series have weathered to form payable bauxite deposits containing 54–56% of alumina and only 6–10% of iron oxides. This gibbsitic residue is dependent on the occurrence of feldspathic gneiss, and forms within well drained profiles beneath ridge tops protected by duricrust. This duricrust, however, contains up to 40% of iron oxides in the top 4 m, suggesting that it may date from the formation of an ancient surface of low relief, while the deeper gibbsitic residue has resulted from subsequent deep weathering and rapid leaching, as dissection has isolated the duricrusted ridge from surrounding terrain.

In the Tonkolili ironstone deposits Gaskin (1975) found evidence for two periods of

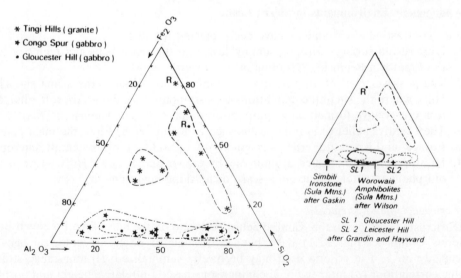

Fig. 22.3 Composition of some duricrusts in Sierra Leone. The left-hand diagram shows samples collected by the writer from the Tingi Hills (granite) and the Freetown peninsula (gabbroid) (analyses by X-ray fluorescence carried out by Mr R. McGill, University of Dundee). The right-hand diagram shows a selection of published data for the Sula Mountains (after Wilson and Marmo, 1958, and Gaskin, 1975), and for the Freetown Peninsula (after Grandin and Hayward, 1975)

rapid water-table fall, as deep weathering proceeded beneath the duricrust. At the Mokanje bauxite mine partition of the deposit by a discontinuous layer of kaolinized rock may also be interpreted in this way, and it suggests responses by the weathering systems to pulses of epeirogenic uplift which have also been responsible for the differential erosion of surrounding terrain.

The duricrusts present in the Freetown Peninsula also occupy elevated sites but in certain cases at least their significance is quite different to the previous examples. Grandin and Hayward (1975) claim the presence of bauxitic residues on Gloucester Hill (530 m) behind Freetown and ferruginous crusts at lower levels, equating these with palaeoforms postulated for Côte d'Ivoire (Grandin and Delvigne, 1969). Grandin and Hayward (1975) offered two analyses, shown in Fig. 22.3. However, detailed sampling from Gloucester Hill reveals a wide range of duricrust composition, different parts of the same boulder yielding highly aluminous or highly ferruginous material (Figs. 22.3 and 22.4). No continuous 'cuirass' exists on this hill, and no deep weathering profile is

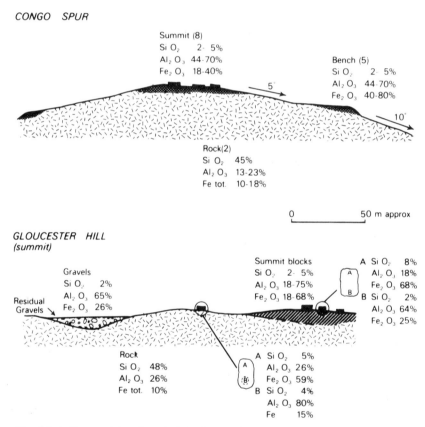

Fig. 22.4 Compositional variations in duricrust samples from two sites on the Freetown peninsula (analyses by X-Ray fluorescence carried out by Mr R. McGill, University of Dundee). Congo Spur and Gloucester Hill are two summit areas of gently sloping land at *ca*. 530 m a.s.l., in the Freetown Basic Igneous Complex. Duricrust blocks from both summits were sampled and the range of composition is indicated. Two blocks from Gloucester Hill were sampled to show contrasts between top and bottom, interior and exterior in terms of SiO_2: Al_2O_3: Fe_2O_3 (shown diagrammatically as 'A' and 'B'. Numbers in brackets refer to number of samples analysed)

evident. Fresh rock crops out at the summit, and the boulders of 'duricrust' are in reality no more than actively weathering blocks of rock similar to those described in detail by Martin and Doyne (1927, 1930). Elsewhere on the summit, residual gravels proved to be highly aluminous, and it is possible that these survive from some higher level duricrust now destroyed. Comparable results were obtained from a 'bevelled' spur at a similar altitude, and it is deduced from this evidence that these features are actively downwasting within a geomorphic system in which rapid rock weathering is matched by dissection and active slope processes. It is not considered that these hills have any 'cyclic' significance at their present altitudes, nor do they relate to the deep profiles of the Kambui Schists and Kasila Gneisses.

It is obvious that duricrusting is controlled by both rock geochemistry and by the environment of weathering. The aluminous and ferruginous bedrock of the Kambui Schist belts and the Kasila gneisses of Sierra Leone give rise to extensive duricrusts under a seasonal tropical climate. These laterites and bauxites with their associated weathering profiles have largely formed *in situ* by relative enrichment of iron and alumina (Maignien, 1966), and their long formational histories have integrated within a single profile perhaps 10^7 or 10^8 years of geochemical evolution. Evidence exists for the early formation of a ferruginous crust under conditions of low relief and weak leaching, followed by dissection and deep penetration of weathering, leading in favourable cases to advanced leaching and bauxitization of the profiles.

It is possible that these profiles record datable palaeomagnetism, although the stability of the relative pole position for West Africa since the early Mesozoic may limit the usefulness of this technique in Sierra Leone (Smith and Briden, 1977). They also appear to record periods of relief development responding to epeirogenic uplift (Gaskin, 1975). In addition, these deposits remain morphogenetically active, as infiltrating water penetrates the cuirass and leads to saturation and failure of the underlying clays. Failure in the form of rotational slumps is common in the Sula Mountains (Wilson and Marmo, 1958; Thomas, 1974; Gaskin, 1975) and the recementation of early slides by iron (Gaskin, 1975) indicates that this process has continued during much of the Quaternary. Local subsidence of the crust may also be responsible for Lake Sonfon (Thomas, 1974).

Such areas may hold keys to unlock much of the gemorphic history of the tropical shields, though the evidence is often complex, requiring care in interpretation. Located by petrographic factors, these duricrusted plateaus and ridges, despite the evidence for marginal landsliding and deep dissection along active drainage lines, have been persistent features of the landscape probably since the Mesozoic. During this time they have emerged into relief by the operation of geochemically determined differential denudation.

Over rocks such as granite, containing little iron or alumina, encrustation occurs only in reception zones, where iron-bearing groundwater or runoff can lead to absolute enrichment of the saprolite by iron. Such areas are found frequently within basins or along piedmonts and are generally discontinuous. Local duricrusting within the intermontane basin of the Tingi Hills (Thomas, 1978a), for instance, may have no significance in 'cyclic' terms, but is more a response to the present-day relief.

Over many areas of subdued relief in Sierra Leone, interfluves are covered by pisolithic, lateritic gravel which seldom forms a coherent crust. According to McFarlane (1976), these deposits may result from a long history of gradual downwasting of the landscape, the iron concretions becoming increasingly packed with time. Such landscapes should be regarded as 'acyclic'.

Granite Massifs

A few kilometres to the west of the Sula Mountains the Gbenge Hills (Fig. 22.1 and 22.2) form a classic group of bornhardt domes of porphyroblastic granite (Marmo, 1956) which are similar to other bornhardt groups in West Africa such as the Idanre Hills of Nigeria (Thomas, 1965; Jeje, 1974). The massive forms and bold relief of these hills obscure the fact that nowhere do they rise above the level of the duricrusted schist surface, which stands in positive relief in relation to all the immediately surrounding basement rocks.

On the other hand, similar domes occur in the Tingi Hills, which rise above 1700 m, and in the Loma Mountains, which culminate in the highest point in West Africa (Bintimani, 1945 m). Suggestions that these higher massifs have been faulted to their present height during the late Palaeozoic or early Mesozoic (Daveau, 1971; McFarlane *et al.*, 1980) must be taken seriously in view of their unusual altitude and evident structural control over their outlines and the major drainage of the region (Fig. 22.1 and 22.2).

The question thus arises as to whether these hill masses are residual from very early landscapes antedating the duricrust formation on the schists. If this is so and they are unaffected by differential crustal movement, then the granites may be considered resistant and durable in relation to the schists. However, the local evidence from the Gbenge Hills and relationships between the schists and adjacent granitoid terrain elsewhere suggest a different conclusion, namely that the apparently resistant granites are in reality lowered differentially by weathering and chemical denudation of the domes. The exposure of the fresh rock at the surface, even though this is in massive and non-fissured form, must lead to some degree of chemical weathering, as shown from studies in serpentinite in the eastern USA (Cleaves *et al.*, 1974). On the other hand, the duricrust is in near equilibrium with the geochemical environment, and once formed may undergo little change except by physical dislocation, unless the environment is radically changed, for example with the development of swamp conditions when the iron may be redissolved.

It seems that there may be three explanations for the altitudes of residual granite massifs on tropical shields. Firstly, they may be erosional remnants from planations at successively lower levels. This is unsatisfactory, because the evidence for the apparent resistance of bornhardts to lateral planation (Twidale and Bourne, 1975; Thomas, 1978b) makes it difficult to argue that their summits indicate former levels of erosional plains. Secondly, they may form by differential erosion of less resistant granite and metamorphic basement rocks at levels pre-determined by their level of formation as porphyroblastic masses within the crust (Thomas, 1965; Twidale and Bourne, 1975). Thirdly, they may be faulted in relation to surrounding country. This last factor could operate in conjuction with the second but is not necessary to it. It is concluded, therefore, that these massifs are located by petrographic and structural factors within a three-dimensional space. Their forms as they emerge by differential erosion are always similar and appear to reach a dynamic equilibrium (Hack, 1960; Gerber and Scheidegger, 1969). Such forms have no easily definable relationship with planation levels if these exist elsewhere; they are acylic.

Granite Basins

Negative relief in granite terrain is well known (Thomas, 1974) and, apart from the so-called 'arenas' and embayments in uplands of more resistant rocks, basin forms exist in an hierarchy of sizes (Thorp, 1967). In Sierra Leone, the Koidu Basin, associated with kimberlitic intrusions and diamondiferous gravels, has the characteristics of an active etchsurface (Mabbutt, 1961; Thomas, 1974). It forms a distinctive, lower landscape adjacent to the duricrusted schists of the Nimini Hills. There are no large bornardts, but on summits and interfluves bedrock is commonly exposed as boulders, tors, and smaller inselbergs, giving the impression of recent stripping of a former regolith. Saprolite is preserved to depths of 20 m or more along valley flanks, and deep weathering beneath swampy valley floors is also known to extend to depths of more than 15 m. Non-rocky interfluves are seldom duricrusted, but may be underlain by indurated concretions which may be fragments of former laterite sheets. These feed downslope in the form of a stone line beneath a creep/termite layer. These intermediate slopes have the form of pediments or glacis cut across the saprolite, and lead down to swampy valley floors containing diamondiferous alluvial sequences from which the oldest wood so far collected is *ca.* 35,000 bp in age.[2] Local field evidence and comparison with Sénégal (Michel, 1973) and the Côte d'Ivoire (Avenard, 1973) suggest that the pediments are probably also late Pleistocene in age and correspond with the 'low glacis' in these other regions (Table 22.1).

Thus, the conclusion from the study of this terrain is that little of it is in any sense 'old'. The general altitude (*ca.* 400 m), slightly below the 'main plateau' (500 m; Hall, 1969), tells us little about the age of the forms and deposits found within the area. It may be described as stripped etchsurface (Thomas, 1974), in which granite cores occur at all levels, from summits to scoured valley floors below the Pleistocene alluvial deposits. Weathering (or etching) continues below the valley floors of headwater streams which have the form of channel-less swamps and undergo little or no mechanical abrasion. Almost the entire landsurface is active in the sense of undergoing continuous morphological change. The preservation of palaeoforms is very limited and few features other than the higher interfluves with their deep weathering profiles and larger outcrops would appear to be older than the Quaternary. The thickness of sand and gravel deposited by the larger rivers (5–7 m) indicates that the products of stripping are still stored at lower levels. The rivers in this area have narrow floodplains and possibly received much of their sediment from hillwash processes or landslides.

The absence of palaeoforms of Pre-Pleistocene age in this area, together with its negative relief within surrounding higher land, must throw doubt on any attempt to relate this stripped etchsurface to any postulated sequence of cyclic erosion surfaces. This type of terrain which appears to have undergone a pervasive areal erosion may be considered to be acyclic for very different reasons to those advanced for the granitoid massifs. Whereas bornhardts develop at predetermined levels in the crust and undergo slow denudation thereafter, the fractured and weathered granites evolve continuously, their altitude being determined by successive uplifts and the control of rock thresholds over the advance of stream dissection.

Hillslopes and Piedmont Zones

The argument developed so far points to an ever increasing differential erosion since the early Mesozoic, between rock formations of varying resistance to the humid tropical denudation system. This mode of landform development has led to the formation and development of structurally and lithologically controlled hillslopes and escarpments. Below these, the piedmont zones have become the loci for the accumulation of waste from the uplands. The transit of this waste to the rivers has in places been arrested by lateritization and duricrusting of the deposits, and this has led to the differentiation of materials of different ages in the piedmont zone.

However, the minor degree of lateral erosion into the hillslopes has led to much reworking of older deposits to form newer ones at lower levels. Over long timespans (10^5–10^6 years) the piedmont zone appears to approach an equilibrium determined by the nature of the contiguous rock masses (Hack, 1960), but over shorter periods disequilibrium is indicated by the occurrence of fragmented fans and glacis, and frequent landslides.

Around granite massifs which are poor in iron few such remnants survive, but around hills of basic igneous rock a succession of ferricreted surfaces can be traced. Episodic fan and glacis deposition, landsliding, and more general colluviation, probably controlled by bioclimatic changes, but at times induced by earth movements, have occurred over a long timespan during which lateritization processes have operated continuously, if with varying intensity (Thomas, 1978a).

Piedmont slopes in the Freetown Peninsula and Kasewe Hills exhibit broad duricrusted benchlands, some intact, others in an advanced stage of disintegration. Subterranean drainage has in places led to cavitation of the surface laterite, to expose sections which in the case of the Kasewe Hills reveal the deposit as a duricrusted rubble which could be ancient landslide debris. Fresh rock-fall and slide material is seen in turn to rest upon these duricrusted surfaces. Similarly, in the Sula Mountains, Gaskin (1975) has argued for two phases of landsliding, the first now encrusted by iron.

In Sénégal, Michel (1973) recognized three glacis developed during the Quaternary around the higher massifs. The High Glacis, thought to date from the early Pleistocene, are strongly duricrusted but partially disintegrated; the Middle Glacis, which are also strongly duricrusted, remain substantially intact; and the Low Glacis continue today as functional units within the present landscape, exhibiting active profile development and segregation of sesquioxides. A comparable sequence is recognized in Côte d'Ivoire by Avenard (1973). Parallels in Sierra Leone are striking, and it appears that the course of landform development has been comparable from 5 to 15° N over much of West Africa, despite the regional differences in rainfall regime and vegetation cover. Although gradations must undoubtedly come to light within this zone, it appears that the oscillations of the Quaternary climates have been more important than zonation of the present bioclimates.

How far back into landform history the palaeoforms of duricrusted piedmonts can be traced is as yet undetermined, though the use of palaeomagnetic studies may provide new clues to the ages of duricrusts.[3] The essential mode of development of these terrains, however, is clear: an episodic formation of hillslope and piedmont deposits has been subject to a continuous process of iron transport and immobilization, to form ferricrete deposits that have led in turn to the partial preservation of a mosaic of palaeoforms (Thomas, 1978a).

Summary and Conclusions

Four essentially different modes of landform development have been described from the emergent basement rocks of Sierra Leone. They may be summarized as follows:

1. Over the Kambui Schist belts and the Kasila Gneisses in particular, lateritic and bauxitic profiles have undergone continuous development at least from the early Cenozoic, protected by an ancient duricrust capping from 2–10 m thick. An ancient level of the landscape has thus been preserved, while sub-surface weathering has operated continuously, as these areas have emerged into positive relief with the lowering of surrounding terrain. Dissection and marginal attrition of these plateaus and ridges have

diversified their relief and led to the development of a mosaic of more recent palaeoforms in the escarpment and piedmont fringes.

2. During uplifts and dissection of the basement, resistant porphyroblastic granite massifs have emerged at levels determined by structure. Once exhumed and modified by deep weathering of shatter zones and less resistant rocks, these massifs develop into bold bornhardt groups such as those found in the Tingi and Gbenge Hills. These domes are probably slowly lowered by chemical denudation, but are essentially survivors from a remote past.

3. Large areas of more easily weathered basement granites and gneisses, together with mudstones of the Rokel River Group, appear to have experienced continuous etchplanation, whereby the weathering systems (Nikiforoff, 1959) produce an easily eroded saprolite which, in the absence of extensive iron encrustation, becomes subject to periodic removal by slope and stream processes. Over the granites of the Koidu Basin, this has led to the formation of a landscape of tors and boulder strewn hillslopes, local pediment formation across the weathered rock, and extensive alluviation of river valleys. The impression is of an entire landscape evolving by a complex of processes to progressively lower levels, without fundamental departure from a plain-like surface of generally low relief, and punctuated only here and there by larger hills. Such surfaces evolve by replacement of one set of palaeoforms by another and retain few elements of ancient relief (Dixey, 1922; Wayland, 1933; Thomas, 1974).

4. Hillslopes and piedmonts evolve by combinations of differential erosion and lateral scarp retreat. The latter appears most effective wherever there are quasi-horizontal discontinuities, as in layered sedimentary formations or at the unconformity between basement rocks and a sedimentary or volcanic cover. Since the stripping of a postulated sedimentary cover during the late Cretaceous and early Cenozoic, the landscape of Sierra Leone has become etched into structurally controlled plateaus, ridges and groups of hills.

Hillslopes and piedmonts inevitably evolve together and as iron has been transported in solution from the more basic igneous massifs, so successive levels of the adjacent piedmont have become encrusted by ferricrete. Much of this zone is reworked with each lowering of the less resistant rock, but a differentiated relief permits survivals of possibly ancient events.

In this analysis there has been no discussion of the river systems or of the sedimentary formations of the Bullom Group that make up the broad coastal plain (Figs. 22.1 and 22.2). However, clearly much of the landform history is recorded in coastal and continental shelf sedimentation (Bezrukov and Senin, 1970; MacMaster *et al.*, 1970). The absence of broad floodplains and extensive terraces in the valleys of the basement rivers has meant that most sediments appear to date from the late Pleistocene. It is therefore apparent that the sedimentary history is transferred to the coastal plain, where the build-up of sands and clays has continued as the basement has gradually subsided throughout the Cenozoic.

Although the geological history of the post-Mesozoic period is to be found in these sediments, and should eventually shed new light on the evolution of the basement landmass, there will always be a spatial discontinuity between the two. In this study, therefore, the mode of evolution of the exposed cratonic area has been discussed, in order to provide a possible framework of argument within which an historical gemorphology can subsequently be considered.

A further problem is to reconcile the published sequences of successive planations (Dixey, 1922; King, 1950, 1962; Hall, 1969; McFarlane *et al.*, 1980; Michel, 1973) with the suggestion that differential erosion has been dominant for the last 50–100 Ma.

Firstly, it may be noted that Michel (1973) offers no regionally extensive planation following the formation of the 'Fantofa Surface' of Palaeocene age in Guinée. In fact, it may be claimed that, following the formation of this 'African Surface' (King, 1962), most accounts of denudation chronology in Africa discuss local planations within major drainage basins or over weaker rocks. Secondly, many type areas for the recognition of these ancient surfaces come from areas of quasi-horizontal sediments, or might reasonably be traced to exhumed unconformities.

It remains clear from recent discussions of the old yet central problem of planation in geomorphology (Melhorn and Flemal, 1977) that evidence and argument often remain inconclusive. The evidence from Sierra Leone suggests that over cratonic areas in the tropics, the answers lie in a full understanding of geological history and the role of geochemical factors in the evolution of terrain. This requires first an understanding of the pulses of epeirogenic uplift, associated with Continental Drift, and reinforcing dome and basin structures of great antiquity. It also involves an appreciation of igneous events such as the intrusion of dolerites and basic igneous rocks in the Triassic or the Kimberlite event ans associated faulting in the Cretaceous.

The sub-areal development of the terrain inevitably responds to these events, but any tendency for the development of stepped erosion surfaces on the flanks of rising domes in the manner of Penck (1924) appears to have been so modified by geochemically determined differential erosion that the nature and significance of local planations remain in doubt. It is the opinion of the author that areas of low relief have developed largely by areal erosion bringing about the simultaneous lowering of valleys and interfluves on less resistant rocks. This is a form of etchplanation, the production of a plain from a plain as described by Wayland (1933). The altitudes of these plains appear determined more by resistant rock formations acting as local or regional base levels rather than by external events.

The timescales within which these landscapes have evolved are long in geomorphological terms, yet the widespread survival of palaeoforms and the continuous evolution of weathering profiles through geological time makes it necessary for the student of recent events to understand the products of this longer history. Moreoever, with new techniques, such as the use of palaeomagnetism, it may become possible to date with greater precision many major events in a chronology of denudation.

Acknowledgements

Fieldwork for geomorphological studies in Sierra Leone has been supported by the Carnegie Trust for the Universities of Scotland, the University of St. Andrews, and the National Diamond Mining Company of Sierra Leone. I thank the following individuals for help in the field and for contributing to many stimulating discussions: Mr. Colin Brown, Mr. Owen King and Dr. Peter Gregory of the Sierra Leone Selection Trust; Mr. Randall of Sieromco; and Dr. Martin Thorp and Mr. Desmond Bowden, formerly of the University of Sierra Leone. I also thank Dr. F. H. Hubbard and Mr. R. McGill for carrying out X-ray fluorescence analyses of duricrust samples in the Geology Department, University of Dundee. My thanks are also due to Mr. C. B. Bremner, who drew the figures, and to Mrs. E. Niven, who typed the manuscript.

Notes

1. The French term 'glacis' is widely used in West Africa to denote both depositional and erosional

surfaces in unconsolidated materials which may be of either sedentary or transported origin. Unlike the term 'pediment', which is commonly used to denote a surface produced by bedrock planation, the term glacis connotes only a more or less undissected surface of wide extent, formed across weathered rock or unconsolidated sediments. In many instances, however, the terms are interchangeable.

2. Taken from preliminary results of a radiocarbon dating programme to date wood from the alluvial deposits of the Koidu Basin. This programme is being undertaken jointly by Dr. M. B. Thorp and the author.

3. Experimental work on the remanent magnetism in laterites is currently being carried out on samples from these areas by Dr. R. Thompson of the Department of Geophysics, University of Edinburgh.

References

Allen, P. M. (1968). The geology of part of an orogenic belt in western Sierra Leone, West Africa. *Geol. Rundsch.*, **58**, 588–620.

Avenard, J. M. (1973). Évolution géomorphologique au quaternaire dans le centre-ouest de la Côte d'Ivoire. *Rev. Géom. Dyn.*, **22**, 145–160.

Bakker, J. P. (1967). Weathering of granites in different climates. In *L'Évolution des Versants* (Ed. P. Macar). *Congr. Coll. Univ. Liège*, **40**, 51–68.

Bardet, M. G., and Vachette, M. (1966). Détermination d'ages de Kimberlites de l'ouest Africain et essai d'interpretation des datations des diverses venues diamantifères dans le monde. *Bur. Rech. Geol. Min.*, Rep. D8 66 A 59.

Beuf, S., Bijou-Dival, B., de Charpal, O., Rognon, P., Gariel, O., and Bennacef, A. (1971). *Le Grés du Paleozoique Inferieur au Sahara.* L'Institut Français du Pétrole, Paris, 464 pp.

Bezrukov, P. L., and Senin, K. M. (1970). Sedimentation of the West Africa Shelf. In *The Geology of the East Atlantic Continental Margin, Vol. 4*, Africa. NERC/IGS, Rep. 70/16, pp. 3–7.

Bleackley, D. (1964). Bauxites and Laterites of British Guiana. *Bull. Geol. Surv. Br. Guiana*, **34**, 156 pp.

Cleaves, E. T., Fisher, D. W. and Bricker, O. P. (1974). Chemical weathering of serpentinite in the eastern piedmont of Maryland. *Bull. Geol. Soc. Am.*, **85**, 437–444.

Crickmay, C. H. (1977). The hypothesis of unequal activity. In *Theories of Landform Development*, (Eds. W. N. Melhorn and R. C. Flemal). Binghamton, New York, pp. 103–109.

Daveau, S. (1971). Etude morphologique des Monts Loma. In *Le Massif des Monts Loma*, Fascicule 1. *Mem. I.F.A.N.*, **86**, 25–53.

Dillon, W. P. and Sougy, J. M. A. (1974). Geology of West Africa and Canary and Cape Verde Islands. In *The Ocean Basins and Margins. Vol. 2. The North Atlantic*. (Eds. A. E. M. Nairn and F. G. Stehli). Plenum Press, New York, 315–390.

Dixey, F. (1922). The physiography of Sierra Leone. *Geog. J.*, **60**, 41–65.

Dury, G. H. (1969). Rational descriptive classification of duricrusts. *Earth Sci. J.*, **3**, 77–86.

Furon, R. (1960). *The Geology of Africa* (English Edition 1963). Oliver and Boyd, London, 377 pp.

Gaskin, A. R. G. (1975). Investigation of the residual iron ores of Tonkolili district, Sierra Leone. *Trans. Inst. Min. Metal., Sect., B., Appl. Earth Sci.*, B98–B119.

Gerber, E., and Scheidegger, A. E. (1969). Stress induced weathering of rock masses. *Ecol. Geol. Helv.*, **62**, 401–415.

Grandin, G., and Delvigne, J. (1969). Les cuirasses de la région birrimienne volcano-sedimentaire de Tourmodi: jalons de l'histoire morphologique de la Côte d'Ivoire. *C. R. Acad. Sci. Paris, Sér. D*, **269**, 1474–1477.

Grandin, G., and Hayward, D. F. (1975). Aplanissements curiassés de la peninsula de Freetown. *Cah. ORSTOM, Ser. Géol.*, **1**(1), 11–16.

Grantham, D. R., and Allen, J. B. (1960). Kimberlites in Sierra Leone. *Overseas Geol. Min. Res.*, **8**, 5–25.

Gregory, S. (1962). The raised beaches of the peninsula area of Siera Leone. *Trans. Inst. Br. Geog.*, **31**, 439–459.

Hack, J. T. (1960). Interpretation of erosional topography in humid temperate regions. *Am. J. Sci.*, **258A**, 80–97.

Hack, J. T. (1977). Dynamic equilibrium and landscape evolution. In *Theories of Landform Development* (Eds. W. N. Melhorn and R. C. Flemal). Binghamton, New York, pp. 87–102.

Hall, P. K. (1969). The Diamond Fields of Sierra Leone. *Geol. Surv. Sierra Leone, Bull.*, No. 5, 133 pp.

Harrison, J. B. (1933). *The Katamorphism of Igneous Rocks under Humid Tropical Conditions.* Imperial Bureau of Soil Science, Harpenden, 79 pp.

Haughton, S. H. (1963). *The Stratigraphic History of Africa South of the Sahara.* Oliver and Boyd, London, 365 pp.

Hawkes, D. D. (1970). *The Geology of Sierra Leone.* African Geology, University of Ibadan, pp. 471–482.

Hawthorne, J. B. (1973). Model of a kimberlite pipe. *Phys. Chem. Earth*, **9**, 1–15.

Hubbard, F. H. (1967). Unmetamorphosed volcanic and sedimentary xenoliths in the Kimberlites of Sierra Leone. *Nature, Lond.*, **214**, 1004–1005.

Hurley, P. M., and Rand, J. R. (1973). Outline of Precambrian chronology in lands bordering the South Atlantic, exclusive of Brazil. In *The Ocean Basins and Margins.Vol. 1, the S. Atlantic.* (Eds. A. E. M. Nairn and F. G. Stehli). Plenum Press, New York, Ch. 10, pp. 391–410.

Jeje, L. K. (1974). Relief and drainage development in the Idanre Hills of Western Nigeria. *Nigerian Geog. J.*, **17**, 83–92.

King, B. C. (1970). Vulcanicity and rift rectonics in East Africa. In *African Magmatism and Tectonics* (Eds. T. N. Clifford and I. G. Gass). Oliver and Boyd, Edinburgh, pp. 263–284.

King, L. C. (1950). The Study of the world's plainlands. *Qt. J. Geol. Soc. Lond.*, **106**, 101–131.

King, L. C. (1961). Cymatogeny. *Trans. Geol. Soc. S. Afr.*, **64**, 1–22.

King, L. C. (1962). *Morphology of the Earth.* Oliver and Boyd, London, 699 pp.

King, L. C. (1972). The Natal Monocline. University of Natal, Durban, 113 pp.

King, L. C. (1976). Planation remnants on high lands. *Z. Geomorph., N.F.*, **20**, 133–148.

Krause, D. C. (1963). Seaward extension and origin of the Freetown Layered Basic Complex of Sierra Leone. *Nature, Lond.*, **200**, 1280–1281.

Ladd, J. W., Dickson, G. O., and Pitman, W. C., III (1973). The age of the South Atlantic. In *The Ocean Basin and Margins, Vol. 1. The South Atlantic.* (Eds. A. E. M. Nairn and F. G. Stehli). Plenum Press, New York, p. 555–573.

Lamotte, M., and Rougerie, G. (1961). Les niveaux d'érosion interieurs dans l'ouest Africain. *Rech. Afr., Études Guinéenes (N.S.)*, **4**, 51–69.

Le Pichon, X., and Fox, P. J. (1971). Marginal offsets, fracture zones and the early opening of the North Atlantic. *J. Geophys. Res.*, **76**, 6294–6308.

Mabbutt, J. A. (1961). A stripped landsurface in Western Australia. *Trans. Inst. Br. Geog.*, **29**, 101–114.

McFarlane, A., Crow, M. J., Arthurs, J. W., and Wilkinson, A. F. (1980), *The Geology and Mineral Resources of Northern Sierra Leone.* Overseas Memoir, Institute of Geological Sciences, **7**, in press.

McFarlane, M. J. (1971). Lateritisation and landscape development in Kyagwe, Uganda. *Q. J. Geol. Soc. Lond.*, **126**, 501–539.

McFarlane, M. J. (1976). *Laterite and Landscape.* Academic Press, London, 151 pp.

Machens, E. (1973). The geologic history of the marginal basins along the north shore of the Gulf of Guinea. In *The Ocean Basins and Margins Vol. 1. The S. Atlantic* (Eds. A. E. M. Nairn and F. G. Stehli). Plenum Press, New York, Ch. 9, pp. 351–390.

McMaster, R. L., Lachance, T. P., Ashraf, A., and De Boer, J. (1970). Geomorphology, structure and sediments of the continental shelf and upper slope off Portuguese Guinea, Guinea and Sierra Leone. In *The Geology of the East Atlantic Continental Margin, Vol. 4, Africa.* NERC/IGS, Rep. 70/16, pp. 109–119.

Maignien, R. (1966). Review of research on laterites. In *Natural Resources Research*, Vol. IV, UNESCO, Paris, 148 pp.

Marmo, V. (1956). On the porphyroblastic granite of central Sierra Leone. *Acta Geog. (Helsinki)*, **15**(4), 1–26.

Marmo, V. (1971). Granite petrology and the granite problem. In *Developments in Petrology*. Vol. 2. Elsevier, Amsterdam, 244 pp.

Martin, F. J., and Doyne, H. C. (1927). Laterite and lateritic soils in Sierra Leone. *J. Agric. Sci.*, **17**, 530–547.

Martin, F. J., and Doyne, H. C. (1930). Laterite and lateritic soils in Sierra Leone, II. *J. Agric. Sci.*, **20**, 135–143.

Melhorn, W. N., and Flemal, R. C. (Eds.) (1977). *Theories of Landform Development.* Publ in Geomorph, State Univ. N.Y., Binghamton, 306 pp.

Michel, P. (1969). Morphogenesis and pedogenesis. Examples in West Africa. *African Soils*, **14**, 109–141.

Michel, P. (1973). Les Bassins des fleuves Sénégal et Gambie—étude géomorphologique. *Memo. ORSTOM*, **63** (3 vols.), 752 pp.

Millot, G. (1970). *Geology of Clays* (Engl. Transl. W. R. Farrand and H. Paquet). Chapman and Hall, London, 429 pp.

Nahon, D., and Lappartient, J. R. (1977). Time factor and geochemistry in iron crusts genesis. *Catena*, **4**, 249–254.

Nieuwenhuis, J. D. (1971). Weathering and planation in the Morvan (Haut Folin area). *Rev. Géom. Dyn.*, **20**, (3), 97–120.

Nikiforoff, C. C. (1959). Reappraisal of the soil. *Science*, **129**, 186–196.

Penck, W. (1924). *Die Morphologische Analyse* (English Edn. 1953, *Morphological Analysis of Landforms*, (Translated and edited by H. Czech and K. C. Boswell). Macmillan, London, 429 pp.

Pillans, B. J. (1977). An early Tertiary age for deep weathering at Bredbo, Southern NSW. *Search*, **8**, (3), 81–83.

Pugh, J. C., and King, L. C. (1952). Outline of the geomorphology of Nigeria. *S. Afr. Geog. J.*, **36**, 1–12.

Rapp, A. (1975). Some views on the Ordovician paleoglaciation in Saharan Africa. *Geol. Foeren. Stockholm Foorh.*, **97**, 142–150.

Reid, P. C., and Tucker, M. E. (1972). Probable late Ordovician glacial marine sediments from northern Sierra Leone. *Nature, Lond.*, **238**, 38–40.

Schumm, S. A., and Lichty, R. W. (1965). Time space and causality in geomorphology. *Am. J. Sci.*, **263**, 110–119.

Smith, A. G., and Briden, J. C. (1977). *Mesozoic and Cenozoic Palaeocontinental Maps*. Cambridge University Press, Cambridge, 63 pp.

Templeton, R. S. M. (1970). The geology of the continental margin between Dakar and Cape Palmas. In *The Geology of the East Atlantic Continental Margin, Vol. 4, Africa*. NERC/IGS, Rep. 70/16, pp. 47–60.

Thomas, M. F. (1965). Some aspects of the geomorphology of domes and tors in Nigeria. *Z. Geomorph., N.F.*, **9**, 63–81.

Thomas, M. F. (1968). Some outstanding problems in the interpretation of the geomorphology of tropical shields. *Br. Geom. Res. Gp. Occ. Publ.*, **5**, 41–49.

Thomas, M. F. (1974). *Tropical Geomorphology*. Macmillan, London, 332 pp.

Thomas, M. F. (1978a). Chemical denudation, lateritisation and landform development in Sierra Leone. In *Géomorphologie Dynamique dans les Régions Interopicale* (Ed. A. Alexandre). Geo-Eco-Trop, **2**, 243–264. Presses Universitaires du Zaïre, Kinshasa.

Thomas, M. F. (1978b). The study of inselbergs. In *Inselberge* (Eds. H. Bremer and J. N. Jennings). *Z. Geomorph., Supplementband*, **31**, 1–41.

Thorp, M. B. (1967). Closed basins in Younger Granite Massifs, northern Nigeria. *Z. Geomorph., N.F.*, **11**, 459–480.

Touraine, F. (1972). Érosion et planation. *Rev. Geog. Alp.*, **60**, 101–121.

Twidale, C. R. (1976). On the survival of paleoforms. *Am. J. Sci.*, **276**, 77–95.

Twidale, C. R., and Bourne, J. A. (1975). Episodic exposure of inselbergs. *Geol. Soc. Am. Bull.*, **86**, 1473.

Umeji, A. C. (1975). Gravity stratification in the Freetown Basic Igneous Layered Complex, Sierra Leone, West Africa. *Geol. J.*, **10**, 107–130.

Wells, M. K. (1962). Structure and geology of the Freetown Layered Basic Complex of Sierra Leone. *Overseas Geol. Min. Resour., Suppl.*, **4**, 115 pp.

Verague, J. (1977). Les alterations des roches du Socle armoricain. *Norois*, **87**, 252–269.

Wayland, E. J. (1933). Peneplains and some other erosional platforms. *Bull. Geol. Soc. Uganda, Ann. Rep. 1933*, Notes, 1, 74, 366.

Wilson, N. W., and Marmo, V. (1958). Geology, geomorphology and mineral resources of the Sula Mountains. *Geol. Surv. Sierra Leone Bull.*, **1**, 91 pp.

Young, A. (1974). The rate of slope retreat. In *Progress in Geomorphology* (Eds. E. H. Brown and R. S. Waters). *Inst. Br. Geog. Spec. Publ.*, **7**, 65–78.

Index